From Prairie to Corn Belt

Allan G. Bogue was born in London, Ontario, and studied at the University of Western Ontario and Cornell University. He is the author of *Money at Interest: The Farm Mortgage on the Middle Border,* as well as several scholarly articles. He is at present Professor of History at the University of Wisconsin.

From Prairie To Corn Belt

FARMING ON THE ILLINOIS AND IOWA PRAIRIES
IN THE NINETEENTH CENTURY

ALLAN G. BOGUE

P963

Q

QUADRANGLE PAPERBACKS
QUADRANGLE BOOKS / CHICAGO

To FRED LANDON
and JAMES C. MALIN

Preface

Although historians have treated particular aspects of middle-western agricultural history in scholarly and perceptive fashion, there are remarkably few accounts that consider the whole range of problems confronting the operator of a farm business on the prairies. It has seemed to me that the need for work of this sort has grown as city-reared and urban-oriented historians come increasingly to dominate our profession. This is, I hope, such a book. I know that some specialists in midwestern history will feel that I have given their favorite topics too little attention. But the effort here is to place the various parts of the prairie farming process in perspective, and I am prepared to plead guilty to some overemphasis on subjects that others have neglected. Some of the material presented here is preliminary in nature, and perhaps this book can best be described as an exploratory essay or progress report. In subsequent work I hope to deal specifically with some of the particularly vital parts of the midwestern agricultural system, with tenancy, with freight rate and marketing problems, and with profits and community economic structure.

In writing this book I received help from many people and am most grateful for it. In some cases my debts are of great magnitude and of long standing. Two of my major obligations are acknowledged in the Dedication: Fred Landon was the teacher who kindled my interest in agricultural history; although he may be shocked at the results, James C. Malin's ideas on research, regionalism, and American agriculture have influenced me deeply. Paul Wallace Gates introduced me to the history of the Corn Belt, and to him I have dedicated an earlier book. I profited greatly also from many discussions with the late Mildred Throne, of the Iowa State Historical Society, whose research in the field of agricultural history earned the respect of all the scholars who knew her. Before domestic concerns forced Margaret Beattie Bogue to withdraw from the venture, we had planned to write this book together. In preparation for it she had already searched and abstracted a considerable body of prairie travel literature. She also allowed me to use some of the notes that she had taken while preparing her study of land use and land tenure in the Grand Prairie. I benefited too from her critical readings of this manuscript. I also received assistance from many county officers, abstracters, and citizens in the prairie peninsula. Typical of their helpfulness was the kindness of Donald R. Murphy, of *Wallace's Farmer*, who publicized my search for farm diaries in his column and gave generously of his accumulated wisdom. Curtis and Frances Frymoyer, of Wilton Junction, kindly allowed me to use two excellent family diaries and shared their very considerable knowledge of the agricultural history of eastern Iowa with me.

The administrators and librarians of midwestern libraries and archives were most kind to me. I remember with particular appreciation the helpfulness of Clyde C. Walton and Margaret Flint, of the Illinois State Historical Society; Theodore J. Cassady and Mrs. Harry E. Pratt, of the Illinois State Archives; Adelaide Seemuth, of the Iowa State Historical Society; Jack W. Musgrove, Bertha Kurth, and Fleming C. Fraker, of the Iowa Department of History and Archives; Margaret Davidson, of the Webster City Public Library; Catherine Reynolds, Julia Bartling, and Ada M. Stoflet, of the State University of Iowa Library.

A number of graduate students at the State University of Iowa have deepened my understanding of midwestern economic development in the nineteenth century. I am indebted particularly to Leonard Ralston, George Boeck, Joel Silbey, George Sieber, Robert Dykstra, Daniel Clynch, Peter Schmitt, and Duane Hawke. In most cases their researches were peripheral to my own, but I was not introduced directly to the many problems of mapping nineteenth-century agricultural census data until I served as adviser for Duane Hawke's M.A. thesis on farming types in nineteenth-century Iowa.

During the process of this research I released a number of trial balloons. The description of John Savage's farm business appeared originally in the *Annals of Iowa*; some of the materials used in chapters ii and x were used in considerably different form in the *Mississippi Valley Historical Review* and in the *Iowa Journal of History*; a discussion of some of my findings was published in the *Journal of Economic History*. The editors of these journals in each instance very kindly consented to such further use of the published materials as seemed appropriate to me.

Professor E. N. Transeau's map of the prairie peninsula appeared first in *Ecology* in 1935 and is reproduced here with the permission of the botany editor of that periodical. Herbert Quick's books, *Vandemark's Folly* and *The Hawkeye*, appeared first in the *Ladies' Home Journal* of 1921–22 and 1923. Quotations are reprinted by special permission of the *Ladies' Home Journal*, the Curtis Publishing Company, and Mrs. Margaret Quick Ball.

I am indebted to the Social Science Research Council for the assistance that I received as a postdoctoral fellow in the year 1955–56. An appointment as research professor at the State University of Iowa during the first semester of academic 1959–60 allowed me to write the preliminary draft of much of this book, and I am grateful also to Deans Walter F. Loehwing and John C. Weaver, of the State University of Iowa Graduate College, for a number of research and typing grants.

Contents

The Land Lies Waiting

By the 1870's Americans had discovered a "corn belt" in the upper valley of the Mississippi. Today the Corn Belt stretches from Kansas and Nebraska to Ohio; its southern boundary embraces parts of Missouri and Kentucky; its northern border cuts through the Dakotas, Minnesota, and Michigan — a uniquely productive region. Some scholars have suggested that use of the phrase "Corn Belt" obscures the importance of the livestock and the diverse field crops that its farmers produce. Nor have the farming patterns and boundaries of the region remained static through the years. But we can agree that in the upper watershed of the Mississippi there lies a great farming region where farmers key their operations to the corn crop as they do nowhere else in the United States. Not even the most chauvinistic Buckeye nor stubborn Kansan will seriously deny that Illinois and Iowa have long been the heart of the Corn Belt. This book is a study of the development of Corn Belt farming in these prairie states. Rather than presenting long general discussions of transportation, agricultural marketing, tenancy, or farmers' movements, I have tried to emphasize the individual farmer — the man with dirt on his hands and dung on his boots — and the problems and developments that forced him to make decisions about his farm business.

When the pioneer farmers came, much of the modern cornland empire was part of a grassland peninsula, a lazy V or triangle of tall grass prairie, that projected eastward into the wooded ramparts of the Lake Plains and the drainage basin of the Ohio River. Grasses, sedges, and forbs contested for most of the land here, although trees often grew along the watercourses or stood in isolated groves on the prairie, and hazel "bushes" were common. Ignorant of the fascinating story of the Pleistocene, which later scientists found written in the prairie landscape, early geologists of the Midwest doubtless longed for bolder profiles and more complex rock strata. Less sophisticated folk merely complained of the monotony of the grasslands.

On close inspection the prairie scene was far from monotonous. Iowa's first state geologist, James Hall, distinguished between the flat prairies like the Grand Prairie of Illinois and the rolling prairies which predominated in

1

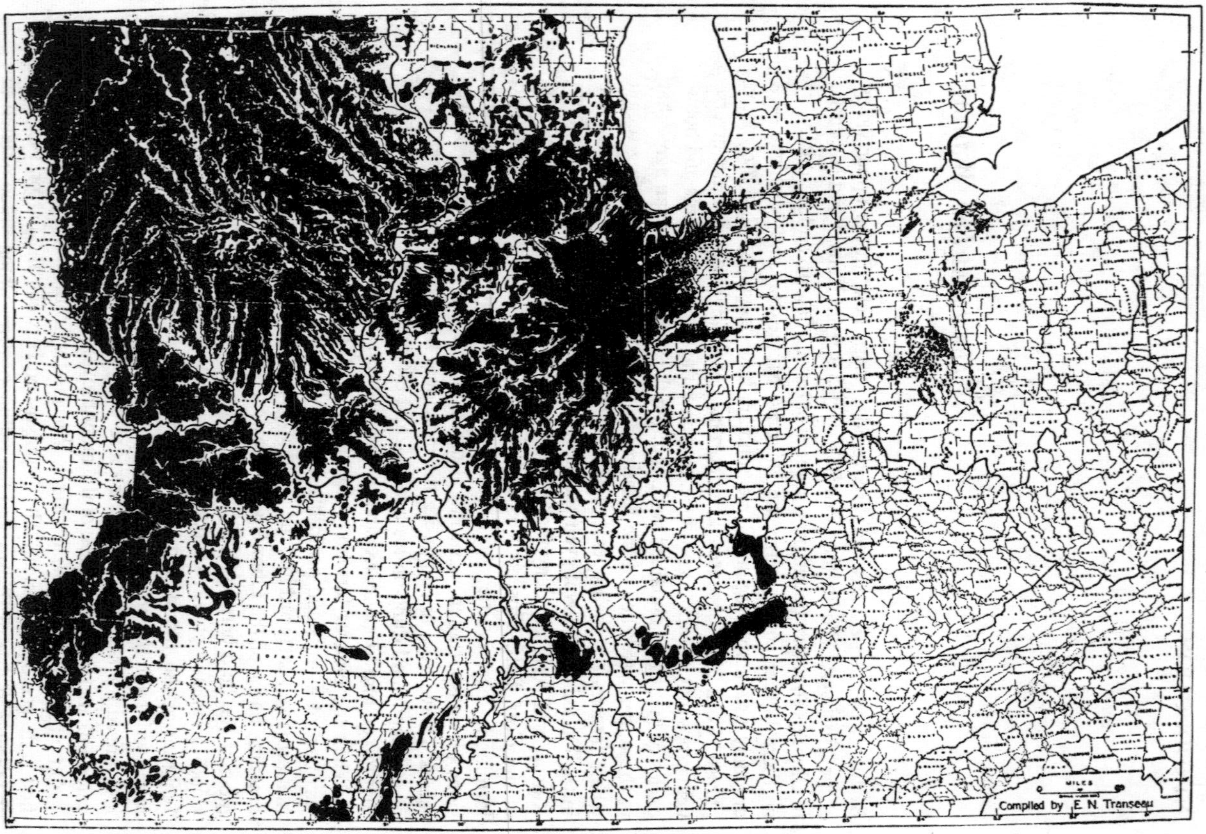

Fig. 1. — The prairie peninsula with outliers

Iowa and other parts of the midwestern grassland.[1] The geographer Leslie Hewes has emphasized that there was "wet prairie" and "well drained prairie."[2] In places the rolling prairie was rolling indeed, and the bluffs of both the Mississippi and the Missouri have their own grandeur. Even in the so-called flat prairie regions the glacial moraines shaped the skyline, and if Mahomet, Illinois, does not today have its mountain, at least it has its "Blue Ridge." When the eye of the traveler turned from the horizon and focused on the plant life of the prairies, there was diversity indeed. The distinguished student of the prairies, Bohumil Shimek, named 271 species in a list of the "typical prairie plants" of Iowa.[3] In the prairie groves, the oak, hickory, and walnut were only the most obvious of a considerable number of species of trees.

Travelers with literary gifts found a challenge in the prairie region during the first half of the nineteenth century. In rolling periods they recounted the beauty and the bounty of the "vast ocean of meadow-land," where a dazzling succession of flowers shone and danced among the grasses, where the wild strawberries, the plum, and the crab apple fruited in wild abundance, and where the nut trees showered the ground of the groves with careless bounty.[4] "God has here, with prodigal hand," wrote Charles Latrobe, "scattered the seeds of thousands of beautiful plants, each suited to its season, where there are no hands to pluck, and but few eyes to admire."[5] Here, he continued rather too simply, the flowers of spring, prevailingly white and blue, were replaced by the reds of summer, to be in turn displaced by a yellow brotherhood that draped the land in cloth of gold.

Some travelers compared the prairies with the parks of English noblemen; more turned to the sea for analogies. Entering the true prairies from the barrens, those stretches of alternating woods, prairie, and hazel brush,

---

[1] James Hall and J. D. Whitney, *Report on the Geological Survey of the State of Iowa: Embracing the Results of Investigations Made During Portions of the Years 1855, 56 & 57* (2 vols.; Des Moines, 1858), I, 20.

[2] See particularly Leslie Hewes, "The Northern Wet Prairie of the United States: Nature, Sources of Information, and Extent," *Annals of the Association of American Geographers*, XLI (December, 1951), 307–23: "Some Features of Early Woodland and Prairie Settlement in a Central Iowa County," *ibid.*, XL (March, 1950), 40–57.

[3] Bohumil Shimek, "The Prairies," *Bulletin of the Laboratory of Natural History*, VI (State University of Iowa, 1911), 174–82. Professor Shimek listed thirteen of the group as "introduced." A recent scholarly study of the prairie which is fully comprehensible to the layman is John E. Weaver, *North American Prairie* (Lincoln, 1954). The origin of the prairie has intrigued several generations of scientists and is still a subject of some scholarly debate. James C. Malin has attempted to put this and many other problems of the grassland into historical perspective, and his writings should be read by anyone seriously interested in the history of prairie agriculture (see, particularly, *The Grassland of North America: Prolegomena to Its History with Addenda* [Lawrence, 1956]).

[4] Charles Casey, *Two Years on the Farm of Uncle Sam: With Sketches of His Location, Nephews, and Prospects* (London, 1852), p. 269.

[5] Charles J. Latrobe, *The Rambler in North America, MDCCCXXXII–MDCCCXXXIII* (New York, 1835), I, 102.

Edmund Flagg saw "the tall grasstops waving in . . . billowy beauty in the breeze; the narrow pathway winding off like a serpent over the rolling surface, disappearing and reappearing till lost in the luxuriant herbage; the shadowy cloud-like aspect of the far-off trees, looming up, here and there, in isolated masses along the horizon, like the pyramidal canvass of ships at sea." [6] For this writer the lesser prairies had a "touching, delicate loveliness"; they were "resplendent in brilliancy of hue and beauty of outline." [7] But, when Flagg reached the Grand Prairie of Illinois, he felt the impact of the prairies at its greatest:

Here, indeed, were the rare and delicate flowers; and life, in all its fresh and beautiful forms, was leaping forth in wild and sportive luxuriance at my feet. But all was vast, measureless, Titanic; and the loveliness of the picture was lost in its grandeur. . . . All was bold and impressive, reposing in the stern, majestic solitude of Nature. On every side the earth heaved and rolled like the swell of troubled waters; now sweeping away in the long heavy wave of ocean, and now rocking and curling like the abrupt, broken bay-billow tumbling around the crag.[8]

The prairies had their psychological effect on the observer. They stirred in him, reported Patrick Shirreff, an "emotion towards God and his fellow creatures." [9] To William Ferguson, however, "the feeling of relief with which one escapes from the interminable forests of the middle states, into these boundless 'earth-oceans,' becomes changed almost to oppression, as you gaze upon the unintermitted expanse of grass." [10] No doubt the emotions of the less articulate settler or land-seeker stirred also when such men halted their wagons to catch a fuller view at the prairie margin or scrambled up a bur oak the better to see the land ahead. In the first volume of his prairie trilogy, Herbert Quick stopped "Cow" Vandemark a few miles west of Dubuque, where the panorama of the prairies opened before him. There follows a passage from which one of the most distinguished of midwestern ecologists quoted approvingly in a book summarizing a lifetime of prairie studies:

It was like a great green sea. The old growth had been burned the fall before, and the spring grass scarcely concealed the brown sod on the uplands; but all the swales were coated thick with an emerald growth fullbite high, and in the deeper, wetter hollows grew cowslips, already showing their glossy golden flowers. The

  [6] Edmund Flagg, *The Far West: or A Tour beyond the Mountains* . . . (New York, 1838) (reprinted in Vols. XXVI and XXVII of Reuben Gold Thwaites [ed.], *Early Western Travels, 1748–1846* [Cleveland, 1906]), pp. 26, 214.

  [7] *Ibid.*, p. 340.

  [8] *Ibid.*, p. 341.

  [9] Patrick Shirreff, *A Tour through North America; Together with a Comprehensive View of the Canadas and United States, as Adapted for Agricultural Emigration* (Edinburgh, 1835), p. 421.

  [10] William Ferguson, *America by River and Rail, or, Notes by the Way on the New World and its People* (London, 1856), p. 393; See also Flagg, *op. cit.*, p. 342.

hillsides were thick with the wooly possblummies * in their furry spring coats protecting them against the frost and chill, showing purple-violet on the outside of a cup filled with golden stamens, the first fruits of the prairie flowers; on the warmer southern slopes a few of the splendid bird's-foot violets of the prairie were showing the azure color which would soon make some of the hillsides as blue as the sky; and standing higher than the peering grass rose the rough-leafed stalks of green which would soon show us the yellow puccoons and sweet-williams and scarlet lilies and shooting stars, and later the yellow rosin-weeds, Indian dye flower and golden rod. The keen northwest wind swept before it a flock of white clouds; . . . The wild-fowl were clamoring north for the summer's campaign of nesting. . . . It was sublime! Bird, flower, grass, cloud, wind, and the immense expanse of sunny prairie, swelling up into undulations like a woman's breasts turgid with milk for a hungry race.

The youth cried in his happiness at "finding the newest, strangest, most delightful, sternest, most wonderful thing in the world — the Iowa prairie." At this, the somewhat tarnished lady in the wagon beside him burst out, "I don't wonder that you cry. Gosh! It scares me to death." [11] Here Quick caught the duality in the impact of the prairie which some of the travelers experienced — uplift and oppression, promise and threat.

To break loose from the timber, to build one's house upon the bare prairie, would be to discard old patterns. For generations pioneers had slashed out their farms from rolling woodlands. The technique of such pioneering was the common heritage of most farm boys, well known if not experienced on their fathers' farms. Now the landscape and the pioneering problems were different. If the country was beautiful, it was also strange, and strangeness bred unease and distrust. With some who came to break the prairie it was love at first sight. But in the minds of most pioneer farmers there was probably nagging doubt as to whether they could solve the obvious problems of farm-making on the prairie and the suspicion that old crops might demand new treatment in a grassland. And, though the prairie flowers stretched out before her to the horizon, the pioneer's wife doubtless found more solace in the blooms rooted in the peony root that she had brought in the wagon from Kentucky or Ohio than she did in the bounty of the prairie. For the immigrant turned prairie farmer such problems were compounded.

In the productivity of its soils the prairie country would not disappoint the pioneers. They were by no means, however, uniformly fertile. Four times during the ice ages glaciers had moved into this region, bringing loads of rock debris and subjecting the old surfaces to relentless, grinding action. Apparently, only the first of the ice sheets, the Nebraskan, covered all of Iowa, and small regions in the southern and northwestern portions of Illinois were not affected by any of the glaciers. But Kansan drift mantled much of

* "Paas-bloeme" one suspects is the Rondout Valley origin of this term applied to a flower, . . . the American pasque-flower, the Iowa prairie type of which is *Anemone patens*: the knightliest little flower of the Iowa uplands. . . .

[11] Herbert Quick, *Vandemark's Folly* (New York, 1921), pp. 111–13.

the two states, and the Illinoian ice front pushed far south in Illinois. Finally, the Wisconsin glacier strewed its drift over much of northern Iowa and Illinois. Deposition was neither a tidy nor an unvarying process. Streams issuing from the glacial front strewed their lines of flow with sands and gravels, creating outwash aprons. Lakes formed temporarily along the glacial borders and laid down characteristic patterns of sedimentary muds. Great stretches of boulder clay or till — and more spectacularly, boulder erratics, moraines, eskers, and the like — emerged as the fronts retreated. During intervals of drought, winds blanketed the region with dust storms, laying down loess deposits of varying thickness.[12]

The glacial drift and loess of the ice ages underwent considerable modification before the pioneers arrived. Water continued to carry, sort, and deposit — robbing the highlands to build up alluvial treasures along the stream courses. Combining with heat, cold, and chemicals, water also broke down the structure of rock fragments and carried away mineral elements to deposit them at lower levels. Even where loess deposits were thick, the underlying drift might greatly affect the nature of the soil-building process by allowing relatively more or less drainage. Meanwhile plant and animal life disturbed and mixed the parent materials and added an organic increment. Time, too, played its part in making soils. In the regions of the Wisconsin drift the soils are generally more productive than are those in the Kansan or Illinoian drift areas, in part because the older surfaces have endured thousands of years more of leaching.

The soils of the midwestern grasslands are dark brown, at times even black in color, reflecting the content of organic materials that have accumulated in them over time, mainly the residue of grassland vegetation and root systems. The massively complex roots of one major prairie resident, the big bluestem, sometimes penetrated more than six feet into the soil, and the roots of some forbs more than doubled this sum. In the woods along the prairie watercourses, the pioneers were to find soils of lighter color, for organic matter accumulated less rapidly in soils under forest cover than under grass. There was less sustenance for the crops of the farmer in these soils than in those of the true prairie. The modern agronomist distinguishes dozens of different soils in Illinois and Iowa that vary from each other in profile, color, texture, and mineral components; on occasion he groups them in a smaller but still considerable number of soil associations.[13] The soil scientist, however, was not on hand to advise the pioneer.

[12] Richard F. Flint's *Glacial and Pleistocene Geology* (New York, 1957) is a helpful recent survey (see, particularly, chaps. XVIII and XX, pp. 320–27 and 335–54).

[13] At this writing the most up-to-date and useful publication on midwestern soils is *Soils of the North Central Region of the United States: Their Characteristics, Classification, Distribution, and Related Management Problems*, North Central Regional Publication No. 76 issued as Bulletin 544 by the University of Wisconsin Agricultural Experiment Station (Madison, 1960). Again, however, the relevant sections should be read in Malin, *op. cit.*

The pioneers divided the prairie peninsula into timber land, prairie, and apparent transition types, the oak openings or barrens. Settlers in older regions had judged the potential of a soil by the kinds of trees that grew upon it. If the farm-makers who faced the Illinois grassland after 1820 still subscribed to such theories, they had good reason to be depressed. But it is doubtful that they were. Smaller prairies had existed in older regions, Ohio and Kentucky, for instance, and here they had proved their productivity. That indefatigable publicist of the Ohio country, Caleb Atwater, termed the prairies and barrens of that state "exuberantly fertile" in 1818.[14] When Morris Birkbeck planted his English settlement in southeastern Illinois during 1817 and 1818, he took the fertility of the local prairies for granted.[15] Farmers brought the greater part of the prairies in Illinois and Iowa into cultivation after 1840, and by that time the judgment of science had been added to the voice of experience. While surveying the mineral regions of Illinois, Wisconsin, and Iowa during 1839, David Dale Owen collected soil samples in an effort to determine the agricultural potential of the region. He found a much higher percentage of organic matter in the soils of Wisconsin and Iowa than in those of Massachusetts. Since he associated organic matter and fertility, he could pronounce the western soils highly fertile and supported his conclusions with the experience of those settlers who had turned to agriculture in the lead region. Here, he believed, farmers could produce Indian corn not inferior to that grown in the state of New York.[16]

[14] Caleb Atwater, "On the Prairies and Barrens of the West," *American Journal of Science . . . I*, No. 2 (1818), 124.

[15] Morris Birkbeck, *Notes on a Journey in America from the Coast of Virginia to the Territory of Illinois* (London, 1818), p. 129.

[16] David D. Owen, *Report of a Geological Exploration of Part of Iowa, Wisconsin, and Illinois, Made under Instructions from the Secretary of the Treasury of the United States in the Autumn of the Year 1839; with Charts and Illustrations* (28th Cong., 1st sess.; Senate Doc. 407 [Washington, 1844]), p. 61.

CHAPTER I

The People Come

Until the 1830's few settlers entered the regions of Illinois that were dominated by the prairies. In 1830 there were six or more inhabitants to the square mile in but two irregularly outlined strips of territory in the state. One of these was based on the Ohio and stretched up the Wabash Valley almost to Danville. The other extended along the Mississippi from the Cape Girardeau area to a point midway between the mouth of the Illinois River and Quincy, projecting inland to include the lower third of the Kaskaskia and Illinois river valleys and the intervening country. North of Knox and Peoria counties, in this same year, there were more than two residents to the square mile only in the Galena lead region. In the interior of eastern Illinois, settlers were few as far south as modern Richland County.[1]

By 1840 there were fewer than two persons to the square mile only in the Grand Prairie counties of Livingston, Ford, Champaign, and Iroquois, together with the southern portion of modern Kankakee. Contiguous counties from Stephenson in the north to Christian in the south, however, still claimed only two to six persons to the square mile. At this time, settlers were increasing in the Illinois Valley, spreading out in a semicircle from Chicago, and moving rapidly into the northern tier of Illinois counties. Here was forecast the final pattern of settlement in northern Illinois. Pioneer farmers reached the interior prairies of northcentral and northeastern Illinois last among all the regions of the state. Lacking adequate water transportation and presenting many problems of adaptation to the farmer, these prairie counties waited for their full quota of settlers until the 1850's and thereafter.

We can deepen our understanding of the settlement process in northern

[1] The basic accounts of settlement in Illinois are: Arthur C. Boggess, *The Settlement of Illinois, 1778–1803* (Chicago Historical Society's "Collection," Vol. V, [Chicago, 1908]); William V. Pooley, *The Settlement of Illinois from 1830–1850* (University of Wisconsin Bulletin, "History Series," Vol. I [Madison, 1908]). The appropriate volumes of the "Centennial History of Illinois" include useful summaries of the settlement process; see particularly the maps in Solon J. Buck, *Illinois in 1818* (Springfield, 1917), p. 59; Theodore C. Pease, *The Frontier State, 1818–1848* (Springfield, 1918), pp. 4, 174, 384; and Arthur C. Cole, *The Era of the Civil War, 1848–1870* (Springfield, 1919), pp. 16, 330.

Illinois by comparing the number of farm units reported in various counties in the census years from 1850 onward with the totals of 1900. In 1850 Du Page and McHenry counties, but one county removed from Lake Michigan, reported 56 and 70 per cent of the farm units of 1900. Among the

Fig. 2. — The counties and major rivers of Illinois

counties of the Rock River Valley, Boone, in the northern tier, reported 68 per cent; De Kalb, 32 per cent; and Whiteside but 14 per cent of the 1900 totals. On the northern edge of the Military Tract, Bureau and Knox counties had slightly more than 20 per cent of the farm units which those counties contained in 1900. The census marshals of Champaign and Livingston counties in the Grand Prairie could find only 4 and 6 per cent of the number of farm units reported by their successors in 1900. The percentage in Edgar to the southeast of these counties on the Indiana line was 38.[2]

If settlers were slow in coming to northern Illinois, the counties of that region filled up rapidly once the full tide of settlement reached them. The pioneers usually needed only twenty or thirty years to open up a number of farms equal to the totals of 1900. Boone County indeed, had reached this figure by 1860 and surpassed it by 8 and 6 per cent in 1870 and 1880. For most counties of northern Illinois, the totals of 1900 represented a decline from maximums, which had been reached by the 1870's. Champaign and Livingston counties, indeed, reported 16 and 23 per cent more farm units in 1880 than in 1900. The farm-making era in the Grand Prairie had definitely ended by 1880.

Settlers crossed the Mississippi during 1833 to establish themselves in the lands acquired by the federal government from the disgruntled Sacs and Foxes in Iowa during the previous year — the Black Hawk Purchase. The river routes provided by the Mississippi and Missouri rivers and their Iowa tributaries shaped the early patterns of settlement in the state. The pioneers fanned out from the Mississippi and penetrated the Des Moines, Iowa, and Cedar River valleys particularly, so that by 1860 the population of the state was concentrated in eastern Iowa, and in the Des Moines Valley as far west as Polk County, seat of Des Moines. Settlement in interior counties between the Des Moines and Mississippi rivers, like Grundy, Tama, and Poweshiek, lagged behind that in the counties both to the east and along the Des Moines River. Meanwhile settlement was radiating from the southwestern counties along the Missouri. In 1870, however, the interior counties between the Des Moines and the Missouri were still being settled, and population was thinly scattered in the northwestern corner of the state generally. Indeed, the population density in Hancock, Ida, and the four northwestern counties of the state was still less than six residents to the square mile.[3]

In a study of the Iowa population, published in 1930, Professors Harter and Stewart, of Iowa State College, concluded that the agricultural settlement of Iowa was complete by 1890.[4] At that date there were more than

[2] These percentages are based on analysis of the county agricultural returns given in the printed federal agricultural censuses, 1850–1900.

[3] Cardinal Goodwin, "The American Occupation of Iowa, 1833 to 1860," *Iowa Journal of History and Politics*, XVII (January, 1919), 83–102; William L. Harter and R. E. Stewart, *The Population of Iowa; Its Composition and Changes: A Brief Sociological Study of Iowa's Human Assets* (Iowa State College of Agriculture and Mechanic Arts, Bull. 275 [Ames, 1930]). There is a series of excellent maps based on the township population figures given in the state censuses of 1856, 1867, and 1875 in G. B. Schilz, "Rural Population Trends of Iowa as Affected by Soils" (unpublished Ph.D. dissertation, Clark University, 1948), pp. 67, 68, 69. See also Clare C. Cooper, "The Role of Railroads in the Settlement of Iowa: A Study in Historical Geography" (unpublished M.A. thesis, University of Nebraska, 1958).

[4] Harter and Stewart, *op. cit.*, pp. 13–14.

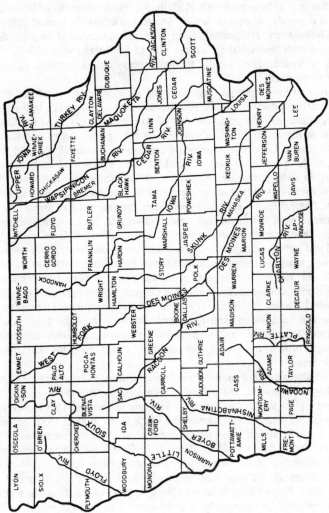

Fig. 3. — The counties and major rivers of Iowa

fifteen people to the square mile in all the ninety-nine counties of Iowa. But, even if a population of that density was all settled on the land, it still provided rather sparse settlement. Except in the oldest sections of the state, most Iowa counties reached their largest total of farm units about 1900, after which a decline began, similar to that experienced in northern Illinois a generation earlier.

It is a striking fact that large areas of a region, now considered to be particularly productive, should have remained unsettled so late in the nineteenth century. While great stretches of northwestern Iowa and the Grand Prairie in Illinois lay in virgin sod, settlers were pushing deep into Kansas and Nebraska. Lack of transportation facilities in interior Illinois and Iowa explains this paradox in part. Navigable rivers, canals, and later railroads not only carried many farm-makers to their destinations in the west but promised markets for the settlers' produce. A recent study, however, shows that settlement lagged for some years after the railroad had arrived in the counties of west, northwest, and west north-central Iowa.[5] As in the Grand Prairie, there was much wet prairie in these sections of Iowa, calling for additional outlays of capital by pioneers before a satisfactory tilth could be achieved. Many a settler turned his back on the potential riches of the Wisconsin drift to gamble five years of his life trying to win a free homestead in the sandhills of Nebraska. In reality a very complex combination of factors controlled the flow of settlement into any particular locality. Transportation routes and facilities, potential markets, the quality of the land, real or imagined, location in relation to older settlements, and the state of the settling-in process there — all had important effects upon the development of new areas.

The Indians but little impeded the flow of settlement into northern Illinois and Iowa. In general, the federal government purchased the Indian title in these regions long before settlers were ready to move in. That unfortunate compound of tragedy and comedy, the Black Hawk War of 1832, occurred when a small number of squatters encroached upon the cornfields of the Sac and Fox in the lower Rock River Valley. Here the Indians were living at the sufferance of the federal government on lands ceded earlier to the United States. At the time many miles of unsettled territory separated the lower Rock River Valley from the Illinois settlements to the south and the lead diggings of the Galena region to the north. The Potawatomis, the Chippewas, and the Ottawas ceded the last major tracts of Indian land in northern Illinois during 1832 and 1833.

A minor land cession in southeastern Iowa for the benefit of the mixed-blood descendants of the Sac and Fox Indians, the Half-Breed Tract, dates from 1824. Federal officers cleared the Indian title from the remainder of the state in a series of major treaties between 1832 and 1851. In less than thirty years the Sacs, Foxes, Potawatomis, Chippewas, Ottawas, Omahas,

[5] Cooper, *op. cit.*, pp. 136–38.

Iowas, Otos, Missouris, Winnebagos, and a number of bands of Sioux relinquished all their rights in Iowa.[6] One incident in the relations between Indian and Anglo-American may have retarded settlement in northern Iowa briefly. This occurred in the spring of 1857 when a group of renegade Sioux, led by Inkpaduta, killed some thirty members of a tiny community at the Okoboji Lakes and Spirit Lake.[7] But the settlers at the lakes were one hundred miles beyond the major settlements in the upper valley of the Des Moines. The massacre probably deterred the flow of pioneers into northwestern Iowa less during the next few years than did the depression of 1857.

Occasionally, settlers did congregate along the boundary line of a new purchase in Iowa, waiting for the opening. This behavior was not so much evidence that the lands in older areas were completely occupied as it was of the speculative bent of the "sooners," who coveted the best waterpower and townsites and the choicer timberlands of the new region. Such a rush occurred in Wapello County on May 1, 1843, and this county, according to one observer, was literally settled overnight.[8] The census figures of 1850 and 1860 tell a different story. Wapello County reported only 36 per cent of its 1900 farm total in the census of 1850 and but 40 per cent ten years later.

If Indians and Indian title little impeded settlement in the prairie triangle, neither did the land survey and sale policies of the federal government. Although in some regions, particularly in portions of Illinois and eastern Iowa, settlers did precede the federal surveyors, these forelopers could organize claim clubs to protect their holdings, and the federal surveyors were seldom long in arriving.[9] The large amounts of land purchased at private entry subsequent to the public auctions at all the prairie-land offices in Iowa and Illinois suggest that the settlers did not press hard upon the available supplies of land in the early years of settlement.

Table 1 shows the state or country of birth of the members of the more

[6] The basic details of Indian land cessions appear in Charles C. Royce, *Indian Land Cessions in the United States* ("Bureau of American Ethnology, 18th Annual Report, 1896–1897" [56th Cong., 1st sess.; House Doc. 736 (Washington, 1899)]), and Charles J. Kappler, *Indian Affairs, Laws and Treaties* (57th Cong., 1st sess.; Senate Doc. 452 [Washington, 1903]). See also Grant Foreman, *The Last Trek of the Indians* (Chicago, 1946). The most useful recent treatment of the problems of the Sac and Fox Indians is by William T. Hagan, *The Sac and Fox Indians* (Norman, 1958).

[7] Thomas Teakle, *The Spirit Lake Massacre* (Iowa City, 1918), and Dan E. Clark, "Frontier Defense in Iowa, 1850–1865," *Iowa Journal of History and Politics*, XVI (July, 1918), 315–86.

[8] William Dewey in *Prairie Farmer*, May, 1844, p. 117.

[9] The following contain material of relevance: Allan G. Bogue, "The Iowa Claim Clubs: Symbol and Substance," *Mississippi Valley Historical Review*, September, 1958, pp. 231–53; Margaret B. Bogue, *Patterns from the Sod: Land Use and Tenure in the Grand Prairie, 1850–1900* (Springfield, 1959), chap. i; Theodore L. Carlson, *The Illinois Military Tract: A Study of Land Occupation, Utilization and Tenure* (Illinois Studies in the Social Sciences," Vol. XXXII, No. 2 [Urbana, 1951]), pp. 49–53; Roscoe L. Lokken, *Iowa Public Land Disposal* (Iowa City, 1942), chaps. i and ii. A comprehensive study of the federal land surveys is badly needed.

important state and national groups in Illinois and Iowa in 1850 and 1870. In both years individuals born in Ohio, New York, and Pennsylvania were numerous in the two states. The figures of 1850 reflected also the large migration of settlers from southern states to Illinois and Iowa. Of the ten States contributing the largest numbers of their sons and daughters to Iowa, five were southern, and undoubtedly the parents of many of the Iowans born

TABLE 1A
MAJOR GROUPS BY NATIVITY: ILLINOIS

1850		1870	
Native-Born			
1. New York	67,180	1. Ohio	163,012
2. Ohio	64,219	2. New York	133,494
3. Kentucky	49,588	3. Pennsylvania	98,614
4. Pennsylvania	37,979	4. Indiana	86,807
5. Tennessee	32,303	5. Kentucky	67,702
6. Indiana	30,953	6. Tennessee	47,523
7. Virginia	24,697	7. Virginia	35,733
8. N. Carolina	13,851	8. Missouri	30,872
9. Vermont	11,381	9. Massachusetts	22,156
10. Massachusetts	9,230	10. Vermont	18,515
Foreign-Born			
1. Gr. Brit. & Ir.	51,647	1. Germany	203,758
2. Germany	38,160	2. Gr. Brit. & Ir.	192,951
3. Brit. N. Am.	10,699	3. Brit. N. Am.	32,550
4. France	3,396	4. Sweden	29,979
5. Norway	2,415	5. Norway	11,880
Illinois population	851,470	Illinois population	2,539,891

TABLE 1B
MAJOR GROUPS BY NATIVITY: IOWA

1850		1870	
Native-Born			
1. Ohio	30,713	1. Ohio	126,285
2. Indiana	19,925	2. New York	79,143
3. Pennsylvania	14,744	3. Pennsylvania	73,435
4. Kentucky	8,994	4. Illinois	65,390
5. New York	8,134	5. Indiana	64,083
6. Virginia	7,861	6. Wisconsin	24,309
7. Illinois	7,247	7. Virginia	19,563
8. Tennessee	4,274	8. Kentucky	14,176
9. Missouri	3,807	9. Missouri	13,831
10. N. Carolina	2,589	10. Vermont	12,204
Foreign-Born			
1. Gr. Brit. & Ir.	9,734	1. Germany	66,162
2. Germany	7,152	2. Gr. Brit. & Ir.	65,442
3. Brit. N. Am.	1,756	3. Norway	17,907
4. Holland	1,108	4. Brit. N. Am.	17,554
5. France	382	5. Sweden	10,796
Iowa population	192,214	Iowa population	1,194,020

in Indiana were southern-born. Numerically, the southerners were a much more important element of the population in both states in 1850 than in 1870.

Yankee, Buckeye, Yorker, Hoosier, and Kentucky "hoss" did not, of course, settle evenly throughout either of the states. The sons of Kentucky, Tennessee, and Virginia settled in southern Illinois and southeastern Iowa particularly. They contributed less to the settlement of the northern prairies in Illinois than did other groups. Especially important in central Illinois were the natives of Ohio and Pennsylvania, while the New Yorkers and New Englanders were most strongly intrenched in the northern section of the state. The southeastern two-fifths of Iowa especially attracted the Ohio-born. New Yorkers and Pennsylvanians settled all along the Iowa side of the Mississippi, but ultimately more of the latter lived in southern Iowa than did those born in New York.

By 1850 considerable numbers of European immigrants had arrived in both Illinois and Iowa. In 1870 slightly more than 20 per cent of the residents in Illinois were foreign-born, and in Iowa the percentage was just under 18 per cent. English-speaking foreign-born from Great Britain and Ireland and from the provinces of British America formed a group larger than that of any other foreign nationality in both 1850 and 1870. Of the British subjects from overseas, one out of every two was an Irishman in 1850, and two out of every three had come from the Green Isle in 1870. Much more striking to the native Americans than the English-speaking immigrants were the Continental-born, with their alien tongues. Natives of the German states made up the major group among them at first, and by the 1860's, Scandinavian elements were also important. The foreign-born settled particularly in central and northern Illinois and throughout the northern half of Iowa, with concentrations extending farther south along the Mississippi in both states. If the Germans, British, Irish, and Scandinavians predominated among the foreign-born of Illinois and Iowa, most of the nations of western Europe contributed in some degree to the settlement of these prairie states.[10]

[10] There is, of course, a very considerable literature dealing with the foreign-born groups. The major relevant works here are: Theodore C. Blegen, *Norwegian Migration to America: 1825–1860* (Northfield, 1931) and *The American Transition* (Northfield, 1940); Thomas P. Christensen, *A History of the Danes in Iowa* (Solvang, 1952); Albert B. Faust, *The German Element in the United States: with Special Reference to its Political, Moral, Social and Educational Influence* (2 vols., Boston, 1909); John A. Hawgood, *The Tragedy of German-America: The Germans in the United States of America during the Nineteenth Century and After* (New York, 1940); Carlton C. Qualey, *Norwegian Settlement in the United States* (Northfield, 1938); Carl Wittke, *The Irish in America* (Baton Rouge, 1956) and *We Who Built America: The Saga of the Immigrant* (New York, 1939); Jacob Van Der Zee, *The Hollanders of Iowa* (Iowa City, 1912). Of the journal literature, the following should be noted particularly: Leola N. Bergmann, "Scandinavian Settlement in Iowa," *Palimpsest*, XXXVII (March, 1956), 129–60, and "The Norwegians in Iowa," *ibid.*, XL (August, 1959), 289–68.

Native Americans from the same state were inclined to settle close to each other. Such bunching was even more pronounced among the Continental-born. Webster, Montgomery, and Page counties, in Iowa, ultimately contained large concentrations of Swedes; in Winneshiek, Allamakee, and Story counties, the Norwegians gathered particularly, and Marion and Sioux counties attracted the Dutch. The foreign-born did not include more than 30 per cent of the population in any Iowa county in 1900, but such statistics are somewhat misleading. To the census-takers, the children of immigrants, born in the United States, were, of course, native-born. In thirty-nine of Iowa's counties in 1900, the foreign-born and their children constituted more than 50 per cent of the population.[11] More important, census statistics may give a misleading impression of the relative numbers of foreign-born farm operators. In Hamilton County, Iowa, for instance, in 1880 the foreign-born made up one-third of the county's population. The manuscript census, however, showed that almost half the farm operators in the county were foreign-born.[12]

We can, of course, make too much of the tendency of members of particular cultural groups to settle in close proximity to each other. The list of nativities in most middle-western counties during the nineteenth century was a long one. Swede rubbed shoulders with German, and he with a Norwegian neighbor perhaps, and they must all deal with the native American. If the latter were all Yankees to the Continental-born, they were certainly not in the eyes of each other. Nor, we can agree, was there complete cultural solidarity among the foreign-born groups if we recall the varied heritages of the German states or the internecine animosities among the Irish.

Historians have suggested many reasons which prompted residents of the older states to come "bag and baggage" to the Illinois and Iowa frontiers. Those who had failed in the older communities, the small farmers who desired more land and could not meet local prices, the farm laborers who wished to be their own masters, the sons who found no farm units awaiting them as they came of age — all these were ripe grain for the western harvest. The swings of the business cycle shook others loose from old surroundings. Regional factors supposedly played their part as well in promoting migration. Writers have pointed to the exhausted soils of the Atlantic states, the competition of western grain, wool, and meat, revulsion against the slave system, and the unrewarding prices of southern staple crops. Illinois or Iowa "fever" fed also on the collapse of internal improvement schemes in Ohio and Indiana and on crop failures and disillusionment with the land in the unglaciated or less fertile portions of these states.[13] In the western states, also, one

[11] Harter and Stewart, *op. cit.*, p. 30 (Fig. 15).

[12] *Census of Iowa for 1880 . . . with Other Historical and Statistical Data . . .* (Des Moines, 1883), p. 216; Allan G. Bogue, "Pioneer Farmers and Innovation," *Iowa Journal of History*, LVI (January, 1958), 32.

[13] Pooley (*op. cit.*, chap. iii) has had an important influence on most subsequent historians. Ray A. Billington, *Westward Expansion: A History of the American Fron-*

writer discerned at work a "general law which seems to have always been fundamental in the westward movement." [14] This, explained William V. Pooley, was the tendency of the younger generation in pioneer areas to move onward to new frontiers.

Intensifying the influence of such factors were letters from friends and relatives who had found success in the western territories and states or conversations with other migrants who had returned for visits or to wind up their affairs. Newspaper accounts and the advertising of land-grant railroads and other large holders played their part as well. The improved roads and the canal systems built during and after the 1820's facilitated migration, as did the expanding services of the steamboats on the lakes and western rivers. Finally, the railroad provided the middle-western pioneer with transportation so speedy and convenient that it would have seemed miraculous to his counterpart of 1780.

Varying somewhat among the European states, a complexity of circumstances set the immigrant tide flowing to the United States as never before during the 1840's and 1850's. [15] Some of the new Americans came, remembering poor crops, absentee landlords, and onerous taxes. Others had chafed under political, legal, or religious grievances. Still others had been set free to migrate — willingly or unwillingly — by the operation of agrarian reforms or changing patterns of agriculture. The unpredictable ebb and flow of economic life had brought others to their decision. Most spectacular, of course, was the migration triggered by the rotting desolation in the Irish potato patches. Least easily explained, perhaps, was the very considerable migration to America of Englishmen or that of residents in the provinces of British North America. The motives of such emigrants were doubtless very similar to those of the native-born Americans who resolved to move west in this same period.

Many circumstances helped to keep the streams of immigration flowing from abroad. Playing a part was the advertising of some American states, including Iowa, the unofficial efforts of American railroads with land to sell and traffic sheds to build, and the assistance given by foreign philanthropists and local and national agencies of foreign governments to indigents who wished to migrate. The decision of the British parliament to abolish the navigation laws fostered competition in the North American trade and

tier (2d ed., New York, 1960), chap. xiv, presents an up-to-date summary of the causes of migration into the Lake Plains. See also Goodwin, op. cit., and Dan E. Clark, "The Westward Movement in the Upper Mississippi Valley during the Fifties," Mississippi Valley Historical Association, Proceedings, VII (1913–14), 212–19.

Early writers overstressed the significance of depressions in causing migration. Although economic distress may have conditioned individuals to migrate later, it is quite clear that migration to the frontier slowed down sharply in depression years. Compare, e.g., the rate of population growth in Iowa during the late 1850's with that of the prosperous early 1850's in the Census of Iowa for 1880. . . , pp. 202–3.

[14] Pooley, op. cit., p. 350 [64].

[15] Marcus L. Hansen, The Atlantic Migration (Cambridge, 1940), pp. 199–306.

helped to keep fares at a reasonable figure. The introduction of steam power and American and British sanitary legislation finally made the sea-crossing a pleasant interlude in contrast to the late forties, when famished Irish peasants rode the fever ships west from Irish ports and Liverpool. But most important probably were the "America letters" which poured into the old European communities, telling of the good life in America. Frequently printed in the old country newspapers, such testimonials from old friends or acquaintances carried a conviction that the advertising of land-grant railroads could hardly equal.

It is always difficult to determine the relative importance of the various factors which promote migration. Revulsion against the southern institution of slavery probably played little part in the thinking of the settlers of Illinois and Iowa. If many southerners joined the flow of pioneers across the Ohio from Virginia, Kentucky, and Tennessee after 1800 because they loathed the "peculiar institution," it is strange that they showed so much attachment for the South and its institutions later. Many residents of southern Illinois hoped indeed to legalize slavery in the 1820's.[16] Although the foreign-born flocked to the Middle West in much greater numbers than to slave territory, it was, no doubt, largely because of the location of the major immigrant ports and interior transportation routes rather than from a conscious effort to avoid the South. Substantial numbers of Germans did go to Missouri and Texas.[17] As for Pooley's law, it is the kind of generalization that must be tested against census data before we can accept it completely.

Whatever the combination of reasons which brought the settlers, native-born or foreign, to Illinois and Iowa, they hoped to improve their circumstances in life by moving. Such ambitions, of course, differed in degree. Note the contrast in tone between the letters of Edwin Terril, a hopeful Iowa capitalist, and Ephraim G. Fairchild, a tenant farmer of the same state. From Jasper County in 1848 Terril wrote:

Since I last wrote to thee I have sold my farm and moved far back westward and settled entirely among the squatters and have become a squatter myself. . . . I have cleared about five hundred dollars since I have been here and my prospects at present are quite flattering. I am now building a saw mill. . . . I am also engaged pretty largely in speculating in land.[18]

[16] Pease, op. cit., pp. 70–91.

[17] Historians have made much of the Germans' antipathy toward slavery (for a review of the problem see Hawgood, op. cit., pp. 50, 123, 130, 134–136, 195, 238, 243–53). Professor Hawgood modified earlier estimates of the significance of the Germans in the antislavery controversy, but he may still have given them more than their due. In an unpublished paper, "Notes on Population and the Decline of the Democratic Party in Iowa, 1850–60," Mr. George H. Daniels has presented evidence to show that the Germans in that state remained opposed to the Republican party in 1860 to a much greater extent than is usually supposed.

[18] Edwin Terril to Walter Crew, Hanover, Virginia, February 24, 1847 ("Terril Papers," Iowa Department of History and Archives, Des Moines, Iowa).

From Jones County in 1857, Fairchild told his family in the East:

> i think that I can plough and harrow out hear without being nocked and
> jerked about with the stones as I allways have ben in Jersey . . . if Father and
> Mother and the rest of the family was out here . . . they would make a living
> easier than they can in Jersey.[19]

Joseph Morton explained emigration fever somewhat differently in 1830,
writing from his home in Hatborough, Pennsylvania:

> Since our visit to the west 3 years ago . . . [your brother Charles] . . . has
> been uneasy and dissatisfyed, he is tired of working days work, wishes to get to
> farming. Land & rents are so high in our section of country that there is nothing
> to be made at the business here. . . . Living here has become so high & the
> people so penurious & selfish as to render life a burthen instead of a pleasure.
> We have therefore come to the conclusion to remove to the West provided
> Charles should succeed in getting a situation.[20]

To Benjamin Harris of Springfield, Ohio, in 1840, the decision to emi-
grate involved deciding whether he should settle down and nurture the
$6,500, accumulated in seven years of cattle-droving, in Ohio where land
was selling for $35 an acre, or go elsewhere. "I concluded," he later wrote,
"we would come back to Illinois and live in a cabbin where we could get
Eight hundred Acres and have 3500 left better land and a chance to get all
the land we might want to buy in the future so we told our friends we would
go to Illinois and grow up with the country."[21] For some it was hard to
explain their decision in such concrete terms. Henry Eno wrote to his
father in New York from Fort Madison, Iowa, in 1837:

> You have doubtless received ere this a letter I wrote from Peoria informing
> you of my intention of leaving there for this place. I am afraid you will think
> that I am feeble minded in leaving a place that offered me so many advantages
> and with which I was so well pleased — but I am still of the opinion that I shall
> better myself.[22]

Many historians have dwelt upon the cultural traits of the native-born
and foreign groups that shared the task of developing the lands of the Middle
West. Following the lead of Frederick Jackson Turner, William V. Pooley
suggested that the southern-born stock moved northward through southern

[19] Ephraim G. Fairchild to his parents, April 9, 1857, in Mildred Throne (ed.),
"Iowa Farm Letters, 1856–1865," *Iowa Journal of History*, XVIII (January, 1960), 40.

[20] Joseph Morton, Hatborough, Pa., to George R. Morton, Sanduskey City, Ohio,
November 6, 1830 (quoted through the kindness of Mrs. Charles M. Ellsworth, Iowa
City, Iowa).

[21] B. F. Harris, "Autobiography," p. 18 (quoted in Margaret B. Bogue, *op. cit.*,
p. 79).

[22] Henry Eno to Stephen Eno, Pine Plains, New York, March 11, 1837 ("Eno
Papers," Special Collections Department, Library, State University of Iowa, Iowa
City, Iowa).

Illinois in three stages. First came the hunter pioneers content to till "little clearings in the timber until succeeded by the small farmer, who, in turn, was succeeded by a third class, the more substantial farmer in search of a permanent location." [23] But, in the Yankee conquest of northern Illinois, the hunter pioneer played little part, thought Pooley. No specialist in the use of rifle and hunting knife was needed there to prepare the way for the oxen and farming implements of the New Englander and his cousin once removed from New York. To Pooley, central Illinois was a cultural battle-ground where "the southern stream . . . met the stream of northern settlers in a contention for the timber lands" and "gave way to the more energetic northern people who took up the land." [24] Yankee determinist that he was, Pooley cheerfully recorded another victory for energy and progress. Questioned by T. C. Pease in the *Centennial History of Illinois*, the theme of cultural conflict was revived in more sophisticated fashion by Richard L. Power in 1953. [25]

The explanation for the failure of the southerners to participate more fully in the conquest of the Illinois prairies probably lies in the mechanics of migration rather than in the theme of cultural conflict. The flow of emigrants from any particular region was anything but constant. From their earliest beginnings, American communities have sent out as well as received. In the early years of community growth inflow exceeded outflow. At some point, perhaps a generation and a half after settlement, the number of those leaving to make a new beginning or a first start elsewhere swelled to considerable volume and some years later declined. Such emigrants did not all seek the same destination. First one region then another might beckon most strongly. Cultural ties and animosities might modify the process; they seldom controlled it. This is not to deny, however, that cultural differences did add spice to life in the prairie communities. Consider the undertones of malice, ridicule, and envy in the following passage from the history of Allamakee County, Iowa.

Makee Ridge, as it was afterwards called, had among her earlier settlers a large per cent from Maine, and being shrewd, prudent, and enterprising Yankees they soon grubbed out, fenced in, broke up, and cultivated farms, built themselves frame houses which they painted white, made a turnpike road through the village one mile in length and were so far ahead of the surrounding country in style and improvements that they soon were dubbed by the settlers who came in from Hoosierdom, with the sobriquet of Nobscotters, and the ridge with the name of Penobscot, and this name like the lingering fragrance of the faded rose hangs round them still. [26]

[23] Pooley, *op. cit.*, p. 309 [23].

[24] *Ibid.*, p. 420 [134].

[25] Pease, *op. cit.*, p. 7; Richard L. Power, *Planting Corn Belt Culture: The Impress of the Upland Southerner and Yankee in the Old Northwest* (Indianapolis, 1953).

[26] Ellery M. Hancock, *Past and Present of Allamakee County, Iowa: A Record of Settlement, Organization, Progress and Achievement* (2 vols.; Chicago, 1913), p. 275.

A number of historians have studied the role of the immigrant in the settlement of the Middle West. Particularly, have they examined the Continental-born, and to a lesser extent the Irish. After painstaking analysis of settlement in a number of Wisconsin counties, Joseph Schafer concluded that there was "a poetic element in the intensity with which . . . [the Germans] . . . pursued the ideal of creating permanent homes on the land, a point in which they differed from the Americans."[27] The Scandinavians would have an even more emotional regard for the land than did the Germans because they came from countries "where land-hunger was more acute than in Germany."[28] In a recent study of the Irish in the United States, Carl Wittke maintained that, "the Irish in Wisconsin, in contrast with German and Scandinavian farmers in that state, were likely to buy and sell several times before settling down permanently."[29] Marcus L. Hansen suggested that the immigrants were "fillers in" who sensibly avoided the labors of the pioneer for which they were untrained, and preferred instead to buy improved farms from the native Americans who moved on to new frontiers.[30] Here again is the suggestion that the Continental immigrants were less mobile than the native-born Americans once they had chosen a place to put down roots.

However accurately Dr. Schafer may have described the behavior of the German settlers in Wisconsin, they, and the Scandinavians as well, settled on many an unimproved prairie section in Illinois and Iowa. So rapidly did the immigrants move into many prairie counties that it was utterly impossible for them to have found enough native Americans willing to sell out. No doubt Professor Wittke was correct when he stressed the Irishman's liking for the city, but anyone who has examined the population census rolls of northern Illinois and eastern Iowa also knows that many prairie farmers gave Ireland as the country of their birth.

How old was the pioneer? What particular paths had led him to the prairies of Illinois and Iowa? How long, once settled, did he stay in the new western community? To the student of agricultural history these questions all have more than antiquarian interest. If the settlers were young, they would perhaps prove more adaptable, more adept, at meeting the challenges of the new environment than the members of an older group. If they came from the next adjacent state, but recently settled, they were perhaps better prepared to face the tasks of settlement than if they had made the long jump from Massachusetts or North Carolina. We are by no means certain of the effect which cultural homogeneity has in shaping community relations, but information about agricultural practices may well have spread

[27] Joseph Schafer, *Wisconsin Domesday Book*, Vol. II: *Four Wisconsin Counties* (Madison, 1927), p. 118 (quoted without page reference in Hawgood, *op. cit.*, p. 31).
[28] Hawgood, *op. cit.*, p. 32.
[29] Wittke, *The Irish in America*, p. 65.
[30] Marcus L. Hansen, *The Immigrant in American History* (Cambridge, Mass., 1942), 76.

more rapidly in communities settled by pioneers with a common heritage. If most settlers moved on again after but a few years in a pioneer community, it may have taken longer for the farmers there to secure a firm understanding of the difficulties of managing local soils or to solve other farm problems linked to the local environment.

Ultimately, we will be able to answer some of our questions about the pioneers with great certainty. Only industry and eyes capable of searching faded manuscript census pages — or worse still their microfilm replicas — are required before we can generalize safely about the age of the settlers. Ten years, however, represented a sixth of a man's life, and the federal census-taker recorded only the state or country of his origin, neglecting periods of residence in other regions before settlement in Iowa or Illinois. The census data, therefore, can provide us with only partial knowledge of the wanderings of the pioneers. Collected in hundreds of county histories, of course, are thousands of biographical sketches of middle-western pioneers. Unfortunately, the sketches are not always reliable or complete, and their proud subjects were not representative of the county population as a whole. The ne'er-do-well and eccentric found scant welcome in the pages of the county "mug books." But, if our sources are incomplete, we can still cast some light on the demography of the middle-western pioneers.

Bureau County lies in the north-central portion of Illinois at the upper bend of the Illinois River. Some 120 miles to the west and slightly to the south in the lower Des Moines River Valley is Wapello County, Iowa.[31] In 1850 Bureau County contained some 23 per cent of the number of farms there in 1900, while in Wapello the figure was roughly 36 per cent. Both counties clearly were in a pioneer stage. The average or arithmetic mean age of 1,155 farmer householders in Wapello County was 42.3; that of 1,161 farmer householders in Bureau County was 38.8 (see Table 2). Seventy-three per cent of Wapello's farmers were thirty-one years of age or more. Of the farm householders in townships in three other widely separated Iowa counties, 78, 64, and 55 per cent fell in the same category in the first federal census year after organization.[32] Evidently, the pioneer was a mature man, and the boy settler and his child wife were rarities. Actually, the 990 Bureau farmers who had children living with them reported that 1,648 of them were born in states other than Illinois, as compared to 1,790 born within the state. The "typical" pioneer of the counties studied was apparently a married man between the ages of twenty-

[31] The material presented concerning Bureau County, Illinois, below is drawn from the writer's analysis of the manuscript population censuses of that county for 1850 and 1860. With one exception, Wapello County statistics are drawn from Mildred Throne, "A Population Study of an Iowa County in 1850," *Iowa Journal of History*, LVII (October, 1959), 305–30. The Wapello statistics in Table 2 were prepared for me by Dr. Throne.

[32] The townships were Springfield, Cedar County; Hamilton, Hamilton County; and Warren, Bremer County.

TABLE 2
Age and Nativity of Farmers in Bureau and Wapello Counties in 1850

BIRTHPLACE	BUREAU		WAPELLO	
	Number	Average Age	Number	Average Age
New England:				
Connecticut	28	43.5	3	48.6
Maine	20	44.6	6	37.3
Massachusetts	87	43.0	12	45.8
New Hampshire	41	41.4	8	44.6
Rhode Island	21	36.8	..	...
Vermont	66	40.4	9	40.5
	263	41.8	38	43.2
Middle States:				
Delaware	10	37.0	5	43.6
New Jersey	22	45.8	16	48.9
New York	165	37.85	53	42.9
Pennsylvania	125	39.0	114	42.6
	322	38.8	188	43.3
Northern Ohio Valley:				
Illinois	7	25.0	19	26.7
Indiana	29	28.0	126	29.5
Ohio	152	32.8	241	33.7
	188	31.8	386	31.9
Interior South:				
Alabama	1	40.0	3	34.3
Kentucky	49	37.5	174	37.9
Missouri	..	...	2	24.0
Tennessee	22	36.8	67	36.2
	72	37.3	246	37.3
Seaboard South:				
District of Columbia	1	46.0	1	50.0
Georgia	2	47.0	1	50.0
Maryland	16	46.3	22	49.4
North Carolina	14	48.3	61	43.4
South Carolina	3	48.3	7	46.7
Virginia	89	40.0	156	43.9
	125	42.1	248	44.4
English-speaking foreign-born:				
England	41	39.7	10	40.4
Ireland	61	40.3	14	40.7
Scotland	10	40.0	1	
Canadas	4	29.5	2	49.5
	116	39.7	27	41.2
Continental foreign-born:				
Denmark	1	38.0	..	...
France	1	52.0	2	43.0
Germany	72	39.8	9	38.4
Holland	..	...	9	39.5
Sweden	..	...	2	35.0
Switzerland	1	40.0	..	...
	75	39.9	22	39.0
Total	1,161	38.8	1,155	42.3

five and forty-five who had started his family before he moved to the Illinois or Iowa frontier.

When considered as a group, the settlers of the Middle West did apparently have a unique age structure. If the midwestern prairies had attracted a cross-section of the general population, the age structure should not have changed substantially over time. The percentage of farmers over forty years of age rose perceptibly during the first twenty or thirty years in the three Iowa townships mentioned earlier. In a study of the Iowa population published in 1930, Professors Harter and Stewart of Iowa State College discovered that Iowans in general were older in those areas of the state that had been settled longest, youngest in those regions that had been settled for the shortest period of time.[33] We can say, therefore, that, although the pioneer farmers were older than some historians have believed, they were probably younger than the farm operators remaining in the communities from which they migrated and definitely formed a younger group than would be found a generation later in the communities which they were helping to build.[34]

Table 2 also shows that the ages of the farmers in both Bureau and Wapello counties in 1850 were apparently related to their states of nativity. New Englanders and farmers who were born in the states of the Seaboard South were on the average considerably older than the farmers who had been born in the Ohio Valley states of Indiana, Ohio, Kentucky, and Tennessee. In Bureau County, for instance, 263 farmers of New England birth were forty-two years of age on the average. The average age of 152 farmers born in Ohio was only thirty-three, while in both Bureau and Wapello counties the Hoosier farmers were younger still. The farther the middle-western pioneer of native origin was from the state of his birth, the older he tended to be. Although older than the Ohio Valley group, the foreign-born farmers were somewhat younger than the New England contingent.

The manuscript federal censuses do not tell us directly of the way stations through which the American emigrant passed on the journey from the state of his birth to the Illinois or Iowa prairies. His children's states of birth, however, do reveal some of them. Unfortunately, we cannot be sure just how much of the story the birthplaces of children provide in any one case. Of the 970 native-born farmers in Bureau County in 1850, 838 did have children living at home. The birthplaces of these children provided

[33] Harter and Stewart, *op. cit.*, pp. 16–17.

[34] Professor James C. Malin was the first western historian to interest himself in pioneer demography in a serious way. He interpreted his findings to show that the frontier population was simply a cross section of the population at large. However, his statistical studies of Kansas farm operators actually showed that, as in Iowa, the average age of farm operators increased for some time after a community was begun (*The Grassland of North America: Prolegomena to its History* [Lawrence, Kan., 1947], p. 289).

skeletal migration charts for their parents. Only 10 per cent of the Ohio-born farmers listed children born in states other than Ohio or Illinois. Somewhat more than half of the farmers born in Virginia and Pennsylvania had resided in states other than Illinois and the state of their birth. The New England— and particularly the New York—born farmers had apparently migrated more directly than had those from Pennsylvania or Virginia. Since the New England—born farmers were in general older than most of their neighbors, children born to them in the earliest years of marriage might have already left home by 1850. The census data showed that 66 per cent of the family men among the Bureau County farmers had lived in another state, approximately 30 per cent had lived in two other states and 0.5 per cent revealed residence in four states in addition to Illinois.

The stopping places of the New Englanders had usually been New York, Pennsylvania, Ohio, or another New England state. Ohio and Pennsylvania served as the main routes of the New York—born. Pennsylvania and Virginia natives had sojourned for the most part in Ohio, although some of the latter had lived in Kentucky or Indiana at one time. As we have seen, the Bureau County pioneers of 1850 brought at least 1,648 children with them. To a considerable extent, migration to the new settlements was a family movement. If some had neither wives nor children to accompany them, and a few thankfully left theirs behind, the majority of settlers brought them along; society on the agricultural frontier was a family society.

Of the 1,115 farmers present in Wapello County in 1850, only some 39 per cent were there ten years later. Of the 1,161 farmers in Bureau County in the same year, 38 per cent remained in 1860. Some of the missing farmers had, of course, died. But, if the farmers of 1850 in these counties were mature, they were not extremely aged. Many of them were undoubtedly living elsewhere in 1860. "Those who stayed" in Wapello County, wrote Mildred Throne, "were more prosperous than those who move on." [35] This was also true in Bureau County. The 438 farmers of 1850 who remained there in 1860 had real estate valued at $1,317 on the average in 1850. The 723 who had disappeared by 1860 reported real estate in 1850 worth only $1,006. In her study of Wapello County, Throne did not compare the ages of those who stayed with those who left. In Bureau County there was no clear-cut relationship between age and persistence.

The Continental-born, some historians believe, were more persistent than the native-born farmers. Table 3 does not show this to have been the case in Bureau County, although it does reveal that the English-speaking foreign-born were the most persistent of all groups in that county. The 72 Germans, however, were highly mobile. The southern stock supposedly were pre-eminently the "movers" among the native-born. It was true in Bureau County that the settlers from Kentucky and Tennessee were the least persistent of all groups. We should remember, however, that the

[35] Throne, "A Population Study," *op. cit.,* p. 321.

Germans and the natives of the interior South were present in relatively small numbers.

TABLE 3
ORIGIN AND PERSISTENCE, BUREAU COUNTY, ILLINOIS

	Number Farmers	Persistence, 1850–60
		(Per Cent)
Great Britain, Ireland, British North America......	116	46.5
New England	263	45.6
Middle States	322	36.9
Seaboard South	125	34.4
Northern Ohio Valley	188	34.0
European Continent	75	28.0
Interior South	72	23.6
	1161	37.7

TABLE 4
FARM OPERATOR TURNOVER
in FOUR IOWA TOWNSHIPS *

	1850		1860		1870		1880	
	No.	Per Cent	No.	Per Cent	No.	Per Cent	No.	Per Cent
Crawford Township:								
Group 1	66	100.0	21	31.8	11	16.6	7	10.6
Group 2	..	....	94	100.0	35	37.2	23	24.5
Group 3	..	....	..	....	141	100.0	36	25.5
Union Township:								
Group 1	81	100.0	35	43.2	22	27.2	11	13.6
Group 2	..	....	84	100.0	41	48.8	25	29.8
Group 3	..	....	..	....	149	100.0	44	29.5
Hamilton Township								
Group 1	..	....	50	100.0	28	56.0	14	28.0
Group 2	..	....	..	....	64	100.0	30	46.9
Warren Township:								
Group 1	..	....	28	100.0	12	42.9	7	25.0
Group 2	..	....	..	....	163	100.0	72	44.2
Continental-born †	..	....	..	....	102	100.0	47	46.1

* The counties were Washington, Davis, Hamilton, and Bremer.
† The Continental-born group consisted mainly of natives of the German states with a few French men and Swiss as well. This group was included in Warren township, Group 2, as well as being placed in a separate category.

Based on manuscript population and agricultural census rolls, Table 4 shows the turnover of farm operators in four Iowa townships between 1850 and 1880. The farmers represented in this table differed from those in the Bureau and Wapello County studies in that they had all made agricultural census returns. Both the Wapello and the Bureau County statistics included a group of "farmers without farms" who described themselves as farmers but who evidently had no farm businesses of their own at the moment. By considering only the farmers who had made an agricultural census return in the townships, we restricted ourselves to those who had made a commitment to their community. In the table the new farmers of each census year stand separately. In Crawford and Union townships we could test the staying power of groups of farmers present in 1850, 1860, and 1870. Settled later, Hamilton and Warren townships provided figures for only the twenty year period between 1860 and 1880.

Table 4 shows that a high proportion of each new group of farmers dropped out early, leaving a core of much more persistent men. Among the ten groups of new farmers in the four townships, the farmers of 1860 in Hamilton Township showed the highest degree of persistence — 56 per cent of them remained there ten years later. The new farmers of 1870 in Crawford Township were least persistent, with only 26 per cent of them remaining after a decade. A considerable group of Continental-born farmers, mostly Germans, entered Warren Township during the late 1860's. Of the members of this group 46 per cent were still there in 1880.

Many historians have followed Turner in accepting the three-stage formula of agricultural settlement, and with even fewer qualifications than those of William V. Pooley. The hunter-farmer or squatter gave way with alacrity, in this interpretation, to the small farmer who obtained title to the land from the federal government and who in turn yielded with few exceptions to the man of property and substance. That there were hunter-farmers and "rolling stones" on the margins of settlement we cannot doubt. But the persistence of a substantial nucleus of settlers from the first census and the fact that all new groups of farmers behaved similarly, whatever the age of the community, force us to qualify the Turnerian formula.

Let us turn from the faceless statistics of Table 4 to discuss the life of one pioneer in Davis County, Iowa. Stephen L. Saunders was born in Pennsylvania in 1813. The family moved to Ohio when Stephen was nine. At the age of twenty-one he went to Michigan, and two years later he married in Indiana. His wife died shortly, leaving one daughter, and in 1837 Saunders went to Iowa. When he crossed the Mississippi, he counted a "York sixpence" as his only capital. After a year in Van Buren County, he worked for the government briefly in the Indian Service at Council Bluffs. Leaving this job, he returned to Van Buren County, joined his parents, who sold their claim, and moved with them to Davis County, still Indian land and unsurveyed. Here they staked out claims, including a number for "friends" in Ohio. A United States marshall arrested young Saunders at this point for trespassing on Indian lands. Fined for the offense, he enjoyed a period of custody by the United States Army, whose officers he found to be "genial, hearty fellows" and "talented drinkers." During 1844 he married again and was still living on his original claim when the county history appeared in 1882. At that time he owned some 1,200 acres, including the home farm of 430 acres, "well improved, with good buildings and orchard." [36]

Until he came to Davis County, Saunders had indeed been a rolling

[36] State Historical Company, *History of Davis County, Iowa* . . . (Des Moines, 1882), pp. 653–54.

stone. Few had better claim to the title of squatter there than did he. But in Davis County the rock stopped rolling and displayed a real talent for gathering moss. Stephen Saunders' career was probably more colorful than most — few settlers crossed the Indian boundary line or fell into the custody of the United States Army. But too many other early comers showed his persistence, once located, for us to dismiss the squatter or early settler simply as a man who left for new surroundings when the first ring of neighbor's axe came floating down wind.

Saunder's story allows us also to qualify our discussion of migration patterns. Had his daughter by his first marriage been living with him in 1850, we could have classified him as a man who had lived in two states, in addition to Iowa. As we know, he had actually resided in four other states, and in Iowa at least had lived in three different localities. Much reading of biographies in the county histories suggests that Stephen Saunders was more than ordinarily mobile as a young man, but he was certainly not unique.

CHAPTER II

They Take the Land

When the surveyors had run their last line and found their last corner in the federal surveys of Illinois and Iowa, they had divided and subdivided some 71,500,000 acres of land, distributed almost equally between the two states. The story of the disposal of this vast acreage to private holders is a complex one — shaped as it was by federal and state legislation, modified by administrative procedures or judicial decision, influenced by the plans of innumerable individuals, enriched by altruism, and marred at times by chicanery.

The registers and receivers of the federal land offices supervised the distribution of some 84 per cent of Illinois and 76 per cent of Iowa. The federal government transferred the remainder to the states for a variety of purposes.

To obtain title to the state lands, the middle-western farmer had to turn to the state land offices or to the corporations and county governments to which the states had transferred control. Although the grant of Section 16 in every township for the support of schools was an important exception, most of the federal grants to the states did not precisely specify the lands included. A number of selection, certification, and sale procedures were involved, and these frequently took considerable time. State officials and the officers of the railroad, canal, or river-improvement companies which had obtained land grants generally hoped, moreover, that they could sell their lands at prices considerably above the price of land sold directly by the federal government.[1] For these reasons, the early comers on the prairie frontier seldom purchased land in the special grants. Instead, they looked to the land that the officers of the nearest federal land office proposed to sell under the general distribution laws of the United States.

[1] Elements in this story appear in Margaret B. Bogue, *Patterns from the Sod: Land Use and Tenure in the Grand Prairie, 1850–1900* (Springfield, 1959); H. S. Buffum, *Federal and State Aid to Education in Iowa* (Iowa City, 1907); Theodore L. Carlson, *The Illinois Military Tract: A Study of Land Occupation, Utilization and Tenure* ("Illinois Studies in the Social Sciences," Vol. XXXII [Urbana, 1951]); Paul W. Gates, *The Illinois Central Railroad and Its Colonization Work* ("Harvard Economic Studies," Vol. XLII [Cambridge, 1934]); Roscoe L. Lokken, *Iowa Public Land Disposal* (Iowa City, 1942).

The prairie triangle was not a homestead frontier. Settlers acquired little land in Illinois and less than a million acres in Iowa under the provisions of the Homestead Act of 1862 and its subsequent amendments. In these states, rather, the registers and receivers of the federal land offices offered

TABLE 5

FEDERAL LAND DISPOSAL
IN ILLINOIS AND IOWA *

	ILLINOIS	IOWA
	(Per Cent)	
Cash sales †	56.1	33.7
Military bounties ‡	26.9	39.7
Agricultural college scrip locations §		0.7
Homesteads	0.1	2.5
Timber claims		0.1
Miscellaneous ‖	0.7	0.1
State grants:		
Swamp and saline lands	4.5	3.4
Educational grants #	2.9	4.9
Internal and river improvements and public buildings....	1.5	3.2
Railroad construction grants	7.3	11.7
	100.0	100.0

* The acreage figures used in the preparation of this table appear for the most part in the Public Lands Commission, *Report*, 1905, supplemented by the *Reports* of the Secretary of the Interior, 1871 and 1921. In the case of Iowa some modifications were made in deference to the findings of Roscoe L. Lokken, *Iowa Public Land Disposal*. The Public Lands Commission reported a land area of 35,842,560 acres in Illinois and 35,646,080 in Iowa. I was unable to make my acreage totals exactly agree with these figures. There are undoubtedly errors and duplications in the basic data. The figures of Table 5 are therefore approximations, but undoubtedly quite close to the fact.
† This category includes sales at land auctions, at private entry, under the graduation law of 1854, and a number of other less important laws.
‡ The basic statistics here are found in the *Congressional Record*, (47th Cong., 1st sess), p. 3973; see Lokken p. 292, n. 180.
§ This grouping embraces the land located by presentation of agricultural-college scrip granted to states without public domain. Iowa's grant of 240,000 acres (204,309 in actuality) was placed under educational grants.
‖ Totaled here are lands granted in satisfaction of private claims, as Indian allotments, and for townsite locations.
Included in this category is the 500,000-acre internal-improvement grant that Iowa diverted for educational purposes.

the lands of their districts for sale at public auction after the surveyors had completed their tasks. Land-seekers could ordinarily purchase those lands that remained unsold when the auction was over by private entry at the minimum price of $1.25 per acre. Adjunct to this method of land disposal was the pre-emption system, outlined first in a number of temporary pre-emption laws and applied generally by the act of 1841. Granted that he was the head of a family or of age, an American citizen or in the process of becoming one, and that he did not own 320 acres of land already in any state or territory, the pioneer could, under the Pre-emption Act of 1841, claim 160 acres upon the surveyed lands of the public domain and purchase this acreage prior to the public sale.[2] A few categories of

[2] The federal land-disposal laws described in this chapter are discussed in Benjamin H. Hibbard, *A History of the Public Land Policies* (New York, 1924), and Roy M. Robbins, *Our Landed Heritage: The Public Domain, 1776–1936* (Princeton, 1942). See also: George M. Stephenson, *The Political History of the Public Lands from 1840*

lands were not open to pre-emption, and the price stood at $2.50 per acre on federal lands within the limits of transportation grants.

Before the passage of the act of 1841, the pioneer who settled anywhere upon the public domain was actually a trespasser. The temporary pre-emption acts of the 1830's applied retroactively and for limited periods of time only. Many settlers could not look to them for protection. They must bid against any rivals who coveted their claims at the public auction. Even after 1841 the squatters sometimes ran their claim lines before the federal surveys or before the district land officers were ready to accept their pre-emption declarations attesting to the fact that they planned to purchase their holdings under the pre-emption law prior to the date of the local land sale. Should the settler fail to amass the $100 or $200 needed to purchase his claim by the time of the land sale, he might well see some large land-buyer, or speculator, purchase his claim and "improvements" at the land sale or acquire them later by private entry. Obviously, the "actual settler" might have many an anxious moment before he held in his hand the cer-tificate that affirmed his legal title to the land he had improved, pending the arrival of his patent from the General Land Office in Washington. It is in this context that we must consider the claim clubs or squatters' associations.

Although the institution was not as common, perhaps, as some have suggested, claim clubs were not unusual among the settlers in Illinois and Iowa during the 1830's, 1840's, and 1850's. Iowa county histories contain specific evidence of the existence of claim clubs in twenty-six Iowa counties and describe half a dozen other settler associations which sprang up where unique local conditions brought land titles under contest.[3] Writing recently,

to 1862: From Pre-emption to Homestead (Boston, 1917); and Thomas Donaldson, The Public Domain (Washington, 1884).

[3] See Albert M. Lea, Notes on the Wisconsin Territory: Particularly with Reference to the Iowa District or Black Hawk Purchase (Philadelphia, 1836) (reprinted by the State Historical Society of Iowa as The Book That Gave to Iowa Its Name [Iowa City, n.d.]), pp. 18–21; John B. Newhall, Sketches of Iowa, or the Emigrant's Guide (New York, 1841), pp. 54–58; Hawkins Taylor, "Squatters and Speculators at the First Land Sales," Annals of Iowa, First Series, VIII (July, 1870), 269–74; Charles A. White, "The Early Homes and Home-makers of Iowa," Annals of Iowa, Third Series, IV (October, 1899), 179–95; Western Historical Company, The History of Appanoose County, Iowa . . . (Chicago, 1878), pp. 364–66; Union Historical Company, The History of Boone County, Iowa . . . (Des Moines, 1880), pp. 326–31; Western His-torical Company, The History of Cedar County, Iowa (Chicago, 1878), p. 325, The History of Clinton County, Iowa . . . (Chicago, 1879), pp. 444–46; Union Historical Company, The History of Dallas County, Iowa . . . (Des Moines, 1879), pp. 324–26; Western Historical Company, The History of Des Moines County, Iowa . . . (Chi-cago, 1879), pp. 377–79; Franklin T. Oldt and Patrick J. Quigley, History of Dubuque County, Iowa . . . (Chicago, 1911), p. 480; Pioneer Publishing Company, History of Emmet County and Dickinson County, Iowa . . . (2 vols.; Chicago, 1917), I, 256–57; Union Publishing Company, History of Hardin County, Iowa . . . (Spring-field, 1883), p. 967; Joseph H. Smith, History of Harrison County, Iowa . . . (Des Moines, 1888), pp. 80–83; Western Historical Company, The History of Jackson County, Iowa . . . (Chicago, 1879), pp. 333–35; Western Historical Company, The

Professor Thomas LeDuc has re-examined the activity of claim associations in northern Illinois, but most accounts describe club activity in Iowa.[4]

In the eyes of many middle-western historians, the claim club was an organization which the settlers used to protect their claims on the public domain until they could obtain title from the federal government. Squatters organized these clubs to forestall the land-speculator and the claim-jumper.[5] Although pointing out that the claim club did allow settlers to transfer claims to which they had not received legal title and that technically the squatters were trespassing, Benjamin Shambaugh emphasized that they were "honest farmers" establishing homes and improving their claims. Representing "the beginnings of Western local political institutions," the clubs fostered "natural justice, equality, and democracy."[6]

The pioneers justified the organization of squatters' associations on a variety of grounds. The preamble to a number of club bylaws in Iowa read:: "Whereas, It has become a custom in the Western States, as soon as the Indian title to public lands has been extinguished by the general government, for the citizens of the United States to settle on and improve said lands, and heretofore the improvement and claim of the settler to the extent of three hundred and twenty acres has been respected by both the

History of Jasper County, Iowa . . . (Chicago, 1888), p. 350; *History of Johnson County, Iowa* . . . (Iowa City, 1883), pp. 323–31; Union Historical Company, *The History of Keokuk County, Iowa* . . . (Des Moines, 1880), pp. 317–25; Union Historical Company, *History of Kossuth, Hancock, and Winnebago Counties, Iowa* . . . (Springfield, 1884), p. 240; Western Historical Company, *The History of Lee County, Iowa* . . . (Chicago, 1879), pp. 440–43; Herman A. Mueller, *History of Madison County, Iowa* . . . (2 vols.; Chicago, 1915), I, 126–37; Union Historical Company, *The History of Mahaska County, Iowa* . . . (Des Moines, 1878), pp. 293–97; William M. Donnel, *Pioneers of Marion County, Consisting of a General History of the County* (Des Moines, 1872), pp. 42–49; Western Historical Company, *The History of Monroe County, Iowa* . . . (Chicago, 1878), pp. 376–77; Johnson Brigham, *Des Moines, The Pioneer of Municipal Progress and Reform of the Middle West, Together with the History of Polk County, Iowa* . . . (2 vols.; Chicago, 1911), I, 602–67; Leonard F. Parker, *History of Poweshiek County, Iowa* . . . (2 vols.; Chicago, 1911), I, 57–60; Union Historical Company, *The History of Warren County, Iowa* . . . (Des Moines, 1879), pp. 304–5; Harlow M. Pratt, *History of Fort Dodge and Webster County, Iowa* . . . (2 vols.; Chicago, 1913), I, 76–78; W. E. Alexander, *History of Winneshiek and Allamakee Counties, Iowa* (Sioux City, 1882), pp. 189–90; A. Warner & Co., *History of the Counties of Woodbury and Plymouth, Iowa* . . . (Chicago, 1890), pp. 70–71.

[4] Thomas LeDuc, "Report of Investigation of the Value of the Land, But Not Including the Value of Lead Mineral Thereon, Ceded by Treaty of 29 July 1829" (presented before the Indian Claims Commission, Docket No. 217, *Citizen Band of Potawatomi Indians of Oklahoma and Potawatomi Nation v. The United States of America* [author's typescript, 1958]).

[5] The pattern was set by two Iowa historians: Jesse Macy, *Institutional Beginnings in a Western State* ("Johns Hopkins University Studies in Historical and Political Science," Ser. II, No. 7, [Baltimore, 1884]); and Benjamin F. Shambaugh, (ed.), *Constitution and Records of the Claim Association of Johnson County, Iowa* (Iowa City, 1894); Shambaugh, "Frontier Land Clubs or Claim Associations," American Historical Association, *Annual Report, 1900* (2 vols.; Washington, 1901), I, 67–85.

[6] Shambaugh, "Frontier Land Clubs or Claim Associations," pp. 71, 83.

citizens and laws of Iowa." [7] Other clubs emphasized the need of protection against "reckless claim-jumpers and invidious wolves in human form," or the need "for . . . better security . . . against foreign as well as domestic aggression." [8] The members of still other clubs were matter of fact, stating merely that the association was designed to assist them in the acquisition and peaceable possession of land.

The squatter could expect that his comrades in the club would come to his assistance if claim-jumpers threatened his holding and that similarly his friends would intimidate speculators who might seek to outbid him at the land auction.[9] In some cases the settlers agreed to protect each other in the enjoyment of their claims for as long as two years after the land sales. The squatters usually placed an upper limit upon the size of the claim to be protected. In ten out of 14 Iowa clubs that ruled on the subject, the maximum was set at 320 acres, but in two instances 480 acres was specified, and on one occasion 200 acres. Club members in another county limited themselves to 160 acres but allowed each other to reserve an additional 160 acres for a non-resident friend. In Poweshiek, Johnson, and Webster Counties, Iowa, one did not have to be a resident to enjoy the protection of the club. Nor was it necessary in some clubs for a settler to have attained his majority. In two cases the minimum age of members was set at sixteen years, in one instance at seventeen, and in two others at eighteen. None of the clubs forbade members to sell their claims; indeed, the right to make such transfers was often specifically guaranteed and the purchaser assured of the protection of the club.

If the squatters of a claim club expected to benefit from membership, they also assumed responsibilities. They pledged that they would assist their officers in maintaining club law in their districts should it be challenged. They promised to co-operate with the other members in intimidatory action at the land auctions if necessary. In some clubs, members paid small sums to the recorder or other club officers for their services. Regulations prescribing the degree to which the members must improve their

[7] Union Historical Company, *History of Mahaska County*, p. 294; John W. Wright and William A. Young, (eds.), *History of Marion County, Iowa, and Its People* (2 vols., Chicago, 1915), I, 61–62; Western Historical Company, *History of Jackson County*, p. 334.

[8] Union Historical Company, *History of Dallas County*, p. 325; Mueller, *History of Madison County*, I, 127; Western Historical Company, *History of Monroe County*, p. 376; Union Historical Company, *History of Warren County*, p. 305.

[9] The following discussion of member rights and obligations is based upon the club rules in force in Boone, Dallas, Des Moines, Dubuque, Dickinson, Jackson, Johnson, Keokuk, Kossuth, Madison, Mahaska, Marion, Monroe, Polk, Poweshiek, Warren, Webster, Winneshiek, and Woodbury counties, Iowa (see n. 3 above for references to published histories of these counties). A typescript copy of the Poweshiek County revised rules and the deed register is available in the Iowa State Historical Society at Iowa City, but the location of the originals is unknown. The society holds the original manuscript rules and claim register of the Johnson County club and a copy of the Fort Dodge club record. The original of the Fort Dodge record is in the Iowa State Department of History and Archives at Des Moines.

claims appear in the manuscript records of the Poweshiek, Johnson, and Webster County, Iowa, associations but not in the selections of the club laws printed in the histories of other counties. The members of the Webster County, or Fort Dodge club, agreed to expend labor worth $10 on their claims each month after the first month. The members of the Poweshiek "Protection Society" pledged in their revised bylaws to put in $30 worth of labor on their claims within six months of registration and $30 worth of additional labor for each succeeding six months that the claim was held. In the Johnson County club, however, only non-residents were obliged to improve their claims to the extent of $50 worth of labor for each six months held.

At the outset these club regulations raise a number of questions. Would it not be reasonable to expect more frequent and more stringent improvement requirements in the club laws if the squatters actually expected to develop their holdings into productive farms and homes? Why protect the claims of minors, who were ineligible to purchase land under the preemption law? Perhaps it was expected that the minors would be of age by the time of the land sales, but squatters may also have sought to acquire additional lands by registering claims in the names of their children. Why, if the public auction was the main reason for the existence of the clubs, did some squatter groups pledge to protect the claims of the members past the date of the sale? Why, finally, did the club regulations allow the members to claim an acreage that was much larger than that needed for a farm unit in the Middle West during the mid-nineteenth century?

It is quite easy to find evidence that shows the Iowa claim clubs in somewhat different light than in the picture painted by Shambaugh. One of the early settlers of Clinton County wrote:

Some of the chivalry, or gentlemen of elegant leisure, followed the business of making claims and selling them to emigrants as they came through. As soon as a new settler arrived, the above named gentry would ascertain his "pile," by some means best known to themselves. They would then have a claim to suit the newcomer's purpose and purse, and, if he demurred paying anything to them, contending that his right to the public land was as good as theirs, they would very soon convince him of his error.[10]

When David Hess and his family arrived in Clinton County, they proposed to settle near the town of Lyons, where they had discovered former neighbors from the East. But they "found that the 'claim-makers' had ploughed their furrows and set their cornerstakes around all the land near the river, leaving their agents to 'sell-out,' while they had sought new fields for similar enterprise."[11] The Hesses decided to go elsewhere, but their old neighbors interceded with the other residents of the settlement, and

[10] Patrick B. Wolfe, *Wolfe's History of Clinton County, Iowa* . . . (2 vols.; Indianapolis, 1911), I, 51.
[11] Western Historical Company, *History of Clinton County*, pp. 444–45.

they were "informed that they were at liberty to settle upon any lands not occupied by an actual settler, and that the settlers would protect them against all claimants." Here, evidently, the early comers had banded together to sell government land to latecomers on the pretext that it was claimed land, although the claims they were selling had no substantial improvements on them and were not occupied.

A similar situation existed in Appanoose County, where a claim club had been organized in 1845. There, the resident friends of a group of newly arrived settlers pointed out to the newcomers good farm locations that were unoccupied but claimed by other settlers. Although the club was called out in force as a result, the local residents who had tried to assist their friends stood fast, maintaining that they would not hesitate to point out surplus lands to inquirers in those instances where the ostensible claimant already held a quarter-section plus a reasonable amount of timberland.[12] Some local historians make it clear that claim-club action was often precipitated not by a threat to a squatter's occupied claim but rather by the effort of a squatter to defend an unoccupied second tract against the claim of a latecomer. The historian of Harrison County tells in language more expressive than precise of a "claim-jumper" who "thought that because the claimant held down a good hundred and sixty acre tract, that, having spread himself over this number of acres, that there was not enough left of the said claimant to amount to [as] much as the additional one hundred and sixty acre claim." Within an hour, according to this account, "a score of earnest, angry men," had brought the "claim-jumper" before a settler jury. This same historian justified club action because the "'home,' the absolute right of all, was invaded."[13]

In his history of Marion County, William M. Donnel pointed out:

Many settlers were not content with the amount of land the law entitled them to, but made pretended claims to so large a portion of the territory that, in some instances, it was difficult for a buyer to find an unclaimed lot. Of course such claims were without improvements, but the pretended claimants, by representing themselves as the real owners thereof, would frequently impose upon some unwary buyer, or, by threats, extort from him sums, varying in proportion to the supposed value of the claim, or whatever sum could be obtained.[14]

James W. Merrill climaxed an account of the claim system in Des Moines County with a description of the land sale at Burlington. In general, the settlers were not an extremely prosperous group, he said, but "some sold claims on lands contiguous to their homestead for enough money to make their entry."[15] Madison County was "singularly free of molestation by land

[12] Western Historical Company, *History of Appanoose County*, pp. 365–66.

[13] Smith, *History of Harrison County*, p. 82.

[14] Donnel, *op. cit.*, p. 49.

[15] James W. Merrill, *Yellow Spring[s] and Huron: A Local History Containing Sketches of All the People, Institutions, and Events, from the Earliest Settlement to the Date of Publication* (Mediapolis, Iowa, 1897), p. 43.

speculators," according to the local historian, but still a small group of settlers organized a claim club. "Half a dozen persons who, in a small and modest manner, were doing something in a legitimate way, at trading in claims to 'accomodate new settlers,' jumped aboard the proposition" to form a club.[16] This squatters' association seems, therefore, to have been organized as a means of protecting the trade in claims rather than as a device to protect the home from the speculator and the claim-jumper. One unusual indication that the clubs were not always considered to be desirable institutions appeared in Monroe County, where the members of a local Presbyterian church declared outright defiance of the claim association and ultimately broke it up.[17]

Available for the use of historians are the claim registers of the squatter associations in Johnson, Poweshiek, and Webster counties. Used in conjunction with the county records, they reveal a good deal about the behavior of the club members.[18] Table 6 summarizes the history of the 671 settlers whose names appeared in the records of the three clubs.

TABLE 6

CLAIM CLUB MEMBERS AND FEDERAL ENTRY

	Members	Acquired Land at Federal Sale (Per Cent)	Aquired Land after Federal Sale (Per Cent)	Acquired no Land in County (Per Cent)
Johnson Co. (1838–43)	325	35	21	44
Poweshiek Co. (1851–54)	91	36	49	15
Webster Co. (1854–56)	255	29	21	50

Of the three clubs, the Poweshiek association had the highest percentage (36) of members who actually acquired land from the government. A considerably larger percentage of Poweshiek club members (49) also acquired lands in the county after the federal land sales than was the case in Johnson and Webster counties. Of the settlers in those counties, almost half evidently failed to acquire land there. Actually, the Poweshiek figures may give a misleading picture of the situation in that county, because the records date only from the revision of the club's constitution and do not perhaps reveal the complete history of squatter activities in the community. Among those who did acquire land at the government sale in all three counties, a considerable number obtained holdings that had not been part of their original claims. Residents of the county seat, hardly striving farmers, formed a substantial element among those who acquired land in each club. In Johnson County, particularly, there was much trading in claims. Indeed, one member of this

[16] Mueller, op. cit., I, 126.
[17] Western Historical Company, History of Monroe County, p. 377.
[18] The relevant county records are the "Book of Original Entries" and the "Index of Deeds," located in the recorder's office at Iowa City, Johnson County; Montezuma, Poweshiek County; Fort Dodge, Webster County; and Dakota City, Humboldt County. The Fort Dodge club had members in both Webster and Humboldt counties.

club participated in twenty-two transactions. Six of the first seven men who signed the club compact in Johnson County appeared in four or more entries on the club record, and, of the eighteen officers who served the club, thirteen fell into the same category. Although the members might describe their activities as "garding our rights against the speculator," [19] the land-dealer and the engrosser were actually in their midst. In the townships subject to claim law in Johnson County, one club member actually purchased 2,834 acres from the federal government.

Apparently, the claim clubs were rather ineffective if designed solely to allow the members to protect their claims from claim-jumpers and speculator-bidders at the land sale. Only about one-third of the group managed to purchase land at the federal sales, and much of this was not included in the original claims. And the members of the successful third ultimately purchased only about one-half the acreage that they had originally claimed. But perhaps the real role of the club was more complex than Shambaugh and his followers have believed. Perhaps some among the successful third used the power of the club to enforce latecomers or speculators at the sale to purchase their claims and then bid in others for themselves. Similarly, perhaps others who acquired but a portion of their original claim had disposed of the rest of it to new settlers for funds, which were then tendered to the receiver at the land auction.

We must pay some further attention to the category in Table 6 of those who acquired land after the federal sale. Certainly, in Poweshiek County, and to a lesser extent in the other two counties, some members of this group had resorted to the time-entry system. Impecunious at the date of the land sale, such men stepped aside for capitalists who pledged to deed the claims back to their occupants if the squatters found purchase money during the next six months or year. To seal such a bargain, the capitalist or money-lender typically gave a bond for a deed to the settler. Such a transaction, of course, was a form of loan, and one which usually involved a high rate of interest. Perhaps the interest rates would have been higher had there been no claim clubs to strengthen the hand of the squatter.

The records of the Johnson County squatters' association allow us to re-evaluate an incident which both Shambaugh and Roscoe Lokken, the historian of public land disposal in Iowa, believed to be illustrative of police action by the claim clubs generally. Lokken, indeed, described it as an example of "pioneer justice." [20] In 1839 the members of the Johnson County club mobilized to drive "a man named Crawford" from a claim owned by William Sturgis. When Crawford refused to abandon the claim, even though Sturgis offered to pay for the improvements, some sixty members of the club under the leadership of its marshal tore down Crawford's substantial log-and-clapboard cabin. Crawford then rebuilt the cabin and moved his

[19] Shambaugh, *Constitution and Records*, p. 21.
[20] *Ibid.*, xv–xvi; Lokken, *op. cit.*, pp. 73, 75.

family into it. The club members returned to the claim, however, and this time Crawford "adjusted" the matter to the "full satisfaction" of Sturgis.

In preparing his account of the clash between Crawford and Sturgis, Shambaugh evidently depended upon an unfinished history of Johnson County which was written by two former members of the association, Cyrus Sanders and Henry Felkner. A second look at the incident reveals a deeper meaning in the affair. The actions of the aggrieved Sturgis did not really conform to the pattern of squatter democracy sketched by the early historians of claim-club activity. Sturgis apparently had not made any improvements on the claim, for, if he had, Sanders and Felkner would certainly have mentioned them. Between April 1, 1839, and March 9, 1843, the name of William Sturgis appeared repeatedly in the club records.[21] He filed three claims, purchased five additional claims for an outlay of $270, and sold five claims for sums totaling $400. The amount of the "adjustment" with Crawford does not appear in the claim record. At the land sales, Sturgis purchased 463 acres in Johnson County — much more than any pioneer farmer needed for farming operations. Patently, he was no hard-pressed pioneer defending his home. In the Crawford incident he played the role of a claim-speculator who used the club for support in extorting tribute from a latecomer in the community. That the club membership would twice mobilize to support Sturgis illuminates the sympathies and aspirations of his fellows in the association.

Heroic squatters, intent on winning title to their little patches of improvements in the public domain, ranged against the greedy capitalist or speculator — this time-honored dichotomy is hardly satisfactory any longer. To many squatters, indeed, the capitalist was a necessity. Induced to buy a portion of the settler's claim, or a source of funds under the time-entry system, the man of capital provided the means by which a penniless squatter could still hope to acquire title to a holding. No doubt the claim clubs did protect many a deserving settler in the enjoyment of improvements and in the purchase of a home from the federal government, but the clubs also shielded the activities of others whose motives and procedures were far less simple. At times the squatters' association was the vehicle of men who sought to capitalize on priority, or to meet the government's minimum price of $1.25 per acre by deriving fictitious values from a cunning mixture of brute force and virgin land. The "actual settler" might be the victim as well as the beneficiary of the clubs. Although our concern here has been with squatters' associations in Iowa, Professor LeDuc has shown that the story in Illinois was probably much the same.

In one respect claim-club activity was linked to the peculiarities of the prairie environment. Had the lands of the Middle West all been equally attractive to settlers, there would have been less reason for clubs; almost in-

---

[21] Shambaugh, *Constitution and Records*, pp. 35, 39, 85, 113, 117, 119, 127, 133, 148, 161, 162, 169, 182.

variably lands remained unsold after the federal auction. But, to the settler, timbered land was much more valuable than plain prairie, and of timber there was not not enough for everyone. Claim-club activity, therefore, was often an effort to corner the wooded land of a new community.

If one scans the tract books of the federal land offices in the prairie triangle and then turns to the agricultural census rolls of the same townships, he will find a surprisingly small number of the original purchasers among the pioneer farmers.[22] The turnover of population in the early days of a community was considerable, as we have seen. To the newcomer, the scanty improvements on the farm of an old settler were handsome indeed when contrasted with the matted grasses, straggling hazels, and timber of the virgin land. Except perhaps in the darkest days after the depressions of 1837 and 1857, the settler who wished to renounce his choice of home was seldom deterred by the lack of purchasers. But the fluidity of the frontier population alone does not explain the small number of original entrants among the early farmers. Local farmers seldom, in fact, claimed as much as half the available farm sites at the time of the land sale. Speculators, willing to buy off fictitious squatter titles or to purchase lands in the sections where the prairies were dominant, easily acquired large holdings at the same time. Speculators bought largely also of the surveyed lands that failed to sell at the land sales and remained thereafter open to private entry at the minimum price of $1.25 per acre. Settlers who arrived in a sparsely settled community often found that large holders owned many of the attractive locations. The title of many pioneer farmers, therefore, was derived not from the federal government but from non-resident investors. The real estate agents, bankers, and lawyers of the struggling prairie settlements counted heavily on the fees that they received for acting as the local agents of non-resident landowners — speculators, railroads, and railroad land companies.

Repeated decisions by Congress to give land to American veterans in reward for their military services influenced the course of land speculation in Illinois and Iowa. In acts of 1812 and 1816 the lawmakers set aside 3,500,000 acres of land in Illinois, between the Illinois and Mississippi rivers, where certain categories of veterans of the War of 1812 might locate the quarter- or half-sections to which their bounty warrants entitled them. Unable or unwilling to grow up with the country, many of the old campaigners transferred their rights to speculators at prices well below the government minimum or lost their lands to buyers at the tax sales. John Tillson, an Illinois resident, acquired more than 290,000 acres, and Stephen B. Munn and Russell Nevins, both of New York, purchased in excess of 130,000 acres in the Illinois Military Tract.[23]

[22] The federal tract books for Iowa are available in the Taxation Division of the Office of the Secretary of State, Des Moines; those for Illinois are in the Illinois State Archives, Springfield. Duplicate sets, of course, are held by the Bureau of Land Management, in the Department of the Interior, Washington, D.C.

[23] Carlson, *op. cit.*, pp. 57–58.

Not until the time of the Mexican War did congressional interest in the landed estate of the veteran reach its height. Major bounty-warrant acts of 1847, 1850, 1852, and 1855, with an amendatory act of 1856, offered 160 acres of land to any soldier who had served at least fourteen days in any war, beginning with the War of Independence. Indian campaigns were included. If death had cheated the old soldier of this earthy reward, his heirs were entitled to the grant. Many veterans were happy to sell their warrants at a sizable discount to warrant-brokers, who in turn sold them to eastern land-speculators or transferred them west for sale in the land-office towns. Warrant-dealers sometimes worked systematically through old regimental muster rolls in their search for veterans who had not yet obtained or sold their warrants.[24]

Since the price of military-bounty land warrants ordinarily was below the government's minimum price of $1.25 per acre, the speculator could make larger purchases of public lands than would have been possible under a policy of cash sales only. Certainly, many large purchasers did use the military-bounty warrants authorized by the major acts of the 1840's and 1850's, even though the act of 1850 ostensibly limited assignment of the warrant until amended two years later. Of 109 buyers who purchased large holdings of land in the Danville Land District of Illinois prior to 1856, sixty-three used warrants for all or for a portion of their purchases.[25] Similarly, warrants figured in a majority of the large purchases in Iowa.[26] That an entryman used a land warrant was not necessarily proof, however, that his purchase was speculative. Many a veteran located his own warrant and made a farm. Warrant-brokers journeyed to the land-office towns and sold their wares to settler and speculator alike.

Speculators in Illinois purchased considerable acreages under the terms of the Graduation Act of 1854, which was in effect until 1862. In this "bit law," Congress set prices ranging from 12.5 cents to $1.00 per acre on lands that had been open to private entry for ten years or more.[27] Provision in the measure called for the buyer to settle on his land and limited the amount to be purchased by one person, but speculators circumvented these requirements.

In the Morrill Act of 1862, Congress assigned lands to the states, in the amount of 30,000 acres for each member of their congressional delegations, to be used for the establishment of colleges of agriculture and mechanic arts. Those states in which there were no public lands still open for entry obtained agricultural-college scrip instead of land. The landless states were expected to assign such scrip to other parties rather than to locate it directly in the public

[24] Nathaniel Gordon of Exeter, New Hampshire, was doing this during the 1850's ("Nathaniel Gordon Papers," Manuscript Division, Baker Library, Cambridge, Mass.).

[25] Bogue, *op. cit.*, p. 20.

[26] Lokken, *op. cit.*, p. 141.

[27] W. E. S. used the expression, "bit law," writing in *Prairie Farmer*, August 22, 1863, 115.

domain. Most of the states in this category sold their land scrip to brokers who disposed of it in much the same way as they handled military-bounty warrants.[28] Its public domain by then exhausted, Illinois acquired scrip under the Morrill Act. Iowa officials, however, located some 204,000 acres under the act in the northwestern section of the state which the board of trustees of the agricultural college ultimately sold on behalf of their institution. Individuals holding the scrip of landless states located some 259,000 acres of land in Iowa, and among these entrymen the speculator was well represented. For a time at least, the ruling of the General Land Office that agricultural college scrip must be applied only in purchase of whole quarter sections caused it to sell at a lower price than 160-acre military warrants, which the land officers accepted for 80's in adjacent quarters.[29]

Speculators acquired large holdings from the public domain in Illinois during the years prior to the depression of 1837 and again during the 1850's, as the public land era in that state came to an end. The greatest years of speculative entries in Iowa came during the 1850's, immediately prior to the depression that began in 1857. But in both states purchasers obtained considerable acreages on speculation during the 1840's, and in Iowa the speculator was particularly active again during the late 1860's and early 1870's.

The speculators did not confine their interests to the federal lands in Illinois and Iowa. They also acquired substantial holdings of swamp and school lands. The activity of the American Emigrant Company in Iowa is perhaps the best-known speculation in swamp land in the two states.[30] Probably it was atypical, however. Administered at the local level as they were, the swamp and school lands, when diverted to speculation, fell more commonly into the control of small, local real estate operators rather than into the possession of non-residents. But substantial acreages of the Illinois and Michigan Canal lands, of the grant for the improvement of the Des Moines River, and of the holdings of the various land-grant railroads in the prairie triangle reached the hands of actual farmers only after passing through the intermediary of the speculator.[31] Occasionally, the historians of the railroads have maintained that the railroads tried to sell their lands primarily to settlers.[32] But they submit no evidence to show that the land-grant roads

[28] Thomas LeDuc, "State Disposal of the Agricultural College Land Scrip," *Agricultural History*, XXVIII (July, 1954), 99–107.

[29] *Prairie Farmer*, December 22, 1866, p. 400.

[30] Daniel F. Clynch, "An Introduction to Swamp Land Disposal in Iowa: 1850–1880" (unpublished M.A. thesis, State University of Iowa, 1957), particularly chap. vii, pp. 57–69; Bogue, "The Swamp Land Act and Wet Land Utilization in Illinois, 1850–1890," *Agricultural History*, XXV (October, 1951), 169–80.

[31] Lokken, *op. cit.*, pp. 210–35; Gates, *The Illinois Central Railroad and Its Colonization Work*, pp. 149–68, 254–79; Richard C. Overton, *Burlington West: A Colonization History of the Burlington Railroad* (Cambridge, 1941). I have myself examined the tract books of the Chicago, Rock Island and Pacific Railroad Company at the offices of the Company in the La Salle Street Station, Chicago.

[32] See, e.g., Overton, *op. cit.*, p. 314.

or their land-company affiliates ever sent away an affluent speculator empty-handed.

Wherever the federal surveyors drove their stakes or built their mounds, the land-speculator or his agent was sure to follow. Indeed, on occasion, he was even ahead of the surveyors. From the entry books of the federal land offices and other sources, Professor Paul Wallace Gates assembled a numerous gallery of such gentry.[33] Gates has argued, indeed, that, of 38,000,000 acres of public lands sold between 1845 and 1857, the sale of some 29,000,000 acres represented speculation. He has suggested also that speculators purchased at least 6,000,000 acres of the 12,000,000 acres that the federal government sold in Iliinois between 1849 and 1856.[34] In her study of land disposal and tenure patterns in eight counties of the Illinois Grand Prairie, Margaret Beattie Bogue showed that at the Danville Land Office there were 109 purchases which ranged in size from 1,000 to 60,000 acres.[35] According to Roscoe Lokken, 140 purchasers acquired a total of more than 1,000,000 acres of land in Iowa.[36] Names like Easley, Willingham, Ogden, Sturges, Cook, Sargent, and many others appear with monotonous regularity on the pages of the federal land-office tract books that record the disposal of vast stretches of the prairie states.

The secretaries of a number of Iowa county agricultural societies estimated the amount of acreage owned by non-residents in their counties in 1865. Although such lands were "becoming very limited" in older counties like Muscatine, Cedar, and Johnson, nearby Linn County reported one-twentieth of its acreage owned by absentees, and Washington County, also adjacent to Johnson, still claimed 30,000 acres of land owned by "speculators, non-residents and corporations." In Decatur County, non-residents owned almost 180,000 acres; the figure was 75,000 in Fremont. In Poweshiek, speculators and absentees owned 123,000 acres, somewhat less than in Story County, where "about one-third" was in similar hands. The correspondent from Taylor County believed that out-of-county folk owned half the land there.[37] Through the mid-nineteenth century, politicians, both eminent and petty, and eastern businessmen of high and low degree cherished with their western counterparts a common concern over the price of land in Illinois and Iowa.

Writers have attempted to classify the buyers of large holdings, to distinguish between those who devoted the bulk of their time and capital to the

[33] Paul W. Gates: "Disposal of the Public Domain in Illinois, 1848–1856," *Journal of Economic and Business History*, III (February, 1931), 216–40; "Land Policy and Tenancy in the Prairie States," *Journal of Economic History*, I (May, 1941), 60–82; "Southern Investments in Northern Lands Before the Civil War," *Journal of Southern History*, V (May, 1939), 155–85.
[34] Gates, "Disposal of the Public Domain in Illinois," p. 228.
[35] Bogue, *op. cit.*, p. 20.
[36] Lokken, *op. cit.*, p. 141.
[37] Iowa State Agricultural Society, *Report, 1865* (Des Moines, 1866). The quoted phrases appear on pp. 523, 533, and 518.

traffic in lands and those who simply took a flyer in land speculation; between the cattlemen and prosperous farmers who amassed great acreages for large scale farming operations and the group, numbering among it the Irish land-lord William Scully, who hoped to build up permanent tenant estates. The phrase "land-speculator" was an indispensable part of the frontier vocabu-lary, but it is not easy to use precisely. To his contemporaries, the speculator of the nineteenth century was an individual who purchased large acreages of unimproved land, intending to sell after land values had risen sufficiently to make the sales remunerative and who was not interested in working the land as a personal enterprise or under tenancy. Under such a definition, motivation becomes crucial in identifying the speculator. But to discover this is often impossible. Large holders who built up tenant estates or large farming enterprises often sold a portion of their original purchases. Avowed speculators might rent some of their holdings for a time, expecting the improvements of the tenants to enhance their value. Local use of the term "speculator" during the nineteenth century was colored somewhat by whether or not the large landholder was a resident in the community where his land lay.[38] Some historians have emphasized correctly that the motiva-tion of the actual settler himself might be speculative — that he often hoped to sell all or a portion of his land at a handsome advance on cost.[39] In em-phasizing the large operators in frontier lands, historians have, however, said too little about the importance of the small speculator, who only purchased a few hundred acres. Difficult to distinguish from the actual settler on the land-office books, such buyers in total were of considerable importance.

Of the speculator's importance in the history of land disposal in the Middle West there can be no doubt. We never will know exactly what proportion of the lands of Iowa and Illinois passed through his hands. Many speculative purchasers of small and medium-sized holdings in the public domain cannot be identified or traced even by the most intensive use of local records. This is true also in the case of many who purchased land from the state agencies and transportation companies. Nor can we ever assess with certainty the profits which accrued to the land-speculator.[40] Manifestly, these varied in proportion to the attractiveness of the holdings acquired and the skill that the speculators displayed in management and in forecasting economic trends. Time of purchase and of sale was important. Lands acquired in the flush times of the 1830's or 1850's and resold before the crashes of 1837 and 1857 might return a handsome profit. Tracts acquired just before depression set in

[38] An outspoken critic of speculators on occasion, the editor of the *Hamilton Free-man* had words only of praise when he reported that Colonel John Scott, a prominent resident of the next county to the south, had resold a school-land section in Hamilton County for $5,200 after purchasing it less than a year earlier for $1,600 (*Hamilton Freeman*, April 7, 1869).

[39] James C. Malin, Paul W. Gates, and Thomas LeDuc have all recognized this fact.

[40] The discussion of profits which follows is based upon Allan G. Bogue and Mar-garet B. Bogue, " 'Profits' and the Frontier Land Speculator," *Journal of Economic History*, XVII (March, 1957), 1–24.

and held for many years while settlers filtered slowly in and tax bills mounted might return a low rate of interest, 3–6 per cent perhaps on the invested capital.

It was the town promoters, rather than the speculators in agricultural land, of course, who made the most fabulous profits and, conversely, suffered the most shattering losses. The speculator who carefully selected agricultural lands in Iowa and Illinois with an eye to their productivity and future markets, who scattered his lands sufficiently so that they would benefit from the improvements of neighboring farmers, but yet concentrated them enough so that administration was not too expensive, probably in the end realized between 6 and 15 per cent on his investment. Of course, there were many unhappy exceptions, and, in cases where the title was in doubt, as in the Illinois Military Tract or in the Des Moines River Lands above the Raccoon Fork, the large holder regretted his involvement. But, if some lost money in land speculation, there were always others willing to take a chance on the raw lands of the frontier. In some cases — the Davenports of Bath, New York, are a good illustration — several generations of the same family made repeated investments in lands farther and farther to the west during the mid-nineteenth century. Such cases hardly support the suggestions of some historians that land speculation was generally unprofitable.

If the land-speculator made profits, he also made himself highly unpopular. "This holding of lands by non-resident speculators," foamed an Iowa editor in 1869, "is one of the most serious drawbacks to the improvement of the western country . . . a regular dog-in-the-manger policy. They will neither improve the lands themselves nor sell them at prices that others can afford to settle on and improve them." [41] Such words would have found favor among the "actual settlers" of most midwestern communities. But somehow the speculator rode out the storm. As an Iowa land agent wrote to his eastern superior in 1876: "The emigration to this state was never greater & mostly locate in [the] western part of the state. At present large share [are] homesteaders, pre-empters & purchasers of railroad land companies but the country is fast settling up and soon the 'speculator' will have his turn." [42] The optimism was justified; the speculator had indeed always had his turn.

Sharing Jefferson's admiration for the virtues of the yeoman, many historians have considered the land-speculator with distaste. [43] The indictment is a long one. The greedy land-jobber despoiled both the helpless Indians and an unwary country. He influenced land policy at both the national and the state levels to the detriment of the actual farmer. He corrupted officers of

[41] *Hamilton Freeman*, May 12, 1869.

[42] John Weare, Cedar Rapids, Iowa, to John Davenport, Bath, New York, June 16, 1876 ("Davenport Collection," Cornell University Collection of Regional History, Ithaca, N. Y.).

[43] For a list of the major treatments of the speculator theme see Bogue and Bogue, *op. cit.*, pp. 2–7, nn. 2–26.

the General Land Office at Washington and the district offices, so that he might select the choicest of lands. Underlying the bitter struggles over the location of western capitals, state institutions, and even, at the local level, the county seats was the pervasive influence of land-speculators who hoped that their holdings would increase in value if the right decision was made. Their holdings forced "widespread dispersion of population," and they refused to bear their just share of the tax burden in the pioneer community. It was the land-speculator who brought tenancy to the Middle West in the first generation. Nor did the effects of land speculation end with the pioneer generation. For "scarcely a city or country town in the West but had its first family whose fortune had been made by shrewd selection of lands and their subsequent sale or rental to later comers. Wealth which had come easily to them through their speculations had become a vested interest, which they sought to protect." [44]

There is, of course, much truth in this case against the speculator. Land-disposal policies did foster inequities at times in the economic and social structure of the western community. In the minds of many of the critics, however, there is the implicit assumption that the nation would have benefited most from its landed heritage if the public domain had been distributed as free homesteads to actual settlers from the beginning. This was usually the position of the farm-makers in the new settlements. But there is another side to the coin. We can rightly regard the operations of the speculator as a means of sending capital to regions that were desperately in need of it. After Congress struck the credit provisions from the land laws in the Revision Act of 1820, the impecunious settler could still purchase land on time from the speculators.

Although they often carried it with poor grace, the speculators in the Middle West did bear a substantial share of the tax burden as new communities developed. True, their lands often remained raw prairie, brush, and woods, while the assessor appraised those of the actual settlers at a higher value because of their improvements. At the same time, as Herbert Quick has suggested, the disparity in valuation between improved, and unimproved lands was much less than it should have been. [45] Prior to sale, also, the speculator lands provided the settlers with hay land, range, building timber, and rails. When actual settlers failed to obtain original holdings large enough to make economic units in the commercial agriculture of the nineteenth century, they were able on occasion to enlarge their farms by purchasing from the speculators rather than by squeezing neighbors from the land.

The settler also benefited from the land-dealer's advertising, which brought newcomers to the community with money to spend and the need to buy food, feed, and stock from their new neighbors before their own

[44] Paul W. Gates, "The Role of the Land Speculator in Western Development," *Pennsylvania Magazine of History and Biography*, LXVI (July, 1942), 332.

[45] Herbert Quick, *The Hawkeye* (Indianapolis, 1923), pp. 21–22.

CHAPTER III

"Free Land" Is Not Free

Land values in the Corn Belt of today seemingly put the judgment of the pioneers to serious question. In general, the first settlers slashed their claim markers on the timber along the streams and in the prairie groves. Broken in surface, their soils comparatively low in organic content, these locations are generally much less valuable now than the prairies which the firstcomers avoided. Undoubtedly, it was the timber that made the early locations so attractive. Here were the rails, the building materials, the fuel, and the sheltered locations for house and stables that the settler desired. Water supplies, nearness to mill sites, the navigability of some of the prairie rivers, and the marshy and "sickly" nature of much prairie ground may have influenced the pioneer as well, but they counted much less in his decision than did the oak, hickory, walnut, and locust trees of the wooded lands. Knowing his need for timber, the farmer "hunting country" was willing to pay $25 or even $100 for a claim rather than to risk the open prairies.

Typically, the settlers encroached slowly upon the prairies, their farms ringing the wooded margins before some hardy or experimental soul ventured away from the timber. In 1837, when the Rowell brothers from New Hampshire chose a farm location in McLean County, Illinois, which was a mile and a half from timber, other settlers believed that "these daring men would freeze to death out there" and called them "fool yankees."[1] As late as 1854, a Pennsylvanian, who started a farm well beyond the timber margin in Livingston County, was "generally pronounced a lunatic."[2] A historian of Cedar County, Iowa, described the early settlements of 1836 and 1837 in that county and remarked, "The prairie land was regarded as worthless for purposes of agriculture, and was considered as a useless waste. There were hundreds of men who honestly believed it would never be occupied."[3] Benjamin J. Rodgers located land there in 1853 and was

---

[1] E. Duis, *The Good Old Times in McLean County, Illinois* (Bloomington, 1874), p. 437 (quoted in Margaret R. Beattie, "Matthew Scott, Pioneer Landlord, Gentleman Farmer, 1855–1891," [unpublished M.A. thesis, Cornell University, 1947]), p. 18.

[2] *History of Livingston County, Illinois* (Chicago, 1878), p. 354 (quoted in Beattie, *op. cit.*, p. 19).

[3] Western Historical Company, *The History of Cedar County, Iowa* . . . (Chicago, 1878), p. 325.

"among the first to move out on the prairie." [4] In systematic studies of settlement in eastern and central Iowa, geographers have confirmed the accounts of the local historians.[5]

When settlers did break free from the timbered stream courses and groves, they would in many cases purchase small timber lots of ten or twenty acres, sometimes as far as ten or fifteen miles from their farms. Here in the winter months they sized out building timber or rails and cut firewood for the summer months ahead.[6]

Were some cultural groups more likely to settle in the timber than on the prairie? Chronology no doubt accounted to a considerable degree for such patterns where they occurred. Even in northwestern Iowa, settlers still preferred locations close to the timber. If particular groups, the Yankees or Danes, say, were more common on the prairie than in the timber, it was largely because they arrived after the timber had passed into other hands.

The pioneer farmers of the prairie triangle have left a cryptic record of their land dealings in the federal entry and tract books and in the county records. We can never fully understand, of course, the plans, hopes, fears, triumphs, and disasters that underlay these entries. But study of the records does reveal to some extent the relationship of men to land in the era of settlement. From the federal entry books, the deed index, the transfer books, and the mortgage records of Hamilton County, Iowa, down to 1896, I have pieced together the tenure histories of the farmers whose farming operations were reported in the agricultural censuses of 1860 and 1870 in Hamilton Township.[7]

When first organized, Hamilton Township included all the lands in Township 87 North, Range 25 West of the Fifth Principal Meridian and parts of the congressional townships to the west, north, and east. Land disposal in this township was similar to that in many areas of the wet prairie in Iowa, although more varied undoubtedly than in some. Federal officers put the lands of this township to sale first in 1849, and 149 purchasers bought holdings there during the next decade. Subsequently, eleven others acquired parcels of land directly from the government. Nine of the latter were home-

[4] *Ibid.*, p. 605.

[5] Leslie Hewes, "Some Features of Early Woodland and Prairie Settlement in a Central Iowa County," *Annals of the Association of American Geographers*, XL (March, 1950), 40–57; Clare C. Cooper, "The Role of Railroads in the Settlement of Iowa: A Study in Historical Geography" (unpublished M.A. thesis, University of Nebraska, 1958); Karl K. Keffer, "Original Land Entry in Eastern Iowa" (unpublished M.A. thesis, State University of Iowa, 1954).

[6] Hewes, *op. cit.*, p. 53. I first noticed this pattern while working in the county records of Hamilton and Bremer counties, Iowa.

[7] The tract books of the federal land offices in Iowa are now held in the Taxation Division of the Secretary of State's Office, Des Moines. The Hamilton County deed registers, mortgage registers, and the appropriate indexes are in the Recorder's Office, Webster City, Iowa. The transfer books are in the Auditor's Office. Here, too, are the minute books of the Board of Supervisors, which contain considerable administrative detail about the disposition of the swamp and school lands in the county.

steaders who obtained forty- or eighty-acre homesteads during the late
1860's and 1870's. These tracts were remnants that, in some instances, were
earlier considered part of the county swamp-land grant. The 151 federal
grantees who did not qualify under the Homestead Law purchased their
lands with cash or land warrants. A majority of them were probably speculators in some degree. Eleven men purchased large tracts, ranging in size
from 483 to 960 acres; of the group apparently only three subsequently lived
in Hamilton Township. Among the large purchasers were Ira Cook, Hugh
Downey, and Charles Barney, land-agents and bankers from eastern Iowa;
a former Iowa governor, Ralph Lowe; and three large buyers from the
Southern seaboard, James S. Easley, William W. Willingham, and Elias
White. Of the 149 individuals who purchased land in Hamilton Township
prior to 1860, only nine were actually farming there in that year.

TABLE 7

FEDERAL SALES TO INDIVIDUALS
HAMILTON TOWNSHIP

ACREAGE	No. OF PURCHASERS	ACREAGE	No. OF PURCHASERS
40	20	321–360	2
41– 80	34	361–400	3
81–120	14	401–440	2
121–160	46	441–480	2
161–200	6	481–520	4
201–240	8	521–560	2
241–280	6	561–640	2
281–320	6	Over 640	3

While the speculators and the actual settlers were making their selections
of land in Hamilton Township, a number of institutional claimants reserved
large acreages there also. During the 1850's the Des Moines River Navigation and Railroad Company, originally a river-improvement concern, and
the Dubuque and Pacific Railroad Company each located approximately
2,500 acres of land in the township.[8] Under the Swamp Land Act of 1850,
the county itself claimed more than 5,000 acres in the township.[9] Since the
validity of the river-improvement titles and some of the swamp-land locations in the county were challenged, the titles to some lands originally in
these categories were uncertain for many years.

This, then, is the general picture of federal land disposal in Hamilton

[8] The most recent and in many respects the best account of the overlapping land
grants in the upper valley of the Des Moines is to be found in Leonard F. Ralston,
"Iowa Railroads and the Des Moines River Improvement Land Grant of 1846," *Iowa
Journal of History*, LVI (April, 1958), 97–128.

[9] Daniel F. Clynch's "An Introduction to Swamp Land Disposal in Iowa: 1850–
1880" (unpublished M.A. thesis, State University of Iowa, 1957), pp. 70–82, deals
with the swamp-land disposal policies of Hamilton County and is based upon my
notes of information in the County Supervisors' Minutes and in the issues of the
Hamilton Freeman (Webster City).

Township. Now let us consider some of the farmers themselves. The census-taker of 1860 found twenty-two farmers in Hamilton Township who either owned or would own land there shortly, as well, evidently, as a few squatters or tenants who never gained title. To the residue of the 1860 group, the marshal of 1870 added sixty-four new farmers.

Among the 1860 group of twenty-two landholders, there were only nine federal purchasers, less than 50 per cent of the whole. Some of the largest resident holders in 1860 had not purchased from the federal government at all but rather from the government's grantees. Of the 1860 group, some half-dozen acquired several hundred acres during the 1850's and then scaled down their holdings over the next decade. In this number was one definite speculator who participated in some thirty-seven transactions in the township prior to 1897. It was with good cause that the census-taker of 1860 listed his occupation in part as "Trader." Most members of the class of 1860 fell far short of the trader's activity, but by 1897, thirteen of the twenty-two had participated in at least six land transactions. Some of the sales of the old settlers in 1860 were undoubtedly linked directly to the locations of their land. Like firstcomers throughout the Corn Belt generally, they had gone to the timber, settling in the northwestern corner of the township along the Boone River. Some of the ten- and twenty-acre tracts that they ultimately sold were timber lots, transferred to settlers on the prairie. The sales of small tracts in the northwestern corner of the township also reflected petty mining activities in the coal outcrops along the banks of the Boone River. We can trace some of the sale activity among the farmers of 1860 also, evidently, to "swapping" as two neighbors agreed that they would both benefit in their farming operations by exchanging forties.

TABLE 8
HAMILTON TOWNSHIP
FARMERS AND LAND TRANSACTIONS

	0–5	6–10	11–15	16–20	21 plus
1860 group (22)	9	6	2	3	2
1870 group (57)	36	14	3	3	1

Of the sixty-four farmers in Hamilton Township who arrived after 1860 and were present in 1870, fifteen did not own land in that year. They were either tenants or residents on county swamp lands, railroad lands, or the holdings of the grantees of the Des Moines River Navigation and Railroad Company. Seven of the fifteen never did acquire title. But fifty-seven of the sixty-four new farmers of 1870 were ultimately landowners in the township. Only four of them, however, obtained land directly from the United States. Of the four, a Pennsylvanian Jacob Omstead purchased 560 acres of federal land in the township during the 1850's. He had sold much of this by the end of 1860 and listed a farm unit of only seventy-five acres in the 1870 census. Quite possibly some of Omstead's federal purchases were made in behalf of another member of his family to whom he transferred several tracts. The three remaining federal purchasers acquired their holdings at the government land office in the 1860's, one by private entry, two by homesteading. There seemed less inclination to deal in land among the new farmers of 1870 than was the case among the farmers of 1860. Almost 60 per cent of the 1860 group had participated in more than five land transactions by 1886; only 37 per cent of the 1870 group were involved in more than five transactions prior to 1897. Perhaps this showed a greater preoccupation with farming and less interest in land speculation on the side among the newer farmers; probably it also reflected the rising value of land and the fact that by 1875, the sale or purchase of a forty might involve more money than the sale of an eighty ten years earlier. Often in both groups, however, a small number of transactions meant simply that the farmer in question had not stayed long in the county.

We find almost endless variety of behavior as we examine the land dealings of the farmers in Hamilton Township. One pioneer might buy an eighty-acre tract and sell it two years later. His neighbor might build up his acreage by acquiring forty-acre tracts one at a time, over a span of ten or fifteen years, and then sell out. Meanwhile, the large holder adjacent to them was selling off his lands. Another farmer built up a large holding by repeated purchases and then, after some fifteen years of acquisition, began to sell off his land at approximately the same rate as he acquired it. His neighbor, meanwhile, was constantly buying and selling. Others, in a series of transactions, bought, improved, sold, and bought again. Linked to such behavior, of course, were a great variety of personal considerations. One farmer sold out after his wife had died of quick consumption; another after diphtheria struck down his growing family. Still another man was, according to reports, "a perennial improver" who improved a series of farms in the county, selling each when he received an attractive offer.[10] Certainly, the man who came west, bought a tract of the size that he thought necessary for his farming operations, and then tilled it for the rest of his life was rare indeed. The more common picture was one of several moves or repeated purchases and sales. Hamilton farmers evidently were ever alert to buy or sell when they saw a chance of making a profit. And all this activity moved, to some extent, in tune with economic conditions — when times were good, more land changed hands.

To some degree, certainly, family plans and aspirations were linked to the patterns of land sales. Five of the farmers of 1860 transferred land to one or more sons; eight young men acquired land in this way in the township. Proportionately fewer of the farmers of 1870 conveyed land to their sons than did those of 1860; eight of the fifty-seven owners assigned land

[10] Obituary of Nelson G. Omstead (*Hamilton Freeman*, September 26, 1919).

to a total of twelve sons. Other degrees of family relationships are discernible in land sales, althought it is difficult to trace them on the female side.

A number of families found a particularly happy environment in Hamilton Township. Several members of the Adams family, of Kentucky stock via Illinois, settled there in the early years, and numerous members of the family farmed, for a time at least, in the township. Six farmers named Adams reported farming operations in the agricultural census of 1870. By 1884, the patriarch of the family, "Uncle Jimmy" to the general community, had given warranty deeds to over 900 acres of land, much of it going to four younger Adams, including at least two sons. Less numerous and perhaps even more prosperous was the Groves family, originally from Pennsylvania. Both Jackson Groves and his son Alexander built up large holdings of land, and were leading cattle-feeders in the township.[11] Ultimately, a grandson of Jackson would sit in the state legislature. No doubt the satisfaction or dissatisfaction of kinfolk reinforced the feelings of the pioneer farmers, making their locations more or less desirable and thus affecting their decisions to buy or sell land on occasion.

The quarter-section farm was not the rule in pioneer Hamilton Township. Fifty-one farmers, who lived there or in neighboring Webster and Marion townships in 1860, reported farm units that averaged 188 acres in size, although the median farm was indeed 160 acres in that year. Thereafter, the size of Hamilton Township farms fell for some twenty years as new settlers opened up smaller units, and the original residents subdivided holdings by transfer to members of their families or by sale to latecomers. The average farm unit included only 85 acres in 1880. The owner-operators of 1860 and 1870 in Hamilton Township participated in 514 separate land transactions between 1852 and 1896. Of these purchases and sales, 53 per cent involved tracts of forty acres or less; only 9 per cent transferred titles to 160-acre units.

A careful student of Iowa agriculture, Earle D. Ross, has argued that in Iowa, at least, there was no land boom until the twentieth century.[12] We may say the same of Illinois, although Illinois settlers of the 1830's or Iowa farm-seekers in the 1850's might have dissented at the time. Still, the long-time investor in middle-western land who considered the history of land prices in these states from the vantage point of 1900 must have felt considerable gratification. The deed records of five Iowa counties show that the average price of lands sold during this year varied from $35 to $47 — a considerable increase over the government minimum of $1.25, for which many of the same tracts had passed into private hands between forty and

[11] There are biographical sketches of James Adams and Jackson Groves in Lewis Biographical Publishing Company, *Biographical Record and Portrait Album of Hamilton and Wright Counties, Iowa* . . . (Chicago, 1889), pp. 248–49, 268–69. See also "The People and School of Pleasant Hill" in the Webster City *Hamilton Freeman*, October 18, 1882.

[12] Earle D. Ross, *Iowa Agriculture: An Historical Survey* (Iowa City, 1951), p. 70.

sixty years earlier.[13] There were wide variations, of course, in the prices for which land sold in the same county or township. Estimates of productivity and nearness to markets influenced the price of even unimproved

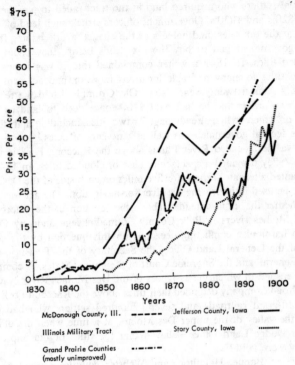

Fig. 4. — Illinois and Iowa land values, 1830–1900

lands. When "Uncle Jimmy" Adams purchased 700 acres of land in Hamilton Township in 1857, he paid $6.00 an acre for it, despite the fact that it was unimproved and had sold for close to the government's minimum price no more than three years earlier. The amount of timber or marsh on a tract, similarly, might affect the price of unimproved land. In Jefferson County, Iowa, where the first land sales occurred in 1838, it was not until 1870 that prairie land, basically the more productive, began to command higher prices than did timberland.[14]

In some restricted areas of Illinois and Iowa, conflicts over land titles

[13] Adrian H. Lindsey, "The Nature and Cause of the Growth of Iowa Land Values" (unpublished Ph.D. dissertation, Iowa State College of Agriculture and Mechanic Arts, 1929), pp. 212–13. The counties studied were Cherokee, Fayette, Jefferson, Montgomery, and Story.

[14] *Ibid.*, p. 144.

depressed land prices below those prevailing in areas that were intrinsically no more productive. Most strikingly was this the case in the Illinois Military Tract between the Illinois and Mississippi rivers. Many of the speculators and actual settlers who acquired land in the tract failed to pay their taxes in the 1820's and 1830's. Government officers struck such land off to purchasers at the tax sales, and holders of the chains of title issuing from the federal government had to buy the tax deeds before they could convey unclouded titles. In 1849 a writer complained that it was impossible to get good titles to many desirable locations in Knox and adjacent Illinois counties.[15] Almost twenty years later "Old Grumbler" told the readers of the *Prairie Farmer* that he had paid $100 for a deed to land in Warren County, on which he had already paid for two titles, including that stemming from the federal government, as well as ten years of taxes.[16]

In Iowa the so-called River Lands above the Raccoon Fork in the Des Moines Valley provided a spectacular case of clouded titles. In 1846 Congress granted alternate sections for five miles on each side of the Des Moines River to be used in improving the river for navigation. The act was unclear as to whether the grant extended above the junction of the Raccoon and the Des Moines rivers in Polk County. Remedial legislation by Congress failed to harmonize conflicting decisions on this question by the commissioner of the General Land Office, the Secretary of the Treasury, the Attorney-General, and the Supreme Court of the United States. A complicated struggle ensued in which the assignees of the Des Moines River Navigation and Railroad Company defended their titles above the Raccoon Fork against three land-grant railroads and several hundred settlers who had entered land in the valley of the upper Des Moines at a time when the officers of the Fort Dodge Land Office believed that the titles of the improvement company were void.[17]

Settlers in Boone, Hamilton, and Webster counties formed a settlers' union, defended their titles in the courts, and sought relief at the hands of Congress.[18] Ultimately, the New York capitalists who had divided the assets of the river-improvement company made good their title to some 100,000 acres of land, but, in the meantime, their agents were hounded and their

[15] *Prairie Farmer*, July, 1849, p. 216.
[16] *Ibid.*, March 9, 1867, p. 150.
[17] Ralston, *op. cit., passim.*
[18] Although a number of articles on the Des Moines River Lands have appeared in the Iowa historical journals over the years, there is still no really adequate treatment of the settlers' union. Great amounts of newspaper and legal materials remain to be exploited. The *Hamilton Freeman*, for instance, maintained a lively interest in the controversy throughout the years. Numerous court cases appeared on the dockets of Webster, Boone, and Hamilton counties. Particularly valuable from my standpoint was a file of letters in the Davenport Collection in the Cornell University Collection of Regional History, written by John Browne of Boone, Iowa, agent of the Des Moines River Navigation and Railroad Company, and Stephen A. Foley, legal counsel of John and Ira Davenport, who inherited claims to river lands in Boone County, Iowa.

tenants and purchasers assaulted. Not until the 1890's did Congress indemnify 163 claimants who were judged to have valid grounds for damages. In all, the federal referee considered almost 600 cases.

In Iowa, conflicts between railroads and counties over the ownership of swamp land also contributed to uncertain titles, and settlers in O'Brien and Monona counties fought for the right to enter their claims under federal law rather than recognizing them as railroad lands.[19]

Not only did fear of obtaining clouded titles deter purchasers and directly depress prices in areas where titles were under contest but there were indirect results as well. Gnawed by uncertainty, settlers there improved their lands with less alacrity than in regions where titles were secure. Mortgage-lenders like the Davenports of Bath, New York, specifically ordered their agents to avoid the Military Tract in Illinois because of the uncertain titles, thus depriving the region of capital that would have otherwise contributed to its improvement.[20]

Aside from local factors, economic conditions in general affected land prices. A graph of land values in McDonough County in the Military Tract in the years between 1830 and 1850 showed that prices reflected the flush times of the 1830's by rising from less than $1.00 per acre in 1830 to almost $4.00 in 1839. In the depressed years of the late 1830's and the early 1840's, values declined to well below $3.00 and then started to rise as the economy prospered and the price level rose toward the heights of 1857.[21] Figures for the Military Tract as a whole, based on census valuations, showed the average value of land there to have been something less than $10.00 per acre in 1850. By 1870 it had risen to a little more than $40.00, but the decade of the seventies brought recession. By 1900 the average value of land in the tract was close to $55.00 per acre.[22] In the Grand Prairie, the average price of unimproved to moderately improved farmland followed a very similar pattern — a strong upward surge from a figure somewhat below $10.00 per acre in 1850 to the mid-seventies, a period of recession to 1880, and then renewed buoyancy. Slightly improved to moderately improved land in the Grand Prairie was worth nearly $55.00

[19] National Publishing Company, *History of Monona County, Iowa* . . . (Chicago, 1890), pp. 202–3; John L. E. Peck, Otto H. Montzheimer, and William J. Miller, *Past and Present of O'Brien and Osceola Counties, Iowa* . . . (2 vols.; Indianapolis, 1914), I, 84–107.

[20] Allan G. Bogue, *Money at Interest: The Farm Mortgage on the Middle Border* (Ithaca, 1955), p. 12.

[21] Theodore L. Carlson, *The Illinois Military Tract: A Study of Land Occupation, Utilization and Tenure* ("Illinois Studies in the Social Sciences," Vol. XXXII, No. 2, [Urbana, 1951]), p. 72.

[22] *Ibid.*, p. 185. Carlson used census estimates for his figures from 1850 to 1900. Some agricultural economists have argued that the census valuations sometimes vary from those derived from an analysis of land transactions. This is undoubtedly true, but the census figures do reflect general trends with some accuracy; their major defect, of course, lies in the fact that they smooth out fluctuations between the decennial census dates.

per acre on the average in 1900.[23] Adrian Lindsey's study of early land
values in three Iowa counties showed that in Jefferson, the longest settled,
land values definitely declined during the 1870's, while they leveled off in
Story and Cherokee counties, only to move upward again to reach values
in excess of $38.00 per acre in 1900. Although the depression of the late
1850's had some effect on land prices, it was evidently not nearly so pronounced as was the case following the depressions of 1837 and 1873.[24]

Many who hoped to farm in Iowa and Illinois during the pioneer period
did not have the money to buy land from the government at its minimum
price, let alone meet the surging cost of unimproved land in the counties
where the public lands were gone. Others with a small nest egg of cash
or a small stock of equipment and livestock could not hope to break, equip,
and stock their new farms if they used their resources to buy them. For
such men, tenancy provided an answer. Tenancy, indeed, was the surest
way for some farmers to guarantee themselves a crop during the first year
of settlement in a new community, no matter what their financial status.
Sod crops on new breaking were uncertain, a much greater gamble than
those sown on the five- or ten-acre field already broken on the partially
improved farms which were often for rent. In Iowa, settlers, on occasion,
rented their claims to tenants before they had actually acquired title from
the federal government.[25] Once a western community took shape, many of
the sons of resident farmers swelled the ranks of farm-seekers; their inadequate means prevented them from becoming owners immediately.

In the biographical sections of the histories of the Corn Belt counties,
published for the most part between 1875 and 1915, the reader discovers
that many prosperous farmers, active or retired, had spent from one to
ten years as tenants before becoming landowners. Tenancy for these successful men had been a step up the tenure ladder, which carried them from
their original status as hired men to positions where they not only owned
their home farms but often owned rental property as well. The agricultural
ladder was an "old reliable" among the concepts of the agricultural economists for many years. We must remember, however, that the county histories contained the biographies only of the successful citizens of the
community. No one bothered to record the histories of the tenants in the
Middle West who failed to climb the ladder to ownership.

If lack of capital was the basic reason for the institution of tenancy in
the prairie triangle during the nineteenth century, one can distinguish
special cases. As we have suggested, some pioneers preferred to rent partially improved holdings in new settlements, because of the slowness with

[23] Margaret B. Bogue, *Patterns from the Sod: Land Use and Tenure in the Grand
Prairie, 1850–1900* (Springfield, 1959), p. 128.
[24] Lindsey, *loc. cit.*, 212–13.
[25] See the documents accompanying Antoine Le Clair's entry under the Pre-emption
Act of 1834 at the Dubuque Land Office, Certificate 401, issued September 20, 1839,
now on file in the National Archives, Washington, D.C.

which a raw holding could be improved. Thus in Hamilton County, Iowa, Amos Julian rented land for a time after his arrival, while at the same time claiming forty acres of government land for a homestead.[26] Others might rent land for a season or two, while they compared the merits of improved farms for sale in the neighborhood, although they had the proceeds from the sale of their old homes in hand. Sons might rent the lands of aged fathers in the expectation that ultimately the home farm would descend to them.

But was there a less happy side to tenancy? Were the tenants in some cases owners who had lost their land through foreclosure and who were actually moving down the tenure ladder rather than upward? In reading the biographical sections of the histories of five Iowa counties, I discovered a number of instances in which individuals reported that they lost farms and became tenants as a result.[27] Such men, of course, had later mended their fortunes; mention of early failures made their success stories all the more successful. Unquestionably, there were others who failed and never attained the affluence which allowed them to insert their biographies in the county "mug book." Although foreclosure rates in nineteenth-century Illinois and Iowa never reached the spectacular heights attained in the Plains States during the 1880's or 1890's, or in the Corn Belt during the 1930's, farmers did lose their land to the moneylender in the years when pioneering difficulties were sternest or in depression years, particularly the 1870's. Such men represented a very small percentage of all farmers, but they did exist, and, no doubt, some of them became tenants.

Most spectacular of the prairie landlords, of course, were a number of large land-holders who acquired considerable acreages of land, particularly in east-central Illinois during the mid-nineteenth century.[28] Of the group, the most eye-catching was William Scully, the Irish landlord who ultimately acquired more than a quarter of a million acres of land in middle-western states and in Louisiana, and whose family still retains a considerable number

[26] Mrs. Elmer Woodmansee, Hutchinson, Kansas, to the Editor, *Webster City Daily News*, May 3, 1923. Mrs. Woodmansee was Julian's daughter, and this letter was the first of two interesting reminiscences about life among the pioneers in Hamilton Township, Hamilton County.

[27] The counties were Bremer, Cedar, Davis, Hamilton, and Mills (Union Publishing Company, *History of Butler and Bremer Counties, Iowa* . . . [Springfield, 1883]; J. F. Grawe, *History of Bremer County, Iowa* . . . [2 vols.; Chicago, 1914]; Western Historical Company, *The History of Cedar County, Iowa* . . . [Chicago, 1878]; C. Ray Aurner, *A Topical History of Cedar County, Iowa* . . . [2 vols.; Chicago, 1910]; State Historical Company, *History of Davis County, Iowa* . . . [Des Moines, 1882]; Lewis Publishing Company, *A Biographical History of Fremont and Mills Counties, Iowa* [Chicago, 1901]; *Biographical Record and Portrait Album of Hamilton and Wright Counties, Iowa* . . . [Chicago, 1889]; S. J. Clark Publishing Company, *A Biographical Record of Hamilton County, Iowa* . . . [Chicago, 1902]; J. W. Lee, *History of Hamilton County, Iowa* [2 vols.; Chicago, 1912]).

[28] Paul W. Gates, "Land Policy and Tenancy in the Prairie States," *Journal of Economic History*, I (May, 1941), 60–82, and *Frontier Landlords and Pioneer Tenants* (Ithaca, 1945); Bogue, *op. cit.*, pp. 85–112, 156–84.

of tenant farms in Illinois, Kansas, and Nebraska. Scully was by birth foreign and aristocratic. His relations with his Irish tenants had been colorful and unhappy; they once tried to assassinate him. Scully's personal background, the scale of his operations, and his manifest intention to develop a long-run tenant operation, all helped to focus attention on him as vacant lands became scarce and times hard in central Illinois during the 1870's. Despite critics and ultimately anti-alien legislation aimed at him, William Scully maintained his Illinois tenant farms centering in Logan County, Illinois.

To the east of Scullyland, in eight counties of the Grand Prairie, there were sixteen landlords who built up aggregate holdings of some 140,000 acres during the 1840's, 1850's, and 1860's.[29] Coming from both the East and the Ohio Valley states, most of them were politicians, lawyers, bankers, and businessmen with little direct experience in farming. A number of livestock men in central Illinois who had invested the profits from cattle-droving and livestock-feeding in land during the 1830's, 1840's, and 1850's developed a portion of their holdings under tenancy also. Men like Isaac Funk, of McLean County; Jacob Strawn, of Morgan County; Benjamin F. Harris, of Champaign County; and John Dean Gillett, of Logan County, accumulated thousands of acres of land and from the 1850's onward established tenants on them. Much of the tenants' corn production went to feed the livestock of the landlord. A number of the Illinois landlords passed on their tenant estates to their heirs who have kept some of the farms into the third generation.

Iowa had its share of landlords, too. Although one of the sixteen Grand Prairie landlords, Matthew T. Scott, developed tenant holdings in southwestern Iowa as well as in Illinois, the Iowa landlords seldom operated on the scale of those in central Illinois.[30] During the 1890's the Litchfield family, however, probably had as many tenants on the lands that it derived from the title of the Des Moines River Navigation and Railroad Company as had all but a very few of the Illinois landlords.[31]

We can overemphasize the significance of large tenant holdings in the broader picture of land tenure in Iowa and Illinois during the last half of the nineteenth century. The 140,000 acres acquired by sixteen large land-

[29] *Ibid.*, p. 85.

[30] Beattie, "Matthew Scott," pp. 41–42.

[31] Edward H. Litchfield filed between 30 and 40 leases in the Hamilton County, Iowa, Deed Register on his lands in that county in 1893. Henry Ten Eyck, Cazenovia, New York, and John and Ira Davenport, Bath, New York, also leased lands that they had acquired from the Des Moines River Navigation and Railroad Company. There is a running commentary on Ten Eyck's operations in the *Hamilton Freeman* from the 1860's to the 1880's. As indicated above, the correspondence between John Browne, Boone, Iowa, Stephen A. Foley, Lincoln, Illinois, and John and Ira Davenport, Bath, New York, 1869–90, Davenport Collection, Cornell Collection of Regional History, presents a highly revealing picture of the problems of the River Land grantees. The Davenport lands lay in Boone County. William B. Welles held 13,000 acres of river lands in Webster County.

lords of the Grand Prairie was only a small part of the 4,000,000-odd acres of land in the eight counties involved. Of the hundreds who acquired large acreages of land in the prairie triangle from the federal government or other public agencies, relatively few passed on tenant estates to their heirs.

Tenancy allowed many land-speculators to derive income from land that could not yet be sold profitably and that was accumulating charges for administration and taxes, while "actual settlers" grazed their livestock upon it and plundered it of timber for their improvements. To rent such land to settlers who would break and improve a portion of it, protect the timber, and pay a small rent, which covered the cost of taxes and a little more, was good business indeed. Most speculators were willing or even eager to make such arrangements. After a few years of renting, the tenant might accumulate enough money so that he could make the first payment on a land contract, and the speculator had found a buyer. Such was the policy which Romulus Riggs followed in disposing of his large holdings in the Military Tract of Illinois.[32] During 1876 a farmer of north-central Iowa wrote, "The last summer we have had parties looking up their wild lands in our township, trying to rent them out."[33]

When titles were disputed as in the Illinois Military Tract and on the Des Moines River Lands of central Iowa, tenancy assisted owners in establishing their titles. Placing a tenant on the land was the initial step in assuming complete control of the land. Such a first step, of course, might be difficult. "I have leased the Sebring farm to four different persons and so far it is not leased," wrote an agent of the Davenport brothers from Boone County, Iowa, in 1884. "These whelps have drove and scared out everyone so far." His superior added, "Those devils destroy all fence put in by us — Fight and flog every man we have put in."[34]

The would-be tenant could find a landlord among other groups in addition to the large holders and land-speculators. The biographical sketches in the county histories and other scattered evidence show that many different types offered farmland for rent at a very early date in the history of western communities. Mechanics and craftsmen — blacksmiths, carpenters, millwrights, shoemakers, and the like — frequently owned farms which they rented to others while they practiced their trades. Merchants, elevator men, druggists, livery-stable proprietors, butchers, even the local marshal might have one or more farms for lease. Once elected to office, county officers frequently moved into the county seat but held their farms as insurance against the uncertain temper of the voters. Lawyers frequently owned farm property which they rented. For the banker and the moneylender, the acquisition of a certain amount of rural property was a logical outgrowth of the business which they followed.

[32] Gates, "Land Policy and Tenancy in the Prairie States," *op. cit.*, pp. 74–75.

[33] O. C. Templer in *Hamilton Freeman*, November 1, 1876.

[34] Stephen A. Foley to John and Ira Davenport, January 17, 1884 (Davenport Collection).

The dust had hardly settled on the new streets of the county towns and villages in Illinois and Iowa before elderly farmers began to move in to spend their remaining years, congregating around the store stoves and on the courthouse steps while they swapped tales of herculean days in the harvest fields and compared notes on the rents that they were receiving from their farms. In the schedules of the second census after the settlement of prairie townships, there were almost always from three to ten widows; some of these also had farms to rent. Less glamorous than the large landlords of central Illinois, seldom having more than 1,000 acres of land to lease, the small landlords in total far outweighed the Scullys and the Scotts as a source of land for rent.

We know far too little about the terms of the leases under which the prairie renters farmed. Many, particularly in the earlier days of settlement, no doubt were verbal. Share leases probably were always more common than cash leases. Under such agreements the landlord shared the uncertainties of nature. Absentee landlords, however, always preferred a cash payment, since share agreements were difficult to supervise from a distance. Declining grain prices during the last quarter of the nineteenth century and an active demand for rental farms also inclined the landlords to ask for cash rather than share agreements. In the very early years of prairie settlement, Patrick Shirreff commented:

Renters of land, or tenants, are common in many parts. . . . The terms of rent are variable. Near towns, and in thickly-peopled districts, a small rent is paid in money, and a lease of several years taken. In remote situations, land is commonly let on shares from year to year. If the owner of the soil furnishes seed and labouring animals, he gets two-thirds of the produce. . . . If the tenant supplies animals and seed, the landowner gets one-third. But terms may vary according to situation, soil, and crop.[35]

Some of Shirreff's generalizations were still valid thirty-five years later.

In the late 1850's, several of Matthew Scott's tenants in east-central Illinois agreed to pay two-fifths of their crops as rent, but the landlord had advanced them money for purchase of work animals, seed, and farming equipment. From the 1860's to the mid-1880's Scott's tenants usually paid one-third of their crops to the landlord when they owned their own work animals and implements.[36] Lacking draught animals and equipment, Ephraim G. Fairchild, tenant farmer of Jones County, Iowa, evidently gave half his corn and small grain to the landlord in 1857.[37] During the late 1870's a

[35] Patrick Shirreff, *A Tour through North America; Together with a Comprehensive View of the Canadas and United States, as Adapted for Agricultural Emigration* (Edinburgh, 1835), pp. 340–41.

[36] Bogue, *op. cit.*, p. 99.

[37] Mildred Throne, ed., "Iowa Farm Letters, 1856–1865," *Iowa Journal of History*, LVIII (January, 1960), 44, 45, 52; William B. Close, *Farming in North-Western Iowa, United States of America, A Pamphlet for Emigrants and a Guide to North-western Iowa* (Manchester, 1880), p. 16.

real estate firm of northwestern Iowa was renting farms with modest but adequate buildings and the breaking done for one-half the crop in the granary. In this case the landlord supplied the seed grain but neither equipment nor work stock. In the Rock River Valley in 1888 the landlord's share was customarily one-third or two-fifths of the tenant's crop.[38]

During the 1850's the cash rent for farmland varied between $1.00 and $3.00 per acre in east-central Illinois. The lower limit for relatively unimproved or unattractive land still stood around $1.00 per acre in the mid- and late 1890's. After rising rather gradually to about $5.00 per acre in the mid-1880's, the upper limit of cash rents rose more sharply thereafter, and by the late 1890's renters in east-central Illinois were paying between $7.00 and $8.00 per acre for good tenant farms.[39] Farther to the west, rents were doubtless lower. The less improved a farm was, the greater the chance that the tenant could negotiate leasing terms that would reward him for improvements. In 1869 Suel Foster, of Muscatine, commented, "Good contracts can often be made with the owner of wild lands, to fence and break prairie, by the owner furnishing posts and lumber, and material for a cheap tenant house, and the renters have the land free of rent two or three years, for the labor of opening the farm."[40] In 1888 a writer described leasing terms on the raw prairies of Iowa in which tenants entered into five-year agreements to erect the buildings they needed and paid on their broken acreage $1.00 per acre in the second year, $2.00 in the third year, and thereafter $3.00 per acre.[41]

The relation of tenancy to ownership and aspects of leasing are illustrated in the story of Peter Nelson, who left his native Denmark in 1871. After working for a time on the railroad and farming rented land in Marshall and Story counties, he came to Hamilton County, Iowa, in 1878. Here he rented a farm for one year and then bought eighty acres of raw prairie. This he improved for two years before selling it. He invested the proceeds in stock and leased half a section of raw land. The owners of this tract paid for the lumber that he used in building fences and buildings and allowed him the crops of three years in return for the labor spent on the improvements. A remunerative crop of flax in the first year more than repaid the cost of his labor, and, in effect, he farmed the place free for the next two years. When his improvements on the farm were complete, the owners offered to sell it to him for $15.00 per acre. He refused the offer because he had ample resources by this time to buy another tract at a lower price.[42]

Peter Nelson's success was not the lot of all tenants. Some of Matthew Scott's renters lost ground, if anything, during the late 1850's; their burden

[38] *Prairie Farmer*, March 3, 1888, p. 149.
[39] Bogue, *op. cit.*, pp. 99–100, 165–73.
[40] *Iowa Homestead and Western Farm Journal*, June 11, 1869, p. 177.
[41] *Prairie Farmer*, March 3, 1888, p. 139.
[42] *Biographical Record of Hamilton County*, pp. 507–9.

of chattel mortgages grew steadily during those depressed years.[43] The letters of Ephraim G. Fairchild and John Kenyon, tenant farmers in Jones and Delaware counties, Iowa, show them struggling desperately and with little success to improve their circumstances in the same years.[44] Paul W. Gates has suggested that the tenants of central Illinois were so hard pressed during the 1870's that, bitter and disillusioned, many of them left the region for locations farther west.[45]

Students of tenure problems during the twentieth century have emphasized that the soil suffers under tenancy. In 1851 the *Prairie Farmer* maintained that the "best of all fertilizers" was "the owner's foot." [46] An agent of eastern speculators noted caustically in 1883 that an unbroken tract under his administration was too good "to be butchered by Iowa tenants." [47] But owners as well as tenants were careless of the soil in nineteenth-century Illinois and Iowa. There were few of either who seriously utilized soil-conservation practices before the 1880's.

The tenants of the region varied in origin and background. There were young men, often from the local community, who leased for a period of from one to ten years while they accumulated the capital to purchase farms. Numbers of the German, Scandinavian, and British immigrants of all ages also leased land in their first efforts to direct their own farming operations. Finally, there was another group of older native tenants, who had failed to move up the tenure ladder at an earlier age. If any tenants deserved to be called "land butchers" during this period, they doubtless came largely from this group—men who were broken by misfortune, congenitally bad managers, or men reluctant to accept the standards of an agricultural society that was rapidly becoming much more businesslike and commercial than ever before. "Men who have for ten or twenty years rented farms, moved from pillar to post, sometimes having a team of their own, and owing for it, and sometimes not having any, I say such men are generally a hard set," wrote a correspondent to the *Prairie Farmer* in 1866.[48] This aspect of tenancy was an old story—older, indeed, than the story of Jesus and the Pharisees in the Temple of Jerusalem.

Not until 1880 did the Census Office instruct its officers to record the tenure status of farmers. In this year tenants operated slightly more than 31 per cent of the farms in Illinois and slightly less than 24 per cent of those in Iowa.[49] Twenty-five Illinois counties with tenancy rates of more than

---

[43] Bogue, *op. cit.*, p. 102.

[44] Throne, *op. cit.*, pp. 37–88.

[45] Gates, *Frontier Landlords and Pioneer Tenants*, p. 51.

[46] *Prairie Farmer*, April, 1851, p. 162.

[47] Stephen A. Foley to John and Ira Davenport, December 6, 1883 (Davenport Collection).

[48] *Verbum Sat.* in the *Prairie Farmer*, March 31, 1866, p. 207.

[49] These comments on the pattern of tenancy in 1880 in the case of Iowa are based on analysis of data in Census Office, *Report on the Productions of Agriculture as Returned at the Tenth Census, June 1, 1880* (Washington, 1883), pp. 50–53. In the

35 per cent were clustered in central Illinois, lying, with only one exception, east of the Illinois River. The counties with the lowest rates of tenancy, from 14 to 25 per cent, were located in southern Illinois or in the extreme northern part of the state. In only six rather widely separated Iowa counties did tenants operate 30 per cent or more of the farms. In general, tenancy in Iowa was lowest in the northern portion of the state. In Winnebago County the rate was only 8.8 per cent. Settlement was still sparse in northwestern Iowa in 1880; pioneer conditions prevailed there to a considerable extent. This was the region in which settlers located most of the homesteads in Iowa under the Homestead Act of 1862 and its amendments. But in the eight northwestern counties of the state the percentage of tenancy in 1880 varied from 12.5 to 24.6 per cent.

Our knowledge of the growth of tenancy before 1880 is most imperfect. Some historians have believed that it was relatively unimportant. "With so much land yet unoccupied, the cultivated portions could command but little rent and tenancy was not common in the fifties," wrote one student of agriculture in Illinois.[50] Recent studies of Illinois landlords and their tenants have shattered such easy generalizations, without, however, presenting firm estimates of the amount of tenancy to be found in the years between 1840 and 1880 in Illinois and Iowa.[51] This situation need not continue because data are available in the manuscript population and agricultural censuses, which can serve as the basis for estimates and at the same time reveal something about the tenants themselves.

In 1860 a census marshal of Jones County, Iowa, interpreted his instructions in an unorthodox but helpful way.[52] Instead of simply recording the occupation of each householder, he noted tenure status in the case of those who did not own real estate. There were 692 farmers and 126 "renters" in Marshal Johnson's territory. If we assume that the 126 were farm tenants, they made up 15.4 per cent of the farmers in the area, a region settled, for the most part, during the preceding twenty years. Many of the 126, however, did not appear in the agricultural census. Such men were perhaps "farmers without farms," mysterious individuals whose status has puzzled a number of students working with raw census data recently.[53] The tenant

case of Illinois, I have depended on Charles L. Stewart, *Land Tenure in the United States with Special Reference to Illinois* ("University of Illinois Studies in the Social Sciences," Vol. V [Urbana, 1916]), p. 50 [444].

[50] Russell H. Anderson, "Agriculture in Illinois during the Civil War Period, 1850–1870" (unpublished Ph.D. dissertation, University of Illinois, 1929), p. 63.

[51] See n. 28 above.

[52] The manuscript agricultural censuses of 1850, 1860, 1870, and 1880 for Iowa are available both at the Iowa State Historical Society, Iowa City, and in the Department of History and Archives, Des Moines, Iowa. The population censuses for the same years are also available at these depositaries, as well as at the National Archives or by order on microfilm from that institution.

[53] Mildred Throne, "A Population Study of an Iowa County in 1850," *Iowa Journal of History*, LVII (October, 1959), 310–11; Merle Curti, *The Making of an American*

who was in his first year on a farm had, of course, no crops to report for the previous season. If such a man had few livestock or was using the work stock of others in the neighborhood, we need hardly wonder that the census-taker failed to report his farm in the agricultural census. Some tenant "farmers without farms" in Jones County were, no doubt, little better than farm laborers, tilling a small acreage with rented or borrowed stock and equipment, and spending most of their time in labor for the local owner-operators.[54]

Our knowledge of tenancy in Jones County, Iowa, in 1860 rests on a fluke, but even without the helpful notations found in the population census of that county, we can still look to the census rolls of 1850, 1860, and 1870 for estimates of tenancy. On the population census record, the census-takers noted the value of a householder's real estate. If a man described himself as a farmer but owned no real estate, he was presumably either a tenant or a "farmer without a farm." The latter classification might, of course, include recently arrived farmers who had not yet bought land in the community or others who were "just passing through" as well as tenants unlisted on the agricultural census rolls. If, however, we find propertyless farmers on the agricultural census rolls, we can be certain that we have identified farm tenants. The total of such proved tenants obviously would make up the minimum number of tenants in a given area and apparently this figure is the one most comparable to those given in the census of 1880. If to this number we add the remaining "farmers without farms," we have arrived at the maximum number of tenants possible. Thus in Clarion and Lamoelle townships of Bureau County, Illinois, in 1850, at least 6.6 per cent of the farmers were tenants, and perhaps the percentage was as high as 10.7.[55] In Union Township of Davis County, Iowa, the percentages were 10.3 and 21.6.

Table 9 shows that the percentage of owner-operators among the farmers in Clarion township in 1860 was little greater than in 1880. Tenancy here, obviously, was not simply a product of the last few years prior to the census of 1880. No doubt as many as 10 per cent of the farmers in the prairie triangle were tenants at a very early stage in the development of most communities, and in areas where the large land-speculator was particularly common, the rate was higher. Year by year thereafter the number of tenants rose during the settling-in process as would-be farmers saw the cost of land rise and the amounts of machinery needed for farming increase.

The agricultural economist has regarded tenancy as primarily a stepping-stone to ownership. It follows then that tenants were normally younger than

Community: A Case Study of Democracy in a Frontier County (Stanford, 1959), pp. 59–60.

[54] Ephraim Fairchild, tenant farmer in Jones County, Iowa, for instance, had no work stock (see Mildred Throne, "Iowa Farm Letters, 1856–1865," *op. cit.*, pp. 38–58).

[55] The manuscript agricultural censuses of 1850, 1860, 1870, and 1880 for Illinois are available at the Illinois State Archives, Springfield, Illinois.

TABLE 9
TENURE CATEGORIES IN THREE
MIDWESTERN TOWNSHIPS

| | Clarion Township *
Bureau County | | | | | | | |
| | OWNERS-
OPERATORS | | FARMERS WITH-
OUT FARMS | | UNQUESTIONABLY
TENANTS | | TOTALS | |
Year	No.	Per Cent	No.	Per Cent	No.	Per Cent	No.	CENT Per
1850	108	89.3	5	4.1	8	6.6	121	100
1860	127	76.0	31	18.6	9	5.4	167	100
1870	151	80.8	13	8.6	16	10.6	180	100
1880	96	73.3	9	3.8	30	22.9	135	100
	Springfield Township Cedar County							
1850	25	58.1	14	32.6	4	9.3	43	100
1860	103	79.8	13	10.1	13	10.1	129	100
1870	111	70.7	3	1.9	43	27.4	157	100
1880	118	71.1	9	5.4	39	23.5	166	100
	Union Township Davis County							
1850	76	78.4	11	11.3	10	10.3	97	100
1860	118	90.8	2	1.5	10	7.7	130	100
1870	145	92.9	2	1.3	9	5.8	156	100
1880	145	73.2	25	12.6	28	14.1	198	100

* 1850 also includes Lamoelle Township.

owner-operators. The mean age of the "renters" in Jones County, Iowa, in 1860 was 37.7 years in comparison to the 42.5 years of the owner-operators in the same townships. The tenants were indeed younger than the resident owners, but they were also older than one might have expected; a substantial number were in their forties and fifties. Figures from Clarion Township tell a similar story. There the tenants of 1850 and later censuses were younger than the owner-operators, but the average age was never less than 36 years. In Clarion the disparity in age between tenants and owner-operators grew over time, largely as a result of the increasing age of the members of the latter group. The average age of owner-operators there in 1880 was 50.2 years.

Writers have pictured tenancy, on occasion, as an aid to acculturation — a status that many of the foreign-born accepted while learning the lessons of midwestern agriculture. This surely was the case. But the Jones County sample of 818 farmers in nine townships in 1860 does not support the generalization that tenants were recruited particularly from the foreign-born. Of the 818 farmers 69 per cent were foreign-born, but only 55 per cent of the tenants reported birthplaces abroad. A township-by-township study of the tenants in Johnson County, Iowa, in 1880 seemed to show mainly that foreign-born tenants were most common in areas where foreign-born owner-operators were most common, and that native-born tenants were most often found closely adjacent to native-born owners.

Just under 50 per cent of the farmers in one Iowa county were tenants in 1900; the maximum in Illinois was over 60 per cent. In general, tenants were most common where the soils were highly productive. How ironic, thought Herbert Quick, that the richest of soils would reduce rather than enhance the freedom of the men who tilled them! [56] The wet prairies of east-central Illinois and central and northwestern Iowa supported a high percentage of tenant operators. Drainage was necessary to make the wet prairies fully tillable, in effect raising the price of the land for the farmer. On the other hand, the high productivity of these soils, once brought to tilth, encouraged businessmen to buy farms as investments. Prosperous farmers invested their savings in tenant farms as well. Some owner-operators amassed competences rapidly and retired to live on their savings and rents. Instead of liquidating estates by cash sale, non-resident heirs preferred to retain or divide the family holdings in the belief that they could find no safer investment. In limited districts long-term tenant estates that dated from the settlement period may have increased the rate of tenancy. Finally, topography, soils, and marketing facilities encouraged cash-grain farming in the wet prairie region — a type of farming operation that was somewhat more adapted to tenancy than those in which greater emphasis is placed on livestock. But in 1900 there was a high rate of tenancy in eight of the nine westernmost counties of Iowa, which lie on the well-drained Missouri loess of the western slope. Here drainage was no great problem, but most of the other factors inducing high tenancy rates were apparently present.

We can be certain that few tenants preferred their status to that of neighbors who were owner-operators. Landownership was the goal of most. But there is little evidence of class consciousness among the tenants in nineteenth-century Illinois and Iowa. If rental terms were harsh or landlords callous, such conditions seldom goaded renters into unified opposition. There was, it is true, some evidence of dissatisfaction at times. A group of renters in McLean County, Illinois, met together in 1879 and agreed that "from and after the fulfillment of the present year's rent, we pledge our most sacred honor to pay grain rents only; provided, the landlords do not rent for a cash rent of $2 per acre, and that only for cultivated land." [57] Other murmurings of discontent occasionally reached the newspapers.[58] Granted the revolutionary developments taking place in agricultural technology at the time and the deflation of the postwar years, it seems surprising that there were not more complaints. Surprising, that is, until we remember that many tenants did, after all, climb the tenure ladder, that farmers of the period still believed in the myth of free land to the west, and that the growing cities of the Middle West offered opportunities as well. These were not conditions to breed a tenant revolt.

[56] Herbert Quick, *One Man's Life* (Indianapolis, 1925), pp. 133–37.
[57] Bogue, *op. cit.*, p. 171.
[58] Gates, *Frontier Landlords and Pioneer Tenants*, pp. 49–53.

CHAPTER IV

Farms on the Breaking

"This is home, is it? Wal, ferever!" These were the words of Selena Prouder as her husband checked the blazed tree and reported that the mare-drawn wagon, the colt, the cow, the dog, and the Prouder family had reached their destination after weeks of jolting travel from Pennsylvania.[1] Now, in Joseph Kirkland's fictional Spring County, Illinois, they would commence the task of subduing a farm — the "woods behind," the "prairie before" them.[2] Though some might live from the wagon box until the men had done some breaking and planted a sod crop, the first step for the Prouders in improving the "farm" was to build a dwelling. So was it also for most settlers.

While the pioneers clung to the timber, there was little challenge in house-building. Prior to the mid-1840's in Illinois, at least, and the 1850's in Iowa, the first house on a farm was usually some kind of log dwelling, although a three-sided camp or dugout might serve for a few months. When the Fraseur family journeyed west from Indiana in two wagons during 1837, the men in the party on arriving in Cedar County, Iowa, immediately sharpened their axes and had completed a shanty by noon of the next day.[3] Soon, of course, a more substantial building rose nearby. After the Gaylord family of Illinois arrived in Fremont County, Iowa, in 1846, the father "built a rude log cabin, sixteen by sixteen feet, with puncheon floor, clay fireplace and mud-and-stick chimney," and roofed, no doubt, with clapboards, although we are not told so.[4] The raising, of course, is standard stuff in the frontier story, and it was common, but the log shanty or cabin presented no structural problems that two men, or a man and a willing boy, could not solve.

Some historians have suggested that northwestern Iowa was a sod-house frontier.[5] Here the occasional pioneer did build a sod house, but such dwell-

[1] Joseph Kirkland, *Zury: The Meanest Man in Spring County: A Novel of Western Life* (Boston, 1887), p. 11.

[2] *Ibid.*, pp. 9, 65.

[3] Western Historical Company, *The History of Cedar County, Iowa* . . . (Chicago, 1878), p. 586.

[4] Lewis Publishing Company, *A Biographical History of Fremont and Mills Counties, Iowa* . . . (Chicago, 1901), pp. 410–11.

[5] William J. Petersen, "The Pioneer Cabin," *Iowa Journal of History and Politics,* XXXVI (October, 1938), 387–409 (see 402–3).

ings were, in general, used only briefly. Some of the sod houses in this region consisted of sod built up around board walls — hardly true soddies by the standards of the Great Plains. By the time that settlers made their major assault upon the Grand Prairie of Illinois and the broader prairies of Iowa, the railroads were carrying the cheap lumber of the Great Lakes pineries from Chicago and the Mississippi River mill towns to stations within reasonable hauling distance of most pioneer farms, as had the Illinois and Michigan Canal in great stretches of northwestern Illinois a few years before. Even earlier, local sawmills supplied the sized stuff and siding for many a pioneer farm home on the prairies. In 1870 the Iowa Railroad Land Company advised the settler interested in its lands in west-central Iowa that he could build a temporary cabin with pine boards and nails, available at the nearest railroad station, for a cost of $50 to $75. The settler who distrusted his own skill with saw and hammer could order a Bridges ready-made house. The company pledged to ship homes that would be ready for occupancy two or three weeks after the order, from Chicago to any station on the Northwestern line. Prices for these houses ranged from the $200 asked for a ten-by-twelve dwelling to $3,000 for an elaborate dwelling garnished with Victorian gingerbread.[6]

The shanty and log cabin phase was, of course, a temporary one in any new community, despite the occasional tale to the contrary. When William Cullen Bryant traveled between Chicago and Princeton, Illinois, in 1846, he was struck "with the difference which five years had made in the aspect of the country. Frame or brick houses in many places had taken the places of log-cabins."[7] In 1850 one of the editors of the *Prairie Farmer* contrasted the appearance of the country in the hundred miles west and northwest of Chicago with the days of its early settlement, some ten years earlier. "The log cabins have not all disappeared"; he reported, "but they are so scarce as to be a curiosity."[8] But in Jefferson County, Iowa, settled during the 1840's and 1850's, the task of supplanting the "log shanty" was still going on in the mid-1870's.[9]

Around the farmhouse a variety of other buildings rose through the years: a summer kitchen, a smokehouse, corncribs, stables, barns, and, perhaps, a roofed threshing floor. If the pioneer was fortunate enough to gather a corn crop in his first season, he must of necessity build a crude corncrib of logs, poles, or rough siding. Stables might be later in appearing. Domestic livestock can survive the middle-western winter in the shelter of

[6] Iowa Railroad Land Company, *Choice Iowa Farming Lands: 1,000,000 Acres for Sale at Low Prices, on Credit or for Cash* . . . (Cedar Rapids, 1870), p. 22.

[7] William Cullen Bryant, *Letters of a Traveller; or, Notes of Things Seen in Europe and America* (New York, 1850), p. 262.

[8] *Prairie Farmer*, September, 1850, p. 266.

[9] Iowa State Agricultural Society, *Report, 1874* (Des Moines, 1875), p. 382. Hereafter cited as I.S.A.S.R. Date of publication was always one year later than the year of the report.

a hay- or straw-stack, and some of the pioneers, through necessity or inclination, allowed them to prove it. If anything, the first stables were further removed from the commodious red and white barns of today than was the log cabin from its frame or brick successor. Although a few pioneers made substantial stables of logs, many others drove notched sticks in the ground, poised a roof of prairie hay on poles resting in the notches, and attached siding of poles and sticks on one or more sides. Sometimes the builder cut back a bank to make one side or built against a haystack. Writers called sheds of this kind "Sucker barns" in the 1830's and 1840's and "Iowa barns" during the 1860's and 1870's. But, like the log cabins, the straw sheds were soon replaced on any particular farm. Settlers had lived in Bremer County, Iowa, less than ten years when David Gillett raised a barn, thirty by forty feet in dimension with 16-foot posts.[10] Painted red, it was the wonder of the neighborhood for some years, but time was on its side.

If the barns or stables of the Corn-Belt pioneers were small and crude, they accurately reflected certain characteristics of pioneer farming operations. Usually the pioneer did not have many livestock initially. Most considered that an unroofed pen was ample protection for fattening hogs, and the idea of stall-feeding beef was one held by only the occasional fanatic or visionary. Nor did the farmer before the 1860's have any great amount of farm machinery that must be housed during bad weather. Capital, John A. Hopkins has suggested, could be put to more remunerative uses than to invest it in elaborate farm buildings during the first years of settlement.[11]

Water supplies for the use of house and livestock seldom provided any great problem for the prairie farmer. The firstcomers settled close to the watercourses, and hillside seeps and springs were common in areas of both Illinois and Iowa. On the wet prairies the supply of surface water was often annoyingly ample. In most prairie districts in Illinois and Iowa, the well-digger could find plentiful supplies of water at depths that were seldom greater than thirty feet. There was little problem either in digging or rein-

[10] Union Publishing Company, *History of Butler and Bremer Counties, Iowa . . .* (Springfield, 1883), p. 1050. Pioneer buildings are described with some cost estimates in Russell H. Anderson, "Agriculture in Illinois during the Civil War Period, 1850–1870" (unpublished Ph.D. dissertation, University of Illinois, 1929), p. 26; Mildred Throne, "A History of Agriculture in Southern Iowa, 1833–1890" (unpublished Ph.D. dissertation, State University of Iowa, 1946), p. 35; John M. Peck, *A Guide for Emigrants; Containing Sketches of Illinois, Missouri, and the Adjacent Parts* (Boston, 1831), pp. 126–27, 190; Elias Pym Fordham, *Personal Narrative of Travels in Virginia, Maryland, Pennsylvania, Ohio, Indiana, Kentucky; and of a Residence in the Illinois Territory: 1817–1818*, Frederick A. Ogg, (ed.), (Cleveland, 1906), p. 120; John Woods, *Two Years' Residence in the Settlement on the English Prairie, in the Illinois Country, United States . . .* (London, 1822), pp. 278–80, 300; Patrick Shirreff, *A Tour through North America; Together with a Comprehensive View of the Canadas and United States, as Adapted for Agricultural Emigration* (Edinburgh, 1835), p. 250.

[11] John A. Hopkins, Jr., *Economic History of the Production of Beef Cattle in Iowa* (Iowa City, 1928), p. 116.

forcing the walls of such wells. With the invention of the drivewell in the early 1860's, underground water at such levels was often tapped very easily, although difficulties in driving the drivewell pipe beyond thirty feet, and the lack of any well reservoir convinced some farmers that the old-fashioned dug well was still superior. By the late 1860's windmills and rotary stock pumps were attracting attention but were considered to be expensive.[12]

The farm-maker, of course, had come to till the land; he would not delay long in beginning his preparations to use it. Until the mid-1840's in Illinois, and some years later in Iowa, the usual farm was located in part, if not wholly, in the timber. Twenty or thirty years later the early settlers of the prairie triangle remembered with chagrin the labor which they wasted in slashing fields out of the timber.[13] Few of the woods were dense, and the pioneers selected the areas of sparsest growth for their first fields. The larger trees they often girdled and left for the time being. To them the pioneers returned at their leisure, cutting them down and burning them or using them for rails as need dictated. Meanwhile, they had cut the smaller trees and hazel brush and grubbed out the stumps and larger roots with shovel and mattock.[14] If the grubbing were done carefully, the turf here offered little resistance to the ordinary plows of the day.

The grasslands presented a different challenge. The thickly interwoven roots of the prairie grasses were especially tough and rank in the marshier spots, interspersed at times with resistant forbs like the redroot, and intermingled on the barrens with hazel roots. Such sod defied the conventional plows of the settlers, who experimented on the smaller prairies of southern Illinois before 1820.[15] Local mechanics met the challenge by building special breaking plows. These unwieldy looking implements ultimately boasted a ponderous beam six to twelve feet long, the fore end resting on small sturdy wheels, the rear end firmly attached to a massive share — ultimately of steel — and mould board as well as to the handles of the plowman. This individual regulated the depth of the furrow by adjusting a long lever which ran from front to rear above the beam and pivoted on a bar above the wheels.[16]

With the largest of their massive plows, the prairie-breakers could turn a furrow of some thirty inches. For such work five or six yokes of oxen or

[12] Earl W. Hayter, "The Western Farmers and the Drivewell Patent Controversy," *Agricultural History*, XVI (January, 1942), 16–28; Herbert G. Schmidt's, "An Economic and Social History of Bond County, Illinois, before 1850: A Type Study of the Development of a Prairie-Forest Region in the Middle West" (unpublished M.A. thesis, University of Chicago, 1936) suggests that windmills were used prior to 1850 in Bond County; *Prairie Farmer*, December 28, 1867, 401–2.

[13] O. M. Culver, *Iowa Homestead and Western Farm Journal*, May 28, 1863, p. 137.

[14] *Ibid.*; *Prairie Farmer*, August, 1847, p. 245.

[15] Solon J. Buck, (ed.), "Pioneer Letters of Gershom Flagg," (*Illinois State Historical Society, Transactions, 1910*), p. 157; Shirreff, *op. cit.*, p. 248; Woods, *op. cit.*, p. 309.

[16] L. S. Coffin, "Breaking Prairie," *Annals of Iowa, Third Series*, V (July, 1902), 447–52.

four horses might draw the plow, and, with the oxen at least, two men were required, one to drive the team and the other to guide the plow and regulate the depth of the furrow. Depending on the width of the furrow turned by the plow and the character of the prairie cover, the breakers turned from one and a half to three acres of sod in a day, with frequent stops along the way to file the cutting edge of the share. Prairie-breaking on this scale required an investment in special machinery and workstock, which many farm-makers were not prepared to make. They turned, instead, to custom breakers, men who maintained plows and teams for the work and who themselves might hire men to work in breaking crews. Many prairie youths amassed the funds for their first farming ventures by working behind the breaking plow.

The prairie farmer who hired his breaking done paid from $2.00 to $4.00 per acre for the service. Prior to 1860 the price was usually closer to the first figure. During the late sixties and early seventies, the cost of breaking ranged, evidently, between $3.00 and $4.00, declining somewhat during the late 1870's. Such prices, of course, varied from place to place, and, no doubt, also according to the capacity of the individual farmer to make special terms or arrangements.[17]

We read much of custom work and the big breaking teams and plows. Many a farm-maker broke his land in much humbler fashion. A pioneer of Adair County, Iowa, wrote: "Prairie breaking is going on in every direction. We break with every kind of team, from two horses up to the heavy team of six yoke of oxen. We use every sized plough, from twelve to thirty inch."[18] Particularly if livestock had grazed the prairie rather closely for a few years, the ordinary two-horse steel plow, available from the 1840's onward, would break prairie, although the work might be slow and the furrow less than half that of the big breaking plow. Neighbors of limited resources might still utilize a breaking plow by pooling their teams and offering them to some other neighbor who owned a plow but lacked the livestock to work it effectively.

By trial and error, and with much discussion, farmers learned the most effective way of breaking prairie. If the breakers attacked the prairies in April, the grasses reclaimed the land during the summer, and the breaking confronted the farmer who tried to cross-plow in the fall with a rough and knotted mass of undisintegrated furrows, which clogged his plow and reduced him to a state of utter frustration. On the other hand, there was too little time for the sods to rot before fall if the farmer allowed the plows to continue much beyond the end of July. "It is conceded," maintained the

[17] Shirreff, op. cit., p. 445; Prairie Farmer, May, 1854, p. 192; Fred Gerhard, Illinois As It Is . . . (Chicago, 1857), p. 311; Throne, op. cit., p. 31; Hamilton Freeman, April 17, 1867, March 8, 1871, April 7, 1880; S. J. Clarke Publishing Company, A Biographical Record of Hamilton County, Iowa (Chicago, 1902), p. 535.

[18] T. M. Ewing in Fontanelle, Adair County Register, June 17, 1869 (quoted by Throne, op. cit., p. 157).

Prairie Farmer in 1843, "that the best time for breaking prairie is when
the grass is in a rapid state of vegetation; in this state the turf undergoes
rapid decomposition." [19] As the farm-makers of the 1840's and 1850's
turned their main energies to the prairies, they were generally agreed that
the proper season for breaking prairie extended from early or mid-May to
the end of July. Every rule of farming has its exceptions, of course. The
farmer who wished to plant sod corn in the new breaking might be willing
to run the risk of breaking somewhat earlier. During the 1870's the farmers
on Iowa's prairie frontier learned that a crop of flax sown on April breaking
could withstand the competition of the native plants and apparently help
to rot the prairie sod.[20]

The pioneers argued also about the proper depth of the breaking furrow
and the way in which the sod should be laid over. Those who first broke
the Illinois prairies evidently plowed to five inches or more in depth and
took satisfaction in overturning the sod in flat even rows. But by the 1850's
these tidy principles of husbandry were in disrepute. Now the trick was to
plow shallowly, one and a half to two inches in depth, and to leave the
upturned sod broken and ruffled.[21] Such breaking rotted more quickly than
did the thicker sod. No doubt, the development of the rolling colter helped
the breakers to cut the shallower furrow.

There were men of capital in almost every community from the beginning.
Such men, once the woods were left behind, might break the greater part
of their land in a season or two with their own equipment and stock or by
custom work. The improved acreage of most farm-makers grew much more
slowly. If they turned to the professional breakers, they could not afford
to have more than a few acres broken in a season. When they used their
own resources, they were hampered because the breaking season lasted
for only a few months and included the period in which the corn crop,
particularly, demanded attention and the harvesting of small grains began.

With the act of breaking, the farm-maker crossed a great divide. Until
that point his land was an investment, perhaps even a home; now it became
a farm. Some have read deeper meaning into this breaking of the prairie.
Herbert Quick had matter-of-fact Cow Vandemark write, "Breaking
prairie was the most beautiful, the most epochal, and most hopeful, and as
I look back at it, in one way the most pathetic thing man ever did, for in
it, one of the loveliest things ever created began to come to its predestined
end." [22] As the youth walked behind the plow, he "heard a curious thrilling
sound as the knife went through the roots, a sort of murmuring as of protest
at this violation — and once in a while, the whole engine, and the arms

[19] *Prairie Farmer*, May, 1843, p. 118.
[20] Coffin, *op. cit.*, p. 450; I.S.A.S.R., 1880, p. 35.
[21] *Union Agriculturist and Western Prairie Farmer*, April, 1842, 34, May, 1841,
pp. 34–35, October, 1841, p. 76; *Prairie Farmer*, July, 1851, pp. 292–93; Coffin, *op.
cit.*, p. 449.
[22] Herbert Quick, *Vandemark's Folly*, (New York, 1921), p. 228.

of the plowman also, felt a jar, like that of a ship striking a hidden rock, as the share cut through a red-root." [23] But this was really the nostalgic poet and twentieth-century conservationist Herbert Quick writing; the prairie farm-maker was seldom a poet and almost never a conservationist.

In 1837 the Duffield family began to improve a farm along Chequest Creek in Van Buren County, Iowa. By mid-May they had cleared and planted a patch of twelve acres on the least timbered portion of their claim. Now father and boys turned to the thicker woods and began to cut rails to protect the growing crops from the family livestock, the wandering strays of other settlers, and, to some extent at least, the deer with which the woods abounded. For several years the valley of the Chequest echoed almost continuously to the axes and mauls of the Duffields as they cut trees and split out the rails to fence their growing patch of crops. George C. Duffield described the fencing process in the county:

A settler dropped down and made a ring of rails. His neighbor did the same. Both enlarged their rings, and so all over the country these rings expanded until they began to 'jine'. They finally surrounded every acre of improved land in Van Buren county. They were established in the heart of the timber, and on the prairies miles away.[24]

The axe, the maul, and the wedges or gluts were more often in the hands of the settler prior to the mid-1850's than were the plow handles or the cradle. One pioneer who arrived in Davis County, Iowa, during the 1840's estimated in 1882 that he had made over one hundred and fifty thousand rails for the people of Fox River Township.[25] Once the fenced-crop area had grown to respectable dimensions, of course, splitting rails became a task for winter and odd times. It was work with its own peculiar requirements of craftsmanship. The placement of the wedges, the knack of making the first one stick, skill in turning the grain or flaws in the wood to the advantage of the axe — all these helped to make the difference between 150 rails and a good day's work, and something far less. The farm-makers of the rail-fence era usually agreed that the Virginia worm with stake and rider was the most satisfactory rail fence. It zigzagged around most pioneer fields, its panels made of seven or eight rails, usually ten feet in length, rider rails cradled securely in the notch made by two eight-foot stakes crossing at right angles to the line of the fence and set at the end of each panel. When carefully laid, the Virginia worm fence was horse high, bull strong and hog repellent. The need for haste, special terrain, or particular requirements might lead the farm-maker to construct variants, like the Shanghai, which substituted blocks or center stakes for the lower rails of the Virginia worm

---

[23] *Ibid.*, p. 229.

[24] George C. Duffield, "Youthtime in Frontier Iowa," *Annals of Iowa, Third Series*, VII (April, 1906), 353.

[25] State Historical Company, *History of Davis County, Iowa* . . . (Des Moines, 1882), p. 666.

and could serve, therefore, as a barrier only against the larger kinds of livestock.[26] More expensive in terms of labor, though saving in rails, was the post-and-rail fence in which rails were mortised into wooden posts sunk into the ground. Later, thin rails would be nailed to wooden posts.

When the Duffields staked their claim in Iowa in 1837, Illinois farm-makers were beginning to venture out on the prairie. A writer in the *Prairie Farmer* told of an Illinois farmer who located himself eight or ten miles from timber in that same year. Starting early, he drove his team each day to the woods, cut and split 50 rails, and drew them home on the same day, laying them around a 40-acre tract. After several months he had cut and hauled enough rails to build a seven-rail fence around the field.[27] Writing in the 1850's, an Iowa farmer maintained that he had cut and hauled the rails for his first fences some twelve miles, which "a New England farmer might think a little inconvenient." [28]

Obviously the labor cost of rail fences rose sharply as the farm-makers invaded the prairies. Even had it been feasible for all of the prairie settlers to haul their rails from woodlots or from the timber on the public domain or the lands of non-residents, there was almost general agreement that the supply of timber on the prairies was simply inadequate to provide fencing materials for all the prairie lands. Writers in the agricultural journals returned to the subject time after time. The major barrier to settlement on the prairies, maintained a writer in the *Union Agriculturist and Western Prairie Farmer* in 1841, was lack of timber for fencing.[29] "It is this deplorable want of fencing material . . . that stays the tide of immigration," argued R. Ferguson of Perrytown, Illinois, in the *Prairie Farmer* during 1848.[30] An Iowa writer declaimed to a war-torn country in 1863, "The subject of fences is as important as that of iron-clads." [31] The problem challenged the inventiveness of two generations of prairie farmers, although the cost of replacing wooden fences each generation made fencing a problem of interest to farmers in older regions as well. One solution, of course, was to plant trees on the prairie, and this the settlers did. But the fledgling prairie groves of poplar, willow, cottonwood, elm, and locust were no answer to the immediate problem of fencing.

When Morris Birkbeck and George Flower began their settlement of English farmers in Edwards County, Illinois, during 1817, they shared few of the native American reservations about the prairies. Birkbeck thrilled to the opportunities which the Boltenhouse prairie offered. For him there was no fencing problem. The traveler Thomas Hulme described the solu-

[26] Peck, *op. cit.*, p. 125; Oliver, *op. cit.*, pp. 239–40; *Union Agriculturist*, January, 1842, p. 8; *Prairie Farmer*, September, 1844, p. 217; Throne, *op. cit.*, p. 73.
[27] *Prairie Farmer*, May, 1846, pp. 156–57.
[28] *Northwestern Farmer and Horticultural Journal*, June, 1857, p. 213.
[29] A. W. Bowen in *Union Agriculturist*, August, 1841, p. 60.
[30] *Prairie Farmer*, August, 1848, p. 250.
[31] J. Sanfield in *Iowa Homestead*, March 19, 1863, p. 58.

tion evolved out of Birkbeck's experience in English farming and his knowledge of European agriculture generally:

He makes a ditch 4 feet wide at top, sloping to 1 foot wide at bottom, and
4 feet deep. With the earth that comes out of the ditch he makes a bank on
one side, which is turfed towards the ditch. Then a long pole is put up from
the bottom of the ditch to 2 feet above the bank; this is crossed by a short
pole from the other side, and then a rail is laid along between the forks.[32]

Ultimately, Birkbeck assured Hulme, he intended to replace the stakes and
rider with a live hedge. When the editors of the *Union Agriculturist and
Western Prairie Farmer* set themselves to serve the unique needs of western
farmers during the early 1840's, the idea of ditch-and-bank fence was still
much alive. A number of agriculturists described their methods of building
the fence, and during 1842 C. K. Bartlett patented a so-called fencing
machine designed to throw two massive furrows back to back with a two-
foot ditch on either side.[33] Prairie livestock, however, treated the bank-and-
ditch fences with contempt. In 1846 a Macoupin farmer explained their
decline and fall:

. . . the frost and hogs would fill up the ditch, and the cattle would horn
down the bank and bawl for help; others hearing them half a mile off, would
bawl and run until all the cattle on the prairie would be in motion, and the poor
unprotected sod fence would come down almost as soon as a hundred cocks
of hay that they could smell a mile.[34]

So passed the sod fence, a victim of herd psychology, and, no doubt, the
rather considerable investment in labor required to build it.

The ditch-and-bank barriers raised by Morris Birkbeck found few admirers among prairie farmers. The superstructure of hedge that, Thomas
Hulme reported, would soon crown the bank fences of the English Settlement enjoyed a longer run. After examining hedges made of Virginia thorn
on the farm of Edward Marshall in Macoupin County, a prairie thinker
burbled in the columns of the *Prairie Farmer* during 1847, "And now sir,
proclaim aloud, this great *problem solved*: a good and permanent live fence
can be made on the prairies from materials within our reach, for less
expense, and with less and far lighter labor, than a rail fence — and in-
comparably better." [35] During the next year, another writer offered to brave
the prairies of Illinois with a bag of hedge seed: "The God of Nature did
not make half the continent prairie without a substitute for timber to fence
with. It is much easier to make hedges and raise timber than to clear

[32] Thomas Hulme, *Journal of a Tour in the Western Countries of America, September 30, 1818–August 8, 1819* (London, 1828) (reprinted as Vol. X of Reuben Gold
Thwaites [ed.], *Early Western Travels, 1748–1846*, [Cleveland, 1904], p. 51).
[33] *Prairie Farmer*, March, 1844, p. 66.
[34] *Ibid.*, July, 1846, p. 222.
[35] *Ibid.*, February, 1847, p. 64.

timbered land." [36] Some twenty years later an Iowan pontificated, "The proposition will hardly be questioned that if the great prairies of Northwestern Iowa ever become densely populated, it must be accomplished by gradually encroaching upon them from the outskirts with timber belts and serried squares of hedge fence." [37]

Noting a considerable "spirit of inquiry about live fences," in the West, the editor of the *Union Agriculturist* listed a number of hedge plants in 1841 and included the hawthorn, the honey locust, the Virginia or Washington thorn, the red cedar, the cottonwood, and the Osage orange. Of the latter he admitted ignorance except that it grew in Arkansas and was "said to be very beautiful." [38] There was admiring mention of the Cherokee rose in the 1840's also, but Solon Robinson directed withering fire on this southern resident which, he suggested, could thrive on the prairies only if the proprietor erected greenhouses along his fence lines.[39] The successful hedges of the early 1840's were evidently of Virginia thorn for the most part. By the late 1840's, however, the Osage orange or Maclura tree had become the most popular of the hedge plants and would remain so during the next thirty years, although the white willow found supporters during the 1860's and 1870's, particularly on the northern prairies of Iowa.

The hedge fence, of course, was a response to the peculiar farm-making problems of the prairie triangle. We would like to know more about the way in which the "hedge mania" spread during the 1850's and 1860's as hedge became one of the major fencing materials of the region. The idea of hedging the prairies must have occurred to many. There were hedges in the seaboard states before the settlers pushed onto the prairies, and European immigrants were familiar with the hedges of England and Europe.[40] As we have seen, Morris Birkbeck had proposed to hedge the prairies as early as 1819. Doubtless during the 1830's a good many Illinois farmers experimented with thorns and other shrubs that, they believed, might make a satisfactory fence. In 1841 the editor of the *Union Agriculturist* described the Osage orange simply as a beautiful plant which grew in Arkansas. By the mid-1850's it had become "the hedge plant" of the prairies.

The champions of Jonathan B. Turner may have distorted the hedging story in their efforts to give him major credit for introducing Osage orange hedging. Early in 1842 B. F. Lodge of Edgar County, Illinois, claimed that he was experimenting with Osage orange as a hedge plant.[41] Although he promised to report further in the *Prairie Farmer*, he evidently did not do

[36] *Ibid.*, May, 1848, p. 145.

[37] *Iowa Homestead*, August 14, 1867, p. 253.

[38] *Union Agriculturist*, September, 1841, p. 65.

[39] *Prairie Farmer*, May, 1846, pp. 151–53.

[40] Mary L. Rice, "The Role of the Osage Orange Hedge in the Occupation of the Great Plains" (unpublished M.A. thesis, University of Illinois, 1937), chap. i.

[41] *Union Agriculturist*, March, 1842, p. 26.

so. In August of 1844 Charles H. Larrabee sent some bois d'arc or Osage orange seeds to the editors of the *Prairie Farmer* and urged that the plants be tried as hedge.[42] Then, the December 1845 issue of the *Prairie Farmer* contained a letter from Alexander McDonald, of Eufaula, Alabama, to Professor J. B. Turner, of Jacksonville, in which he gave Turner the names of nurserymen in Cleveland, Buffalo, Flushing, Long Island, and Baltimore who could supply the seed of the Osage orange or bois d'arc. To this communication Turner added his own experience with Osage orange, writing that he had several Osage orange trees in his garden, one of which had "stood the climate well . . . for six or more years." He added, "Three years will make a hedge from it which nothing can pass, on good soil, if the plants will not thin themselves out."[43] Evidently, Turner had not yet tried the bois d'arc as a hedge plant, although it is clear that he was experimenting with other hedge plants by this time.

In mid-1846 S. Edwards, of Bureau County, reported in the *Prairie Farmer* that a nurseryman of Cincinnati, William Neff, had just sent a shipment of Osage orange plants to be planted on his farm in Bureau County.[44] In November of 1847 Turner reported that he had become interested in hedging during the 1830's when he was stumping the state on behalf of a state-wide system of common schools and realized that the state must be more thickly settled than the prairies had yet allowed if he were to realize his objective. He had first learned of the Osage orange in the mid-1830's, he said, and had soon obtained one plant. Gradually he had added to the number and was now, in 1847, preparing to set out several miles of the hedge, having arranged that seed enough for 200,000,000 plants be brought from Texas.[45] Turner now improved his own considerable holdings with Osage orange hedge and also developed a considerable nursery business, specializing in the sale of Osage orange seedlings.

During 1848 William C. Greenleaf, a nurseryman of Sangamon County, declared for Osage fence, although he had a "vast number of thorn plants for sale."[46] He based his decision on having seen growing in the state a number of fine hedge rows of the plant that had survived severe winters unprotected. Although we cannot know the exact date of his conversion to the southern tree, Cyrus Overman, nurseryman of Fulton County, also began to grow Osage orange plants for sale "soon" after 1844.[47] Obviously, we can hardly say that Jonathan Turner "introduced" the Osage orange hedge in the prairie country. Once committed to the nursery business, however, he promoted the Maclura with great energy, advertising vigorously

[42] *Prairie Farmer*, September, 1844, p. 217.
[43] *Ibid.*, December, 1845, p. 284.
[44] *Ibid.*, June, 1846, p. 184.
[45] *Ibid.*, November, 1847, pp. 346–47.
[46] *Ibid.*, October, 1848, p. 313.
[47] *Ibid.*, July 29, 1865, pp. 72–73.

and writing to the press about the most successful methods of growing Osage orange hedge. To his friends, however, it was he who "buffeted the waves of opposition; wrote down, lived down, and *hedged* down the gibes and jeers and doubts of unbelievers. *He* who shed first his sweat and then his ink, freely and without pay, till universal conviction crowned his success . . . the father of our system of hedging." [48] Conviction, of course we may note, did bring its rewards to nurseryman Turner.

Although many farmers obtained Osage orange seedlings from the prairie nurseries or raised their own from seed, hedge fencing presented a variety of problems. Those who purchased seed in the early years often found it difficult to make it germinate. Whether the seed should be frozen for a time, soaked in water prior to planting, or started in a plant house at 70° were all questions which perplexed the pioneer growers. Turner reported an "Osage Weevil" that attacked the seed in transit. The Civil War interrupted the flow of seed northward from Texas and Arkansas despite dramatic efforts on the part of Turner to maintain his supplies. (His agent ultimately fled the South in fear for his life). Although efforts to save seed from the seed balls of mature plants in the northern states were successful in some instances, the price of Osage orange seed rose to $87.50 per bushel from the prewar price of $20.00.[49]

Farmers and nurserymen debated methods of culture with considerable difference of opinion. By the early 1850's, hedge-contractors were offering to save farmers from the worry and effort of planting their own hedges. Contractors in southeastern Iowa during the mid-1850's asked 37.5 cents per rod for their services, "twelve cents per rod at the time of putting in, five cents per rod in each of the two following years, and the balance, fifteen and a half cents per rod at the completion of the hedge or at the end of four years." [50] Some of the contractors, unfortunately, were rascals who collected as large a down payment as possible at the time of planting and then left the country.[51] The Osage hedge was disease free and unattractive to pests with the exception of marauding gophers.[52] Its greatest enemy all too often was the master's hand. In the beginning the spacing between plants and the methods of trimming and thickening were very much argued. Gaps in hedges remained unfilled, trimming was often perfunctory, the hedge plants turned into trees, and livestock found gaps that they could pass through with little discomfort. Sceptics quickly pronounced the Osage orange to be one more "prairie humbug." The criticism subsided somewhat when men with a knowledge of English hedging methods introduced the "plashing" technique, cutting the plants partially off a few inches above

[48] *Ibid.*, September, 1855, p. 270.
[49] *Ibid.*, September, 1849, p. 273, March, 1850, pp. 91–92, October, 1850, pp. 314–15; Rice, *op. cit.*, pp. 46–49.
[50] *Prairie Farmer*, March, 1854, p. 93.
[51] I.S.A.S.R., 1858, p. 386.
[52] *Ibid.*, 1879, p. 403.

the ground to bend and thoroughly intertwine them.[53] But as late as 1872, a writer from southwestern Iowa commented:

. . . the hedges are receiving a great variety of treatment in different men's hands — some planting three inches apart, others twelve inches, some trimming up and plashing, others thickening up from the ground, while others let accident and nature have free course without any interference on their part. . . .[54]

Many farmers did not succumb to "hedge fever." Depending on their location, they might still continue to "maul and haul" rails, construct picket fence, or, as in Fayette County, Iowa, make poplar-pole fence.[55] From the 1860's onward, particularly, many farmers looked to the Wisconsin pineries for their fencing material, making post-and-board fence. In the late 1840's there was a flurry of interest in wire fencing. The wire available at this time was ungalvanized and must be painted to prevent rust. Farmers learned also that they must stretch it taut to make a secure fence and that the frost heaved the fence posts, loosening the wire each spring. Cattle and horses viewed the wire fences of the 1840's and 1850's with friendly tolerance; after they had scratched out their winter coats upon them, they found easy passage. Pigs scorned them utterly, unless the lower strands ran expensively close together.[56]

In 1871 the United States Department of Agriculture surveyed the fencing of the various states. Although based on incomplete county returns, the results do give some idea of the fencing decisions which the prairie farmers had made. In fifty-six Illinois counties, 43 per cent of the fences were worm-fence, 32 per cent board, with hedge fence making up 20 per cent of all fencing in thirty-four counties where Osage hedges were "particularly mentioned." In Kankakee County on the Grand Prairie, however, 75 per cent of all fencing was hedge. "No greater variety of fencing exists in any State" than in Iowa, reported the Commissioner of Agriculture. Forty-eight counties reported that 24 per cent of the fences were worm, 23 per cent board, 14 per cent of post and rail, and 39 per cent of miscellaneous construction. Osage hedge dominated this last category, and in Cedar County accounted for 60 per cent of the total. But in Muscatine County, close by the busy sawmills of Davenport and Muscatine, 90 per cent of all fencing was of boards.[57]

Comparison of the cost of the various types of fencing is difficult. Contemporary observers treated the labor factor differently and did not always

[53] *Prairie Farmer*, August 12, 1865, p. 111, April 11, 1868, p. 233; I.S.A.S.R., 1871, pp. 410–14.
[54] *Iowa Homestead*, March 8, 1872, p. 74.
[55] I.S.A.S.R., 1877, p. 337; *Northwestern Farmer and Horticultural Journal*, July, 1858, p. 223.
[56] *Prairie Farmer*, September, 1845, p. 227, February, 1847, pp. 67–68, November, 1848, p. 353, December, 1848, p. 375, February, 1849, p. 53, July, 1849, p. 211, March, 1850, p. 76, April, 1850, pp. 117–18, July, 1850, pp. 212–13.
[57] U.S. Commissioner of Agriculture, *Report, 1871* (Washington, 1872), pp. 504–5. The quotation appears on p. 505.

specify the height of the fence in rails, boards, or strands. For the settler with woods on his farm or a timber lot in some nearby grove or valley, rail fence represented an outlay of labor only, aside from the initial cost of the timberland and the taxes on it. But if, like some farmers, he had to haul his rails between five and ten miles, the labor outlay became considerable. If he hired his rails split on his own property, the cash cost of seven-rail Virginia worm stood, in the 1840's or 1850's, at roughly 40¢ a rod. It is clear from the estimates of fencing costs that board was the most expensive of the inert fences, and wire the next most costly (see Table 10). The initial cash cost of hedge fence, eight to fifteen cents per rod for

TABLE 10

AVERAGE FENCING COSTS PER ROD, 1840–74.

	Board	Wire	Picket	Sod	Worm	Post and Rail	Four-Strand Barbed Wire
1840–1860* ..	$1.75	$0.83	$0.43	$0.40	$0.55–.75	....	....
1871 Illinois † .	1.31	....	....	....	.99	$1.27	....
Iowa ...	1.31	....	....	....	.91	0.94	....
1874 Iowa ‡ ..	....	....	....	....	....	....	$0.60

* *Prairie Farmer*, March, 1846, pp. 90–91, July, 1846, pp. 204–5, February, 1847, p. 67–68, April, 1848, p. 113, May, 1848, p. 144, October, 1848, p. 302, July, 1849, p. 211, March, 1850, p. 76, April, 1850, pp. 117–18, April 2, 1864, p. 226; *Union Agriculturist and Western Prairie Farmer*, October, 1841, p. 77, November, 1841, p. 43; *Northwestern Farmer*, April, 1856, p. 104, *Iowa Homestead and Western Farm Journal*, Jan. 3, 1873, p. 1; Fred Gerhard, *Illinois As It Is* . . . (Chicago, 1857), pp. 311–12. The estimate for seven-rail worm is the writer's, based on a rail cost of 2c per rail.
† United States Commissioner of Agriculture, *Report, 1871*, p. 509.
‡ I.S.A.S.R. *1875*, p. 43. By 1885 barbwire fencing costs were probably well below 30c per rod, depending upon the local cost of labor and posts. The wire for a rod of four-strand fence cost 10c at that time. *Prairie Farmer*, April 4, 1885, p. 209. Three-strand fencing was probably always much more common than four.

the plants, was lower even than the cost of rail fences when the rails were custom split, but the continuing charge for maintenance was heavy. One Illinois property owner's accounts showed that it cost 51¢ per rod to start a hedge in 1868 and some 33¢ per rod each year thereafter for upkeep.[58] In four years time this fence had cost as much as board fence, and the cost of upkeep continued unabated. The estimate of one historian that the western farmer must pay two or more dollars in fencing costs for every one dollar paid initially for land is hardly an exaggeration.[59]

Shortly after the Commissioner of Agriculture made his survey, a veritable fencing revolution was under way. During the late 1860's inventors in New York and Ohio had patented types of barbed wire. During the early 1870's J. F. Glidden and Jacob Haish, of Dekalb, Illinois, perfected types of two-strand, twisted, barbed wire that farmers accepted with approval. Like most of the technological adaptations to the prairie environment, the barbed wire that became so popular was not the brainchild of any one man. Of 394 early barbed-wire patents, Illinois inventors obtained 176,

[58] Margaret B. Bogue, *Patterns from the Sod: Land Use and Tenure in the Grand Prairie, 1850–1900* (Springfield, 1959), pp. 119–20.
[59] Clarence H. Danhof, "The Fencing Problem in the Eighteen Fifties," *Agricultural History*, XVIII (October, 1944), 173.

and the Dekalb men owed much to a technological climate developed by twenty years of fretting over the fencing problem.[60] During the mid-1870's a barbed-wire fence of four strands might cost 60¢ a rod, but wire prices would fall rapidly from the 20¢ per pound of 1874 until it cost as little as 2¢ a pound in the early 1890's.[61] Some stockmen complained of the injuries which barbed-wire fence inflicted on cattle and horses, but farmers used it more and more. In the 1890's wire manufacturers produced a satisfactory and reasonably priced woven wire, but for all practical purposes the fencing problem had ended on the prairies during the late 1870's.

As the prairie farmers hauled rails, stabbed themselves on hedge thorns, and deplored the cost of board fencing, some of them called for a "non-inclosure system" on the prairies. The advocates of the "no fence" proposal did not, of course, intend to eliminate all fences. They wished simply to reverse the custom of frontier Illinois and Iowa and make the owners of livestock responsible for fencing them in rather than allowing them to range as free commoners. The question of stock confinement in the counties of the prairie triangle was a free flowing source of community conflict. Depending somewhat, of course, on the locality, it ranged livestock men against grain farmers, town and village dwellers against farmers, old settlers against new settlers, timbered sections against prairie, the well-to-do farmer against his poorer neighbor, and resident farmers of the county or township against the owners of "foreign herds".

Supporters of stock-confinement measures or herd laws stressed the cost of fencing and presented elaborate estimates of the expense that prairie settlers must meet if they fenced all of their farms.[62] Conversely, they stressed the limited means of the prairie farm-makers. Money otherwise spent on fencing, if judiciously expended, would make them prosperous farmers in short order. As things stood without a herd law, the prairie farmers must use whatever poor fencing they could, and writers contributed touching accounts of prairie herds, led by some " 'lantern jawed' old ox that . . . [had] . . . served the season out at the breaking plow — working probably at the center of the team, because he was too unrully and mean to be made to work anywhere else," [63] bearing down on flimsy "shang highs" as soon as the prairie grasses lost their succulence.

Quite understandably, the opponents of stock confinement professed to

[60] Earl W. Hayter, "Barbed Wire Fencing — A Prairie Invention: Its Rise and Influence in the Western States," *Agricultural History*, XIII (October, 1939), 190.

[61] *Ibid.*, p. 195.

[62] The agitation in Illinois had begun by the 1840's. See *Union Agriculturist*, August, 1842, p. 67; *Prairie Farmer*, February, 1843, p. 35, May, 1843, p. 118, February, 1847, p. 58, November, 1848, p. 859, May 2, 1863, p. 273, May 7, 1864, p. 322, April 29, 1865, p. 327. The problem became pressing in Iowa at a later date: *Iowa Homestead*, March 16, 1864, p. 57, February 26, 1868, p. 58, July 29, 1868, p. 237, December 31, 1869, p. 1, January 14, 1870, p. 2, February 4, 1870, pp. 4–5, March 11, 1870, p. 2, October 7, 1870, p. 4, February 9, 1872, p. 43, March 22, 1872, p. 92, January 30, 1874, p. 36.

[63] *Iowa Homestead*, October 7, 1870, p. 4.

believe that fencing was no great problem. Their opponents' plan was a "no fence–no sense system." The northern pineries and hedging would provide the materials for prairie fences. As farm-makers took up the open ranges, of course, herd laws might have a place, but not until then. In the meantime such laws would encourage the non-resident owners of grassland to try to rent it. As for the small farmer, the range was open to his cattle no less than to those of the larger stockman. Nor could the quality of livestock improve rapidly under a herd law, for the breeder of purebreds must ward off the forays of his neighbor's "*Scrawny Pennyroyal* Durham" dangling the remnant of his tether and unimpeded by intervening fences.

Slowly, sentiment in favor of stock confinement gathered strength as the settlers invaded the prairies. During the 1850's the legislators of both Illinois and Iowa restricted the freedom of swine and sheep. In Illinois, a series of laws allowed the voters of particular counties to restrain these animals, and in 1857 the Iowa legislature passed a law which allowed the voters of any county to deny the commons to sheep and hogs, outlining a procedure of distraint, sale, and damages. Another law of the same year provided that a three-rail or three-board fence was a legal one in actions for trespass, provided that the structure was fifty-four inches in height and that the bottom rail was between sixteen and twenty inches from the ground. Clearly the Iowa legislators hoped to save fencing materials, as well as to confine animals whose depredations might be particularly costly or annoying.

In the next decade the lawmakers of Illinois and Iowa considered the larger domestic animals, horses, mules, and particularly, cattle. A series of Illinois herd laws, beginning in 1861, allowed the voters of townships or counties to restrict the larger farm stock.[64] Between 1868 and 1874 the Iowa legislators also provided the procedures by which the residents of counties or election precincts could restrain stock from running at large, or establish limited bans, calling for restraint between sunset and sunrise during certain periods of the year.[65] Much backing and filling marked the passage and application of these laws; statutes conflicted, and residents questioned their constitutionality. Apparently, the herd laws inspired more than their share of political maneuvering in the state legislatures. While Iowa legislators were working out a practical herd law that would be applied on an optional basis, they returned to the problem of restraining the smaller animals and passed a law in 1872 that made confinement mandatory throughout the state. One observer hailed this as a healthy step toward the common-law principle that owners must confine all stock.[66]

Once the state legislators had approved the basic statutes, acrimonious

[64] Margaret Bogue has discussed this legislation in *op. cit.*, pp. 120–21, 133–36.

[65] Iowa, *Laws*, 1856–57, chap. cxciii, chap. ccxxxv; 1868, chap. cxliv, pp. 202–5; 1870, chap. xxiv, p. 23, chap. xxvi, pp. 24–26; 1872, chap. xviii, pp. 19–20; 1874, chap. lxx, pp. 91–93.

[66] Iowa, *Laws*, 1872, chap. lix; I.S.A.S.R., 1872, p. 34.

battles over the herd law occurred at the county and township level. In some localities, residents voted time after time on the question and filled the columns of the local newspaper with arguments pro and con at each election. In Hamilton County, Iowa, in 1877 "R" bared the feelings that such contests could provoke:

Now I want to tell you who wants a herd law. Some men in Webster City [the County Seat] who own land that is broken up but not fenced and who want to save every dollar they can; they want a herd law. A few men who own many cattle and want all that their poor neighbors own, they *want* a herd law. Land sharks, land agents and lawyers; they want a herd law. Some men living along Boone river, who want to keep the cattle off from the grass nearest them, so that they may cut their hay nearer home (they don't care whether we out on the prairie have any hay or not), they want the herd law. Some other honest men want the herd law.[67]

When herd-law votes were held at the county level, farmers protested the town vote cast, according to one bitter writer, by "every Irishman who pastures his cow and pig on the curb stone, and imagines they are stealing a living." [68] In some areas the contest became one between grain farmers and stockmen, or the timbered areas against the prairies, but the lines were seldom drawn so simply.

Many of the prairie counties, or townships within them, adopted the herd-law. In northwestern Iowa, unquestionably, the herd law did ease the financial burden of many farm-makers, as well as put change in the pockets of farm youths who herded stock on the prairies. But in the communities where even the bitterest fights had occurred over the herd law, the farmers had fenced their farms by the 1880's and 1890's. In part, cheap barbed wire explained this fact. But prairie agriculture was not to be all grain-farming or all stock-raising. Rather, judicious combinations of the two developed, combinations that only fencing allowed.

"'Iowa sloughs,' have long had a notoriety as wide-spread, at least, as from Maine to California," maintained a writer in the *Iowa Homestead* in 1869.[69] Perhaps he drew the longbow somewhat, but at the same time he quite properly emphasized a feature of the land in both Iowa and Illinois. Particularly in the areas of Wisconsin glaciation the natural drainage patterns were poorly developed, much of the land lying sodden or, indeed, under water during long stretches of the year. Typically, the farmer who settled on the wet prairie broke his high ground first and looked to lowlands and sloughs for pasture and prairie hay. "Knoll farming" one granddaughter of the pioneers called such practice.[70] But prairie farms of this sort were not fully improved until artificial drainage had tamed the wet prairie.

[67] *Hamilton Freeman*, September 26, 1877.
[68] *Iowa Homestead*, March 11, 1870, p. 2.
[69] C. A. Johnson in *Iowa Homestead*, October 8, 1869, p. 1.
[70] Mrs. Percy Neese, Stanhope, Iowa, in conversations with the writer in May, 1956.

The war on the wet prairie was to be a long one, and drainage efforts prior to 1870 were little more than skirmishes. By the 1850's some of the large landholders of central Illinois were ditching in an effort to drain their holdings. About 1854 the mole ditcher came into use. A farm editor likened this to a "wedge of iron . . . attached to a sharp coulter, some three or four feet long . . . fastened to a frame, so as to work above the surface of the ground. In lands inclined to be wet . . . this instrument is plunged into the ground the desired depth, and with two yoke of cattle attached to a windlass, it can be forced readily through the earth at the rate of one-half a mile a day." [71] At the end of the decade the secretary of the Iowa State Agricultural Society claimed that this machine was "the very thing needed to do our draining at a merely nominal cost." [72] But despite rather wide use, the mole ditcher was not an unqualified success either in Illinois or Iowa. A farmer from Cedar County, Iowa, reported in 1863 that more than half the mole drains in his neighborhood were failures.[73] In some clay soils they worked well for a time, but in the more porous soils they broke down almost immediately — a disaster forecast occasionally by the sudden appearance of dangerous holes along the line of the drain.

In the meantime the middle-western press featured articles on the under-ground drains of board and stone constructed on British farms and on the pioneering efforts in America of John Johnson, "The Great Tile Drainer," of Geneva, New York.[74] During 1861 the *Prairie Farmer* carried the advertise-ments of tile-manufacturers in Chicago and Joliet, the latter willing to ship to all parts of the West by canal or railroad. Tile factories were operating in Polk and Henry counties, Iowa, by 1869.[75] But, if the family farmer of the prairie triangle drained his land at all prior to 1870, it was generally by running a few ditches with plough and shovel or by hiring the services of a custom ditcher in an effort to dry up the more irritating sloughs on his property. Some of the landowners who did experiment with minor ditches or tile drains during the 1860's discovered that drainage on the prairies had broader implications than they had imagined. If surface ditches or tile drains were to do their work properly they must feed into larger ditches, which might run for several miles before reaching a creek or river. Adequate drainage for many prairie lands could be the product only of joint effort. The landowners who pioneered in prairie drainage found also that neighbors might object violently to drainage projects which diverted additional water onto their acres. During the 1860's and 1870's the legisla-tors of both Illinois and Iowa turned to these problems and provided the legal machinery by which one landowner could obtain right-of-way for his

[71] Margaret Bogue, *op. cit.*, p. 122.
[72] I.S.A.S.R., 1859, p. 9.
[73] O. M. Culver in *Iowa Homestead*, January 1, 1863, p. 385.
[74] See for instance *Hamilton Freeman*, November 26, 1859.
[75] *Prairie Farmer*, July 18, 1861, p. 44, September 5, 1861, p. 140; I.S.A.S.R., 1869, pp. 248, 290.

drainage lines across the property of others, and by which farmers could group themselves together into drainage districts where county officers supervised the construction of major drainage channels with funds derived from tax levies on the property benefited.[76] Not until the counties were allowed to spread the cost of the work over a term of years by issuing drainage bonds, however, were some of the larger drainage projects of northern Iowa and Illinois possible.

Led by the larger operators and owners, Illinois farmers of the "black earth" counties turned to tile drainage enthusiastically during the late 1870's. Exceptionally heavy rainfall during these years as well as rising land values undoubtedly fostered this enthusiasm. Comparable interest in drainage in Iowa would not come for another ten years although a considerable number of Iowa counties reported tile draining under way by the late 1870's. But settlers did not begin farm-making on much of the Iowa wet prairie until the 1870's and 1880's, and it would be some years before they or their assignees could turn to the problem of draining their farms. In northern Iowa, drainage-district activity culminated after the turn of the century.

[76] Margaret Bogue, *op. cit.*, p. 146; Iowa, *Laws,* 1870, chapter clix; *Iowa Homestead,* January 7, 1870, p. 4.

CHAPTER V

The Passing of the Lean Kine

Among Corn Belt farmers today none is more respected by his fellows than the cattle-feeder. In part this is a recognition of the exacting skills, the judgment, and the capital required in a successful cattle-feeding enterprise. It is also an attitude rooted in the history of the prairie peninsula, going back to the first generation of prairie agriculturalists when cattle kings rode the Illinois prairies and the famous Texas cattle trails were still unknown. Then, as now, the cattle-drovers and feeders were a minority of the agriculturalists in Illinois and Iowa. But cattle played some part in the farm business of almost every farmer in the prairie triangle from the earliest days.

TABLE 11

CATTLE IN ILLINOIS AND IOWA*

YEAR	ILLINOIS			IOWA		
	Milk Cows	Other Cattle	Oxen	Milk Cows	Other Cattle	Oxen
1850	294,671	541,209	76,156	45,704	69,025	21,892
1860	522,634	970,799	90,380	189,802	293,322	56,964
1870	640,321	1,055,499	19,766	369,811	614,366	22,058
1880	865,913	1,515,063	3,346	854,187	1,755,343	2,506
1890	1,087,886	1,968,654	6,579	1,498,418	3,394,765	2,367
1900	1,007,664	1,373,024	.....	1,423,648	2,653,703	.....

* Compiled from the federal census, 1850–1900.

During the 1840's and 1850's most farmers owned from one to six cows and a somewhat larger number of young stock. From this herd came cream for the family butter as well as a supply of beef and veal. Typically, the prairie farmer butchered several animals each year. He might sell several others for cash. In most communities a few farmers kept a larger number of cows, selling milk in a nearby town, or more likely, making larger amounts of butter than that needed for home consumption or casual trading at the local store. In less frequent instances they made cheese. Here were the beginnings of the western dairy industry, although it was not until the 1860's and 1870's that the northern fringe of Illinois and, somewhat later, the northeastern corner of Iowa began to assume the character of a dairy region. When our average farmer sold a few animals for cash, they went often to a traveling stock-dealer or drover who either carried on feeding operations himself or sold the herds that he gathered to feeders in regions of surplus corn production. Smallest in numbers among prairie stockmen were the breeders of improved or purebred stock who hoped to sell breeding stock to other farmers.

The varied cattle operations were not, of course, mutually exclusive. The breeder of "fancy" stock might also feed native cattle or try to upgrade common cattle while maintaining improved cattle for sale as breeding stock. As he bettered his fortunes, the drover or feeder who had originally evinced no interest in purebreds might build up a herd of them. Given the inclination, ability, and some good luck, the small farmer of one year might become the proprietor of a large feeding operation. Although blooded stock was most frequently the province of the man of some capital or the gentleman farmer, the breeder of fine stock was sometimes a relatively small operator.

The French settlers in the Illinois country had originally reared the black French-Canadian cattle, but these beasts evidently had little influence upon the herds of the later settlers.[1] Into Illinois and Iowa the American pioneers brought cattle of the native stock, descended from colonial herds that traced back to the various shires of England, to Holland, and even to Denmark. As late as 1868, Lewis F. Allen wrote of the western natives:

They are of all possible shapes, colors, and character, from the very worst to tolerably good, except in those districts where 'improved' blood has been introduced. . . . The chief defects of these common cattle are in *their lack of early maturity*, (requiring five to seven years to mature them,) hard 'handling,' prominence of bone, a large proportion of offal to flesh, and an uncertainty both as to the quantity and quality of milk with the cows. . . . It would appear from the looks of these animals, that the best bull calves — if there were any best about them — were made into steers, and the meanest kept for propagating their race, and the best heifers, tending to early maturity, were turned into beef, while the worst were reserved for breeding, and the dairy.[2]

Despite the slowness with which they matured, the common stock of the 1830's and 1840's seldom attained any considerable size either by modern standards or by those of the older states. William Oliver estimated that some Illinois cattle might attain weights of up to 840 pounds.[3] It was Shorthorn blood that first improved the quality of cattle in Illinois and Iowa. The

[1] William Oliver in *Eight Months in Illinois; with Information to Emigrants* (Newcastle upon Tyne, 1843), (reprinted Chicago, 1924), p. 102, did, however, remark upon the French influence in the Randolph County area at the beginning of the 1840's.

[2] Lewis F. Allen, *American Cattle: Their History, Breeding and Management* (New York, 1868), p. 38. Representative descriptions of Illinois cattle at an earlier date are found in *Prairie Farmer*, June, 1844, p. 133; Oliver, *op. cit.*, 102–4; John Woods, *Two Years' Residence in the Settlement on the English Prairie* . . . (London, 1822), (reprinted in Reuben G. Thwaites, [ed.], *Early Western Travels*, 1748–1846, Vol. X, [Cleveland, 1904]), 281–82.

[3] Oliver, *op. cit.*, p. 104; See also John M. Peck, *A Guide for Emigrants, Containing Sketches of Illinois, Missouri, and the Adjacent Parts* (Boston, 1831), pp. 166–71.

leavening process was slow, but it had begun by the 1830's. During 1834 the
Kentuckian James N. Brown established his Grove Park Herd in Sangamon
County, Illinois. Several other breeders introduced Shorthorns into central
Illinois during the next decade.[4] These pioneers obtained their stock almost solely from the breeding herds of Kentucky and Ohio. During the first
years the work went slowly, but in the flush 1850's interest in improved
stock in Illinois became much keener. The fact that grade Shorthorn steers
could reach gross weights in the neighborhood of 2,000 pounds impressed
Illinois farmers, and prosperous times gave them the means to improve
their stock. Now for the first time, Illinois stockmen imitated the breeders
of Ohio and Kentucky by forming an importing company to bring a shipment
of Shorthorns directly from England. The Illinois Stock Importing Association sold twenty-seven head of English Shorthorns at Springfield, Illinois,
in August of 1857.[5] During the same years "Long John" Wentworth, Chicago politician, journalist, and businessman, was establishing his famous
Summit Hill Farm near Chicago. In 1855 the Illinois Breeding Association,
a Wentworth alias, announced the arrival of a number of superior animals,
some of them from New York, and advertised service charges of from $10 to
$20. The eccentric Wentworth shocked other breeders by his practice of
asking $100 for young bulls on a first come first served basis rather than
basing his price on blood lines or conformation.[6]

The second Shorthorn Herd Book, which went to press during 1854, included pedigrees from some fifteen Illinois herds located in nine Illinois
counties.[7] The twenty buyers of the importation of 1857 were scattered
through eleven counties. Taking the two lists together, we know that there
were breeders of purebred Shorthorns during the mid-1850's in at least
eighteen Illinois counties, stretching from Edwards in the south to Cook and
Winnebago in the north but concentrated particularly in west-central Illinois.
Sangamon County was apparently the center of activity among the breeders
of Shorthorn cattle, with at least seven breeders located there. Scattered
through the Illinois counties there were, no doubt, also numbers of grade
herds headed by sires obtained from the breeding herds or tracing back, more
or less irregularly, to the blood lines of Kentucky and Ohio.

No pedigrees from Iowa appeared in the second Shorthorn Herd Book.
There is, however, record of the occasional well-bred animal in Iowa prior
to 1854, and already Timothy Day of Van Buren County had a small herd

[4] Alvin H. Sanders, *Shorthorn Cattle: A Series of Historical Sketches, Memoirs and Records of the Breed and its Development in the United States and Canada* (Chicago, 1916), pp. 264–356.

[5] W. W. Corbett in U. S. Commissioner of Agriculture, *Report, 1862* (Washington, 1863), p. 330.

[6] Sanders, *op. cit.*, p. 319; Don E. Fehrenbacher, *Chicago Giant; A Biography of "Long John" Wentworth* (Madison, 1957), pp. 115–16, 209–11.

[7] Lewis F. Allen, *The American Herd-Book Containing Pedigrees of Short-Horn Cattle, with Introductory Notes* (Buffalo, 1855).

of Kentucky origin. During the spring of 1857 the former editor of the *Ohio Agriculturist*, George Sprague, supervised a drive of some sixty pure-bred Shorthorns from Ohio herds to the lands of the Ohio Stock Raising Company in Butler County, Iowa.[8] A list of pedigrees collected by the secretary of the Iowa State Agricultural Society in 1858 showed that twenty-three individuals or companies owned purebred Shorthorn stock.[9] Most of the members of this group, however, listed only one animal, a bull, and were evidently maintaining grade herds rather than purebred breeding establishments. The Ohio Stock Raising Company was short lived. As late as 1872 an Iowan wrote, "The most noteworthy thing about our breeding farms at present is their newness." [10]

A student of the American livestock industry has pointed out that interest in improving the quality of American cattle developed primarily during periods of high beef prices.[11] The long gestation period of nine months and extended growth span of cattle, of course, made improvement a much slower process than in the case of hogs or sheep. Breeding animals from the improved herds of Ohio and Kentucky cost at least several times the prices asked for animals of native stock, an English animal, much more. Particularly in the days before the coming of the railroad, a slow and sometimes hazardous journey faced the blooded animals. The twenty-seven members of the Illinois importation of 1857 brought an average price of $1,165.[12] The purebred fancier must, therefore, be a man of some capital. He needed other qualities as well. In the first generation of settlement it was only the dedicated, the foolish, or the very farsighted who brought purebred stock to the prairies.

When beef prices were extremely satisfactory in comparison to the prices of other farm products during the late 1860's and early 1870's, a "boom" began in the purebred Shorthorn business.[13] The wonderful effect which even one cross of Shorthorn blood could have upon the rate of gain and ultimate size of the native stock was well known by the 1860's. As cheap Texan feeders invaded the Illinois and Iowa prairies, farmers there tried to compete by rearing animals which would return a premium for superior quality. At the same time a market developed on the western ranges for improved breeding stock that stimulated the growth of prairie breeding farms. The region surrounding West Liberty, Iowa, for instance, had be-

---

[8] Earle D. Ross, *Iowa Agriculture: An Historical Survey* (Iowa City, 1951) pp. 45, 46.

[9] Iowa State Agricultural Society, *Report, 1858* (Des Moines, 1859), pp. 441–68. Hereafter this series will be cited as I.S.A.S.R.

[10] G. W. J. in *Iowa Homestead and Western Farm Journal*, August 2, 1872, p. 242.

[11] Charles T. Leavitt, "The Meat and Dairy Livestock Industry, 1819–60" (unpublished Ph.D. dissertation, University of Chicago, 1931), p. 51.

[12] Corbett, *op. cit.*, p. 331.

[13] Russell H. Anderson, "Agriculture in Illinois during the Civil War Period, 1850–1870" (unpublished Ph.D. dissertation, University of Illinois, 1929), p. 94.

come known for its concentration of such farms by the early 1880's.[14] Finally
the boom generated its own momentum as speculators invaded the field,
gambling on the continued gain in the price of purebreds, particularly animals of the Booth and Bates strains, the royal families of the British Shorthorn kingdom. The climax of this phase of the interest in Shorthorns came
at the famous New York Mills dispersal of 1873, when the herd of 109
Bates Shorthorns put to auction by Samuel Campbell sold for an average
price of $3,504. For the eighth Dutchess of Geneva alone a British buyer
bid the fabulous price of $40,600.[15]

Such speculative prices had little place in practical farming operations;
they were sustained by speculators and rich men for whom blooded stock was
a hobby rather than a business. In the meantime, owners with stock tracing
back to the Kentucky importation of 1817 writhed in frustration as purists
impugned the legitimacy of their animals' ancestry and suggested that they
were only pampered grades.[16]

Speculation and faddism played their part in discrediting the Shorthorn
somewhat. Philistines pointed out that the mellow-handling Bates and Booth
stock and their relatives lacked in girth and stamina, and the first attempts
to grade up the range herds with Shorthorn blood bore out the charge. Ultimately, the conformation of the Shorthorn changed drastically as breeders
turned to the stockier and hardier Scotch breed. In the meantime, the Here-
fords and the Aberdeen Angus had usurped the field. Although hardly popular, the Hereford had been known in the United States since Henry Clay's
importation of 1817, but the "bonnie doddie" was a comparative upstart.
The first importation of Aberdeen Angus occurred in 1873.[17] From the
late 1870's considerable numbers of both reached the United States as
stock-importing became a considerable business. Lost in the shuffle was
the Devon, often mentioned during the 1850's as a possible rival of the
Shorthorn and promoted by men like Horace Capron and John Wentworth,
of Illinois, and Josiah B. Grinnell and George Sargent, of Iowa.[18]

The major breeders of improved cattle exhibited their choicest animals
at the larger fairs and exhibitions, seeking to prove their stock superior to
all others and to attract the attention of humbler breeders and farmers who
might wish to buy breeding stock. The pioneer purebred stockman of Illinois,

[14] I.S.A.S.R., *1877*, pp. 495–96; *Iowa Homestead*, September 3, 1875, pp. 276–77
and September 17, 1875, p. 292.

[15] Sanders, *op. cit.*, pp. 424–26.

[16] Paul C. Henlein sketches the origins of the "Seventeens" controversy in *Cattle
Kingdom in the Ohio Valley, 1783–1860* (Lexington, 1959), pp. 33–39; The *National
Live Stock Journal* devoted many columns in 1873 to the problem.

[17] Donald R. Ornduff, *The Hereford in America* (Kansas City, 1957), pp. 1–151;
Charles S. Plumb, *Types and Breeds of Farm Animals* (Boston, 1906), pp. 213–24.

[18] John Wentworth to the editors, *Prairie Farmer*, January 18, 1868, p. 37, maintained that there were many Devons in the West. (see also *ibid.*, July 11, 1863, p. 19
and October 17, 1863, p. 19.) The "Iowa Devon Herd Book" of 1859 listed six
owners of Devons. I.S.A.S.R., *1859*, pp. 462–68.

James N. Brown, had won more than 1,100 fair premiums and had sold "not less than 500 head" of cattle as breeding animals when he died in 1870.[19] Since there were initially classes for graded stock and categories for steers on the basis of their beef qualities, the fairs attracted exhibits from feeders or stockmen who were not purebred breeders. But, although the feeding and breeding fraternities overlapped, the purebred stock business was also a world of its own with little respect for national boundaries. It had its own peculiar enthusiasms, its own saints, devils, humor and pathos. So calculating a business on the one hand that an animal of a given strain might be sent to the shambles simply to "bull" the value of the remainder, it could be marked on the other by sentiment like that of John Hope, manager of the great Bow Park breeding farm in Canada, whose feelings toward the great herd sire, the 4th Duke of Clarence, "seemed deeper" than a veteran livestock journalist had "ever observed elsewhere on the part of an owner or herdsman toward a beast of the bovine species." It was so deep, indeed, that Hope chose the box stall of the aged Duke as the spot for his own suicide.[20]

It is difficult to estimate the speed with which prairie farmers discarded "piratical bellowing machines" and "little scrubby bulls." From the 1850's onward, improvement was probably rather rapid. One writer has suggested that "nearly all the common stock [of Illinois] had an infusion of more or less Shorthorn blood" by the early 1860's.[21] Another, writing in 1878, argued that the Shorthorn "had almost completely changed the color and form of Illinois cattle." [22] A little improved blood could go a long way. When Oliver Mills settled in the Nishnabotna country of southwestern Iowa during the late 1850's planning to carry on large scale feeding operations, he distributed twelve highbred Shorthorn bulls free of charge to the farmers of the district. As a result, according to Colonel John Scott, this district boasted the best grade cattle in Iowa during the early 1870's.[23] Not until this decade did purebred stock become relatively common in most farming communities of Iowa, and even in 1870 an Iowan from Fort Madison reported the farmers of his district "very tenacious of the old malt-head scrubs." [24]

It was unnecessary, of course, for a farmer to buy a purebred Shorthorn to grade up his herd. In the depth of the depression of the late 1850's, Coker F. Clarkson, later a journalist and politician in Iowa famous as "Father" Clarkson, obtained the use of a bull from the Ohio Stock Farm for a year by consenting to serve as agent, and to collect $2 service fees from farmers

[19] *National Live Stock Journal*, November, 1870, p. 66.

[20] Alvin H. Sanders, *At the Sign of the Stockyard Inn* (Chicago, 1915), pp. 95, 105.

[21] Helen M. Cavanagh, *Funk of Funk's Grove: Farmer, Legislator and Cattle King of the Old Northwest, 1797–1865* (Bloomington, 1952), pp. 59–60.

[22] Paul W. Gates, "Cattle Kings in the Prairies," *Mississippi Valley Historical Review*, XXXV (December, 1948), 382.

[23] *Iowa Homestead*, October 18, 1872, p. 331.

[24] I.S.A.S.R., *1870*, p. 482.

wishing to breed their cows to the beast. At the end of the year he returned the bull and a roll of bills — a reflection of stock improvement in Grundy County.[25]

Some circumstances slowed down the process of improvement. The best animals in a farmer's herd often caught the eye of feeder or butcher. Pure-bred or high grade stock might produce a better quality of beef somewhat faster, but the animals also required more careful feeding and handling than the frontier farmer was prepared to give. Before herd laws became general, it was difficult to keep blooded females safe from the overtures of bulls that lacked every desirable quality but ambition. When the cows pastured on the open prairies, farmers preferred to keep all calves irrespective of quality so that maternal instinct would bring the mother home at milking time.

Few settlers had the capital necessary to exploit the grasslands stretching away from their doors at the timber's edge, but a grazing industry did develop on the open ranges of the prairie triangle at an early stage of settlement in the region. Drovers from Ohio were scouring the settlements on the prairie margins by the 1820's, purchasing a few steers here, a couple of animals there, until they had accumulated a sizable herd. They often pastured the animals for a time on the prairies before guiding them eastward to Ohio.[26] Here, particularly in the Scioto Valley region, the cattle enjoyed another interval of grazing, perhaps, followed by a period of feeding on corn, before the drovers headed them east to the shambles of Philadelphia, Baltimore, or New York. It was a profitable business which continued in this fashion until the 1850's, when the development of the railroad network and the growth of population in the Upper Mississippi Valley disrupted the pattern and forced the Ohio graziers and feeders to modify their system of operations.[27]

Meanwhile there was developing in Illinois a group of drovers and feeders who sought themselves to exploit the supplies of native cattle and surplus corn in the central portion of the state where transportation facilities were too inadequate to encourage much growing of wheat. The Illinois stock-dealers drove cattle east to the seaboard markets on occasion, and supplied also the butchers and packers of Chicago and St. Louis as these centers became increasingly important as livestock markets during the 1840's. These

[25] *Iowa Homestead*, June 8, 1877, p. 181.

[26] Oliver, *op. cit.*, 105–7 described the beginning of a cattle drive in a colorful account that a number of writers have quoted. If the testimony of the veteran Iowa drover and feeder Moses W. Robinson can be trusted, however, Oliver described an atypical incident. Rather than assembling the herd at one time and risking the mass bovine rebellion portrayed by Oliver, most drovers built up their herds gradually, adding animals a few at a time, as purchased, to a nucleus supervised by a herder on the prairie. *Iowa Homestead*, March 8, 1872, p. 75.

[27] Percy W. Bidwell and John I. Falconer, *History of Agriculture in the Northern United States, 1620–1860* (Washington, 1925), p. 399; (see also Henlein, *op. cit.*, passim.)

men purchased supplies of corn from the farmers of central Illinois and fattened their own cattle before driving them east. Some evidently filled a kind of intermediary position in the trade, carrying herds of stock cattle or stockers through one winter on less than a full corn-feeding program and selling them during the next grazing season to the Ohio men who completed the fattening process during the next winter. With the coming of the railroad, the long drives east came to an end, and Chicago and St. Louis became the major objectives of the herds, although shipments of live cattle east or south were, of course, made from there.

In their search for cattle the Illinois stockmen did not confine themselves to the farming districts of Illinois, but followed the settlers westward into Iowa and Missouri as well. During the late 1840's and the 1850's a trickle of cattle from Texas began to flow into central Illinois.[28] Dammed by the Civil War, this trickle became a tick-infested river during the late 1860's when hog and cattle prices rose relative to the price of corn.[29] Despite the furor caused by Spanish fever and charges that their meat was merely "vitalized rawhide," [30] history was on the side of the Texans; they were the forerunners of generations of range cattle that have come to Illinois feedlots.

As soon as areas of surplus corn production began to develop in Iowa, residents of this state, too, turned to droving and feeding operations. Not all of the surplus cattle produced by Iowa farmers in the early days found their way to an eastern market. Western migrants and gold-seekers provided a market for beef and workstock as well, and when the trans-Missouri freighting business boomed during the 1850's, the outfitting towns of the Missouri Valley became an increasingly important market for cattle from interior Iowa. On the western slope a unique method of wintering and fattening developed for a time as stockmen pastured their herds on the succulent rushes and wild pea patches of the Missouri bottoms.[31]

The Illinois prairies produced a crop of cattle kings, no less colorful in their way, if slightly less fragrant perhaps, than the prairie flowers. A number of writers have portrayed the more famous of them in loving detail — Isaac Funk, of McLean County; Jacob Strawn and John T. Alexander, from Morgan County — men who ran empires "larger than some of the kingdoms of the Old World and a good deal more active." [32] In each case they utilized the profits of extensive stock-dealing and feeding to buy land, so that

[28] Margaret B. Bogue has summarized the material on the Texan episode in Illinois in *Patterns from the Sod: Land Use and Tenure in the Grand Prairie, 1850–1900* (Springfield, 1959), pp. 58–68.

[29] Anderson, *op. cit.*, p. 273.

[30] *Iowa Homestead*, February 23, 1877, p. 60.

[31] I.S.A.S.R., *1866*, pp. 284–85.

[32] This description was actually applied to Edward C. Sumner by George Ade in "Prairie Kings of Yesterday," *Saturday Evening Post*, July 4, 1931, pp. 14, 75–78. (see Paul W. Gates "Hoosier Cattle Kings," *Indiana Magazine of History*, XLIV [March, 1948]), pp. 1–24, p. 15, fn. 34; "Cattle Kings in the Prairies," pp. 379–412.

Isaac Funk accumulated some 26,000 acres, Jacob Strawn acquired about 20,000, and John T. Alexander held title at one time to an even larger estate. During the 1850's the first two were marketing more than 1,000 head of cattle along with large numbers of hogs per year, and in 1859 Alexander reportedly sold some 15,000 head of cattle.[33] The agricultural census of 1860 reveals that Strawn slaughtered, or sold for slaughter, $150,000 worth of livestock in 1859; Alexander's total was $115,000. Comparable figures are apparently not available in the case of Isaac Funk, but he did value the livestock on his farm, including 1,000 "other cattle" at $31,480 in 1860. This amount was $5,000 more than the value of Strawn's livestock, which included 500 other cattle. Seven other stockmen in Morgan County reported numbers of other cattle ranging from 200 to 600 head, and in both that county and in McLean there were many farmers with herds of fifty other cattle or more. It is clear from the census records of Morgan, McLean, and adjacent counties that Funk, Strawn, and Alexander were doing business on an exceptionally large scale.

Paul W. Gates has detected a kind of progression in land use on the part of the larger cattlemen in central Illinois. Depending on the open range for their grazing during the 1830's and 1840's, these men then built up large landed estates which they ran as bonanza farms for a time, seeking to raise much of the corn needed for their feeding operations with the help of hired labor. But management difficulties encouraged a transition to tenancy. From the tenants the cattlemen obtained their rent in corn and might also purchase the tenant's share of the crop. The cattle business as known by Funk and Strawn was an exciting one, calling for sound business sense and a good eye for the weight of a steer, since scales were seldom used before 1850. Isaac Funk and Jacob Strawn died in 1865, both of them millionaires. John T. Alexander was hardly so fortunate. Although he made great profits during the Civil War, he experienced a series of disasters later, including expensive damages payable to neighbors for cattle infected with Spanish fever by his Texan feeders.

In the early 1860's Funk and Strawn revealed the dollar and cents boundaries within which they operated.[34] Good two-year-old steers cost Funk between $18 and $25. After keeping them one summer, one winter, and half the next summer, he hoped to sell them as prices ranging from $45 to $52 per head. Buying older cattle in general, Strawn expected to pay from $25 to $30 for his feeders and to sell them ultimately at prices between $50 and $60. He contrasted these prices with those of the early years of his business, in the 1830's, when he bought steers for $8.00 and sold them for $16. The feeder thus expected to sell at approximately double the purchase

[33] Joseph G. McCoy, *Historic Sketches of the Cattle Trade of the West and Southwest* (Kansas City, 1874), (reprinted [Washington, 1932]), pp. 171–78.
[34] Corbett, *op. cit.*, pp. 333–34.

price. A full-fed steer might eat seventy-five bushels of corn, and Strawn, at least, figured that one feedlot attendant was necessary for every 100 head of cattle. But taken into calculation also must be the return from the fat hogs that were also fed on the same seventy-five bushels of corn.

Spectacular as the great cattlemen were, there were few of them in any particular locality of central Illinois. By the late 1860's there were forty-five holdings in the eight counties of Champaign, Ford, Iroquois, Kankakee, Livingston, McLean, Piatt, and Vermilion, ranging in size from 920 to 26,500 acres that were primarily livestock enterprises, an average of only six per county.[35] The number was somewhat higher, perhaps, in counties like Morgan and Sangamon. By 1880 the northern portion of the Military Tract and the counties immediately adjacent to the north comprised the major feeding area in Illinois. Almost 21 percent of the farmers in Clarion Township, Bureau County, bought and sold twenty or more cattle in 1879 as compared to 10 per cent in Towanda Towship, McLean County, and 7 per cent in Philo Township, Champaign County.[36] For every farmer in these localities with a major interest in cattle, there were between four and thirteen farmers who concentrated on grain or some other combination of enterprises. Yet the fortunes of these men were in part linked to those of the cattle-feeders, since they sold their surplus corn to them and might sell a few steers or hogs to them as well.

Iowa feeding enterprises were less spectacular for their times than those of Funk or Alexander, perhaps, but fattening operations began quite early in that state, sometimes involving several hundred animals. As early as 1845 Moses Robinson fed and drove a herd of cattle from Des Moines County to Philadelphia. In the spring of 1871 Robinson was managing an 1100-acre farm north of Des Moines on which he had wintered 260 cattle, 200 of which were destined for the spring market, the remainder to be finished off on grass.[37] During the summer of the same year, N. M. Letts of Louisa County had some 500 steers on pasture.[38] By this time a livestock economy somewhat reminiscent of central Illinois in the 1850's was developing in southwestern Iowa. Oliver Mills of Cass County reported that he had slaughtered, or sold for slaughter, stock to the value of $30,000 in 1869. At the time of the census enumeration in 1870 he owned 600 other cattle. Both Josiah and Otha Wearin of Mills County reported livestock sold for slaughter worth $10,000 in 1869. The number of cattle increased rapidly in Iowa during the 1870's, and by the end of the decade there were many stock

[35] Bogue, *op. cit.*, p. 48.
[36] Statistics of cattle movements must be compiled from the manuscript census of 1880 because the relevant columns were not summarized for publication in the printed census reports of that year. The Illinois manuscript agricultural census is available at the Illinois State Archives in Springfield.
[37] *Iowa Homestead*, April 21, 1871, p. 4.
[38] *Ibid.*, August 11, 1871, p. 3.

businesses of considerable size on the western slope. John R. Blair of Mills County, for instance, reported that he had purchased 1,200 cattle and sold 1,197 during 1879.

Iowa, too, had its Texan interlude when stockmen, mainly in the western and southwestern portions of the state, handled large numbers of "rangers."[39] Late in 1872 Oliver Mills of Cass County shipped 700 head to his feedlots at Lewis, Iowa.[40] Since the Texans had come north to Iowa over the trails and spent a considerable time in reaching the state, there was less difficulty with Texas fever here than in Illinois, where the large feeders of central Illinois brought their animals up the Mississippi by steamer — a rapid trip that gave the animals little time to lose their ticks.[41] There were, however, outbreaks of Texas fever in southwestern Iowa during the 1870's. Even cattle bearing Oregon brands arrived in Des Moines in 1879, destined for feed yards in Polk County.[42] John Hopkins' suggestion that the feeding of range cattle in Iowa was unimportant until the 1880's and 1890's is much too conservative.[43]

Analysis of cattle movements during 1879 in all ninety-nine Iowa counties shows that farming units on which the operator bought and sold a total of twenty cattle made up from 15 to 8.5 per cent of the whole in the counties of the top quintile. These counties lay for the most part on the lower Western Slope and in east-central Iowa. Most counties of the frontier fringe in northeastern Iowa or in the developing dairy region of the northeast lay in the lower two quintiles in which the farmers who bought and sold as many as twenty cattle made up 4.2 per cent or less of the total number of farmers. There were in all 12,679 farmers in Iowa who bought and sold a total of twenty cattle in 1879. Only 441, however, purchased or sold 300 or more. The greatest number of large operators resided in Woodbury County, where there were seventeen, But Dennis Mahanah of Muscatine handled the greatest volume of stock, buying 4,000 head and selling the same number.[44]

No doubt there were many stockmen in both Iowa and Illinois during the early 1870's whose businesses were somewhat similar to that of George F. Green, of Jackson County, Iowa. With the help of a foster son and usually two hired men, Green farmed 340 acres of land, handling between 100 and 200 head of cattle each year and a like number of hogs.[45]

[39] *Ibid.*, April 8, 1870, p. 2, November 15, 1872, p. 364, November 24, 1876, p. 376; I.S.A.S.R., *1868*, p. 15, 1872, p. 32, 1873, p. 14, 1874, pp. 318, 427, 464.

[40] *Iowa Homestead*, November 15, 1872, p. 364.

[41] Agricultural society reporters noted Texas fever outbreaks in Appanoose County in 1872 and Montgomery County in 1873. I.S.A.S.R., *1872*, p. 32 and *1873*, p. 14.

[42] *Hamilton Freeman*, October 29, 1879, quoting the *Des Moines State Register*.

[43] John A. Hopkins, Jr., *Economic History of the Production of Beef Cattle in Iowa* (Iowa City, 1928), p. 42.

[44] This paragraph is based on research in the manuscript rolls of the federal agricultural census of 1880 in the Iowa State Historical Society, Iowa City.

[45] For the following account I have drawn on the diaries of George F. Green, made

Green's diaries reveal the pattern of his stock operations in some detail. Ordinarily he maintained between fifty and 100 steers. Some of these he acquired in small lots of one to four animals from the farmers who lived within a day's drive from his farm. But at times he purchased droves of from fifty to seventy steers from the proprietor of a cattle-auction business who drew stock from a broader region and perhaps shipped in cattle from the West. Green did not confine his attention to steers alone but bought fat cows and yearlings also from local farmers. He did most of his small lot buying between April and September. His larger purchases occurred during the summer or fall. Typically, he bought steers at weights between 800 and 1000 pounds. When sold, his fat steers usually averaged between 1200 and 1300 pounds "well shrunk," that is, held from feed and water from ten to fourteen hours. Sometimes he shipped fat steers directly to Chicago; at other times he evidently sold to another local dealer who presumably shipped there.

George Green was a dealer as well as a feeder. If he frequently purchased steers from local farmers, he also sold stock on occasion to neighbors or relatives who needed animals to fill their feedlots. On one September day in 1872, for instance, he purchased thirteen steers for $500 and resold them to a brother-in-law for $550. He maintained particularly close relations with his son-in-law, purchasing steers for him at times and also making arrangements to sell such animals when he sold his own. Green sold most of his fat cows in small lots to a buyer who was probably a butcher in one of the nearby river towns. Although the diary record does not give the details of all his dealing, Green purchased between 155 and 180 head of cattle in 1871 and between 180 and 200 in 1872.

Beef cattle and hogs went together in the livestock economy of eastern Iowa. The notations in which Green described the sales of hogs are less complete than those concerned with cattle transactions, but clearly he sold more than 100 fat hogs in both 1871 and 1872. With the exception of twenty-eight hogs that he sold in July of 1872, these went to market in the winter or early spring months. Most of Green's hogs were farrowed on the farm, but usually he purchased a number of shoats or young sows each year. The weights of his hogs at sale varied considerably. In early January of 1871 he sold twenty pigs, which averaged 358 pounds apiece, at $5.47 per cwt. In June of 1872 he let a few go at an average of 202 pounds and received only 3.5 cents per pound.

The agricultural census of 1870 shows that Green raised 4000 bushels of corn during 1869, and his diary entries indicate comparable crops in the early 1870's. But Green was still obliged to purchase additional corn in the neighborhood from farmers who either through lack of inclination or capital had not the livestock to use their crop. In some cases he obtained grain

available to me through the kindness of Mrs. Curtis Frymoyer, his great-granddaughter of Wilton Junction. Microfilm copies are now available in the Special Collections Department of the State University of Iowa Library.

from landlords who rented their land under share leases. Occasionally, he sold some wheat and oats, but, in general, he derived his income from sales of livestock.

Green's feeding regime was apparently a flexible one. From 1871 through 1875 he sold large lots of steers on dates as diverse as March, July, and November. In 1872 he sold to a local dealer in March for July delivery. He did full-feed steers each winter, however, even though he ultimately sold many of them off grass. On occasion he began to feed stalk corn in September and, like most feeders, he utilized his stalk fields for a time after corn picking. In December 1875 Green put seventy-four steers into Henry Bryant's stalk field for a fee of 50¢ per animal per month, with the understanding that Bryant should stand all losses. Sometimes Green's men drove steers to the farm of his son-in-law to utilize the later's surplus corn or hay. The stockman's operating unit had originally been two farms, and he maintained "the Davis place" in pasture to a considerable extent. There was much driving of cattle to and from the pasture, and, at times, when his own stock was depleted, he allowed other stockmen to put in animals in return for small monthly pasture rents. Tame grass, probably timothy, carpeted Green's pastures at the beginning of the 1870's. In these years, however, he began to grow seed clover and by the middle of the decade had at least one clover pasture.

One can discern a number of elements in George Green's income from livestock. In the first place there were the quick returns from dealing. These he derived from the fat cows which remained in his feedlot for just a few days before a buyer appeared, or from the feeder or stocker steers which a neighboring feeder purchased after Green had acquired them from the farmers of the district. In such cases his pay was, in effect, brokerage — payment for bringing buyer and seller together. But his earnings from steers or cows long-kept were of a different nature. In this case he tried to profit from feeding pasture, hay, and particularly corn, home grown or purchased locally at from 20¢ to 30¢ per bushel, to stock, usually bought at 3¢ per pound. In part he hoped to derive profits from the spread between cost and sale prices. Typically, feeder cattle in this era brought more per pound as they grew heavier. A contract under which Green sold steers to his brother-in-law in 1872 illustrated this fact. For 1100 pound steers he received $4.30 per cwt., for 1000 pounders $4.20 and only $3.80 for 800 pound animals. There was, therefore, normally a growth differential in the prices received as well as the possibility of shifts in the market price generally. The ideal situation for Green, obviously, was one in which he sold steers that had gained several hundred pounds in his pastures and feedlots in a market where a general price structure prevailed at levels above that current when he bought the steers. Yet the growth differential and the increased weight of steers sent to the shambles allowed profit even when prices were much the same at both the date of sale and the time of purchase.

Finally, of course, there was income from the hogs that so industriously scavenged the feedlots.

We cannot with certainty separate Green's household and family expenses from those of his farm enterprises. But in 1871 he recorded total receipts of $26,672 and expenditures of $25,208. In the following year the figures were $35,830 and $31,550, to show a clear return of $4,290.

It would be easy to envy Green those years of the early 1870's. The famed monotony of rural life could hardly have borne heavily upon him, as he rode behind a jogging horse on cattle-buying forays through much of Jackson and Clinton counties. There were periodic trips as well to Chicago to sell stock. The needs of the cattle called him frequently from the routine of the crop fields to weigh animals, to salt them, to drive lots from one pasture to another, or to dicker with traveling buyers. Despite these tasks, Green found time to notice when the first frogs cheeped and blue birds sang or when the first squadrons of Canada Geese pressed their flying V's against the sky. Well-respected in the community, Green found his advice on the cattle and hog markets sought by relatives and neighbors. And finally, there was the pleasure of directing the farm work force in profitable labor. It must have been a rewarding life.

During the 1870's and 1880's many midwestern stockmen sought to add an element of vertical integration to their businesses by developing or sharing in the development of western ranch properties. The Swan brothers, famous pioneer ranchers of Wyoming Territory, maintained a feeder and breeding farm at Indianola, Iowa, their original home.[46] But less prominent stockmen of Iowa dabbled in western ranching in considerable numbers. A.D. Arthur, for instance, settled in Hamilton County, Iowa, during 1863 and in the following years became one of the leading stock-dealers in the county. By the 1880's he was "getting to be a 'cattle king,'" according to the local paper, and in company with other stockmen of Hamilton County was developing a ranching operation in Montana to which he shipped a large number of Iowa young stock during the spring of 1884.[47] Another Hamilton County businessman and stock-dealer L. L. Estes acquired a large cattle ranch in Utah in the same period.[48] The histories of other Iowa counties yield many more illustrations of intimate relations between midwestern stock enterprises and those in the northern range country. The pattern should not, of course, surprise us if we remember that the promoter of the first of the great Kansas cow towns, Abilene, was an Illinois stockman. Emphasis upon the Texan contribution to the range economy sometimes hides the fact that

[46] Don L. Berry, Tucson, Arizona, to George M. Sheets, Iowa City, Iowa, March 1, 1958.

[47] *Hamilton Freeman*, September 12, 1883, April 30, May 14, 1884, May 20, 1885; Lewis Biographical Publishing Company, *Biographical Record and Portrait Album of Hamilton and Wright Counties, Iowa* . . . (Chicago, 1889), p. 290.

[48] S. J. Clarke Publishing Company, *A Biographical Record of Hamilton County, Iowa.* (Chicago, 1902), pp. 446–48.

the entrepreneurial élan, business ability, and capital which built the northern range industry was often midwestern in origin.

There is in the report of the Commissioner of Agriculture for 1862 a brief account of the feeding methods followed by Isaac Funk and Jacob Strawn.[49] Although the scale of their operations was unusual, their feeding methods probably reflected common pratices. When buying cattle, it was Funk's preference to buy two-year-old steers in the spring of the year. After a summer of grazing, he might put these cattle on strong feed, that is, enough corn to keep them growing, and gaining in flesh somewhat as well. These steers he sold in the next summer or fall, after a period of grazing on the prairie had made them fat. Funk almost invariably sold grass-fed beef in Chicago prior to the reorganization of markets that followed the development of the western railroad net during the 1850's. Those steers that, he believed, would benefit by extra fattening were held, along with others purchased at the age of three years or better, and full- or stall-fed for a winter. Under this regime the steers obtained all the corn they could eat "and a good deal more." The term "stall-fed" was not used literally in the West, however, referring simply to the extra rations involved rather than to the system of inclosure.

Funk's "stall-fed" cattle, like his "strong-fed" steers, spent the winter in timbered feedlots, where attendants spread shocked corn before them each day. He believed that the optimum arrangement was to have two such fields for each herd of cattle, to be occupied day about by the steers and hogs. The optimum number of swine or scavengers was one hog for each strong-fed, and two for each full-fed, steer. Funk estimated that for the latter class of animal an acre and a half of corn was necessary; for the former, but an acre. Salt and water were available in abundance for the animals, of course.

The system of Jacob Strawn was much the same as Funk's, except that his preference was to buy three- and four-year-old steers. In terms of grain he estimated the average allowance of corn for stall-feeding was half a bushel daily, although larger animals were given as much as three pecks. Some stockmen drove herds to areas of corn surplus and contracted with farmers there to winter the animals. A common price for wintering two- and three-year-old cattle in the region of Putnam County, Illinois, about 1850 was $2 to $2.50 per head.[50]

The practice of feeding shocked corn was often described as the Virginia, Kentucky, or ever Ohio system of feeding. In 1845, Henry L. Ellsworth believed it to be "the usual mode" of procedure.[51] But sometimes hogs and cattle were simply turned into the cornfields for a period each day. Critics

[49] Corbett, op. cit., pp. 333–34.

[50] U. S. Commissioner of Patents, Agricultural Report, 1850 (Washington, 1851), p. 404.

[51] Ibid., 1845 (Washington, 1846), p. 384.

usually stigmatized this "Illinois plan" as wasteful practice, but it was common.[52] As early as the 1870's in Iowa, and probably earlier in Illinois, the practice of feeding husked or snapped (pulled in the husk) corn had become common. At first the stockmen merely scattered such grain on the ground, but soon they were saving grain by constructing feeding bunks or troughs. Cattle required hay or other fodder under this regime. Intermittently, the champions of ground corn, fed as meal or even mash, preached their message in the agricultural journals, but they failed to convert the feeding fraternity.[53] One writer quoted Isaac Funk in the 1860's to the effect that corn fed to cattle netted him 75 cents per bushel.[54] A few years later another stockman estimated that a bushel of corn would make ten pounds of beef and three pounds of pork.[55]

Before the settlers encroached on the prairies, they were the domain of the herds, even though the land might already be the property of some non-resident owner. Here grazed the stock that large stockmen had placed out for the summer under the supervision of mounted herdsmen. Over the prairies, too, there passed intermittently the herds of drovers or groups of farmers on their way to market or being driven to feedlots in the older settlements. During the herd-law era the farmers in communities where settlement was well advanced might pool their stock, with the exception of milk cows and calves, and send the herd out to the open prairies. Here one or more neighborhood lads watched these animals lest they wander away or raid the growing crops along the farming margin. As the settlers occupied the prairies, the herds retreated. In 1866 an Illinois observer noted that cattle were becoming fewer on the open prairies of Ogle and adjacent counties.[56] In these same years the open range was coming to an end in the Grand Prairie region. The same process was taking place more slowly in Iowa, where herding came to an end in the southwest during the 1880's and in the northwest during the 1890's.

When their access to the range was gone, stockmen concentrated increasingly on corn feeding. Some of the Illinois stockmen who owned large acreages made the transition slowly, and many believed that Texas cattle returned a larger profit if grass-fattened. The Brown brothers of Sangamon County described their system of grass-feeding in 1874, arguing that their large pastures of bluegrass gave them at least 6 per cent on their investment when used for the pasturing of steers.[57] Just at this time they were feeding considerable numbers of Texans, which required only half the capital necessary for handling native cattle. They maintained, however, that Illinois land

[52] *Prairie Farmer*, March 14, April 11, 1868, pp. 163, 236. Among secondary works, Hopkins, *op. cit.*, pp. 122–42 has a particularly useful account of feeding methods.

[53] *National Live Stock Journal*, January, 1875, p. 11.

[54] *Prairie Farmer*, February 6, 1864, p. 83.

[55] *Ibid.*, March 10, 1871, p. 2.

[56] Old Firkin in *ibid.*, June 16, 1866, p. 411.

[57] James N. Brown's Sons in *National Live Stock Journal*, April, 1874, pp. 123–24.

was too valuable to be used for the rearing of any young stock except the purebreds then in demand as breeding stock on the western ranges.[58] But soon most of the inclosed grassland pastures gave way to cornfields, unless the land was broken or less fertile than the average soils of central and northern Illinois. Somewhat later, but just as inexorably, the same development occurred in Iowa. Stockmen placed more and more dependence upon the range country for feeder stock.

Although Funk and Strawn in the early 1860's expressed preference for three- and four-year-old steers, many animals went to the shambles at an even more advanced age. It was possible to feed steers to monster proportions. Exhibited before the Chicago Board of Trade in the New Year holiday season of 1867, "Bob Burns," "Abe Lincoln," and "John Williams" averaged almost 3,200 pounds in weight.[59] The efforts to produce a larger market steer climaxed in the 1870's. In these years the Illinois stockman John Dean Gillett became famous for the mammoth ton-plus steers which he exhibited at the major exhibitions. The shipment of Gillett animals to England caused a minor panic among the hard-pressed farmers of that country. But even as Gillett received his plaudits, others were taking advantage of the improvement that the Shorthorn blood had worked in American cattle to emphasize that animals could be fed to respectable weights at two years of age, producing a superior quality of beef and returning a greater profit on the overall investment in the animal. These men were the true prophets of the future, and Gillett himself supposedly vowed in 1883 that he would never have another three-year-old steer on his farm.[60]

[58] *Ibid.*, May, 1872, p. 155.
[59] *Prairie Farmer*, January 4, 1868, p. 9.
[60] *Ibid.*, August 18, 1883, p. 516.

CHAPTER VI

The Lesser Beasts and Draft Stock

As night overtook the Yancy family of Harold Sinclair's *American Years* on the Illinois prairie in 1830, they came upon an abandoned cabin. They counted themselves lucky to find shelter, but around midnight a horde of grunting, clattering animals poured through the door to contest their claim. These were Ike Frink's hogs, and for two hours Yancy and his wife fought them off with billets of stovewood. Sinclair's Ike Frink strongly resembled Isaac Funk, the McLean County drover, even to naming one of his sons LaFayette.[1] Nor were Frink's half-wild, ill-tempered, and nimble-footed

TABLE 12
SWINE, SHEEP, AND HORSES IN ILLINOIS AND IOWA*

	ILLINOIS			IOWA		
	Swine	Sheep	Horses	Swine	Sheep	Horses
1850 ...	1,915,907	894,043	278,226	323,247	149,960	38,536
1860 ...	2,502,308	769,135	563,736	934,820	259,041	175,088
1870 ...	2,703,343	1,568,286	1,017,646	1,353,908	855,493	482,786
1880 ...	5,170,266	1,037,073	1,023,082	6,034,316	435,359	792,322
1890 ...	5,924,818	922,631	1,335,289	8,266,779	547,394	1,312,079
1900 ...	5,915,468	1,030,581	1,350,219	9,723,791	1,056,718	1,392,573

* Compiled from the federal census, 1850–1900.

hogs unlike the Illinois swine of the time. Few of them ventured to attack people, but the behavior of many of them suggested that they would enjoy doing so.

To cast the early hogs of Illinois as second rate villains, however, is to do them less than justice. The hog was as important on the farms of the prairie triangle as the steer or milk cow. Nor should we portray hog and steer in competition with each other for the grain crops of the region. There is some truth in such a picture, but the hog and the steer actually complemented each other on many farms. For cattle-feeders the margin of profit was often represented by the nutriment that his hogs gleaned from the droppings of the steers. For dairymen the hog strained out the last bit of usefulness which remained in buttermilk or whey.

[1] Harold Sinclair, *American Years* (New York, 1938), pp. 4–6.

None of the American farm animals can convert grain into meat of high quality with greater speed or efficiency than can the hog. Agricultural scientists have determined that the modern hog retains some 35 per cent of the energy in its feed, as compared to the 11 per cent that cattle and sheep derive from their rations. Depending on its age, the hog needs between three and five pounds of feed to gain one pound of weight. Calves require five pounds of concentrate and five more of roughage for each pound that they add to their weight. When dressed, the carcass of the hog weighs between 65 and 80 per cent of its live weight. Cattle generally dress out 50 to 60 per cent of live weight, while sheep and lambs lose between 45 and 55 per cent of their weight in the dressing process.[2] Many generations, of course, separate the western hog of the 1820's and 1830's from his modern descendants. During the interval, breeders have worked assiduously to improve his capacity to fatten quickly and to provide a carcass with little waste. Since stockmen have, during this same period, improved the fattening qualities of cattle, it is reasonable to assume that the hog of 130 years ago was also a more efficient meat producer than the steer of his day, although perhaps the difference was not so pronounced. The cattleman has ministered to fewer generations than has the swine-breeder.

Our comparisons between the hog and other meat-producing animals have simply stressed, thus far, the efficiency with which the individual hog converts feed into meat. Consider for a moment the capacity of the pig to reproduce. The cow freshens with one calf, occasionally two, between two and three years of age after a gestation period of nine months. The sow can farrow at about a year of age and can drop two litters in a year, since the gestation period is just under four months. One litter of pigs will produce as much or more meat than a steer in half the time. By the time a calf born on the same date as a female pig has dropped its first offspring, the sow may have numerous grandchildren, her owner, of course, permitting. Frontier hogs matured more slowly than do those of today, and doubtless, few frontier sows mothered two litters in a year, but the multiplication table of the western pioneer hog was still impressive.

Important also in this catalogue of the virtues of the hog was the fact that little capital need be involved in raising pigs. The capital necessary before a farmer could feed cattle with safety was considerable; a litter of weanling pigs cost less than half the cost of one steer ready for the feedlot. A writer in the *Iowa Homestead* during the 1870's was uncertain about the origin of the saying that hogs allowed Iowa farm boys "to go a courting in store clothes," but affirmed, "It is the small farmer's crop — his dependence and often his all."[3] Just as applicable to the nineteenth century as to the twentieth, to

[2] This paragraph and the following are based largely on Charles W. Towne and Edward N. Wentworth, *Pigs: From Cave to Corn Belt* (Norman, Okla., 1950), p. 7.

[3] R in *Iowa Homestead and Western Farm Journal*, October 19, 1877, p. 332.

which it was applied, was the comment of a Department of Agriculture specialist, "The prolificacy of hogs, their early maturity, the inexpensive equipment, and small capital investment needed likewise help to put hog production within reach of almost every farmer." [4] Given the matchless capacity of the prairie triangle to produce bumper corn crops, and given the ability of the hog to convert this cereal into succulent meat, it is little wonder that the corn plant and the hog have come to symbolize the agriculture of the region. "The hog," proclaimed a flamboyant speaker in the 1860's, "eats the corn, and Europe eats the hog. Corn thus becames incarnate; for what is a hog but fifteen or twenty bushels of corn on four legs?" [5]

In 1820 John Woods found many pigs in the Wabash settlements of Illinois. They were, he wrote, of "various sorts; but many of them are of a sandy colour, and some with wattles." In size they were "middling" but seldom attained great weight because of the "very hard keep." [6] Some twenty years later William Oliver reported from Randolph County that "the breed of hogs in this part of the country is very bad; they are long-nosed, thin creatures, with legs like greyhounds, and, like the greyhound among dogs, seem to be the kind formed for speed and agility among swine, as they think nothing of galloping a mile at a heat, or of clearing fences which a more civilized hog would never attempt." But he concluded philosophically, "Still, as the hog of a pioneer settler has, at some seasons, need for all the activity he can exert to procure a subsistence, he may after all be the best fitted for the backwoods." [7] Writers in the agricultural journals and in the agricultural society reports called the hogs of the prairie margins, the long-snouted "woods breed," wind-splitters, thistle-diggers, prairie sharks, hazel-splitters, and stump-suckers. From the perspective of 1879 the featured speaker at a fair in Clayton County, Iowa, spoke nostalgically, and a little loosely, of the:

. . . pioneer breed of hogs, provided by nature with snouts not less than a yard long . . . they could lift the top rail off of a ten rail fence, and breechy shoats were more numerous than fence-jumping steers. . . . A lean-sucked sow . . . could outrun Rarus, and had to be hunted down in the timber with fast

[4] E. Z. Russell *et al.*, "Hog Production and Marketing," U.S. Department of Agriculture, *Yearbook, 1922* (Washington, 1923), p. 182.

[5] S. B. Ruggles quoted by Howard C. Hill in "The Development of Chicago as a Center of the Meat Packing Industry," *Mississippi Valley Historical Review*, X (December, 1923), 259–60.

[6] John Woods, *Two Years' Residence in the Settlement on the English Prairie, in the Illinois Country, United States* . . . (London, 1822) (reprinted in Vol. X of Reuben Gold Thwaites, [ed.], *Early Western Travels, 1748–1846* [Cleveland, 1904]), p. 285.

[7] William Oliver, *Eight Months in Illinois; with Information to Emigrants* (Newcastle upon Tyne, 1843) (reprinted Chicago, 1924), pp. 80–81; (see also John M. Peck, *A Guide for Emigrants, Containing Sketches of Illinois, Missouri, and the Adjacent Parts* [Boston, 1831], pp 171–73; *New Guide for Emigrants to the West* [Boston, 1836], pp. 284–85).

horses. . . . A good specimen, well fed, for four or five years, would produce a fine mass of pork weighing not less than 200.[8]

By 1840 the days of the prairie shark were numbered. Abundant supplies of corn, the rapid development of the packing industry in Illinois and Iowa, and a market eager for fat pork ended his reign. It was among the swine that improvement of livestock on the prairie was first most clearly evident. Improved breeding stock represented no great capital outlay, and the early maturity of swine allowed breeders to work changes with great rapidity. Here the American lard hog developed to its fullest potential. On a trip to McHenry County in 1854, the editor of the *Prairie Farmer* noted great improvement in the hogs along the way in comparison to those in new communities ten years earlier.[9]

By the early 1840's there was keen interest in improving the swine of the West, and indeed, the interest in Berkshires amounted almost to a "mania." [10] At this period also a number of Irish Graziers reached the West, including the boar Daniel O'Connell.[11] Less spectacular, but probably more important, was a flow of stock from eastern regions where swine improvement was far advanced, especially Chester and Delaware counties, Pennsylvania, source of the Chester White hog. By the mid-1840's also, Ohio breeders had fixed the characteristics of the spotted hog, which ultimately became the Poland China. The Illinois Stock Importing Association of 1857 brought eighteen improved British boars and sows to Illinois, of which nine were Berkshires.[12]

Hog-breeders mingled a great variety of blood strains in the three major American breeds that they produced during the nineteenth century: the Chester White, the Poland China, and the Duroc Jersey. During colonial times and in the first sixty years under the republic, swine reached North America from Spain, France, Great Britain, Holland, Sweden, Germany, the West Indies, Italy, Africa, China, Siam, Burma, and other sections of the Orient. Relatives of the European wild boar, the breeds from Europe grew to large size under favorable conditions and were sometimes of combative temperament. Their flesh revealed an intermingling of fat and muscle fiber. Hogs of Oriental stock were more docile and fattened more easily, but they tended to secrete their fat in a thick layer between the skin and bone structure. To determine the exact legacy of any particular strain in the American breeds, and especially in the Poland China, would be impossible.[13]

Corn Belt hog-breeders of the nineteenth century sought particularly to

[8] Iowa State Agricultural Society, *Report, 1879* (Des Moines, 1880), p. 364. This series is hereafter cited as I.S.A.S.R.
[9] *Prairie Farmer*, July, 1854, p. 250.
[10] *Ibid.*, January, 1851, p. 1; June 27, 1863, p. 403.
[11] *Union Agriculturist and Western Prairie Farmer*, March, 1841, pp. 18–19; September, 1841, p. 69.
[12] *Prairie Farmer*, June 27, 1863, p. 403.
[13] In this paragraph I have followed Towne and Wentworth, *op. cit.*, pp. 165–68.

increase the rate of gain and the size of their hogs. The most important physi-
ological change that the breeders worked in the hog was a lengthening of
the intestines, thereby improving the animal's ability to absorb food nutri-
ents.[14] They altered the animal's outward appearance considerably also. For
the long-legged fence-jumper of the early 1840's they substituted animals
with thick cylindrical bodies and very short legs. When consumers revolted
against extremely fat pork in the last quarter of the nineteenth century,
breeders concentrated on fine-boned pigs that had not attained great size
by the time they were ready for market. But these so-called "hot bloods"
lacked vigor and were shy breeders. The breeding pendulum swung again
toward a larger, rangier animal.[15] By giving premiums for the kind of animals that they wanted, the packers played a part in these changes. The
efforts of some packing houses with British antecedents, however, to promote a bacon-type hog for the British market during the last twenty years
of the nineteenth century were hardly successful. Despite their efforts to
encourage the use of Yorkshire boars in the districts from which they drew
their hogs, they failed to make Corn Belt farmers abandon the lard hogs.[16]

Although the Poland China never completely outdistanced its American
rival, the Chester White, and both shared place with British breeds like
the Berkshire and Suffolk, the "spotted hog" was the most typical of improved western hogs in the nascent Corn Belt. The Poland China breed
developed in the Miami Valley of Ohio between 1816 and the mid-1840's.
Mingled in its veins were the bloods of the Warren County, the Russian, the
Byfield, the Big China, the Irish Grazier, and the Berkshire hogs; and,
perhaps, the list should not end there. Ironically, the historians of the breed
concluded finally that no Poland strain was involved, although a farmer of
Polish ancestry played a part in developing the breed.

The Poland China was the work of a series of intelligent breeders, beginning probably with the Shakers, of Union Village, in Warren County,
Ohio, and extending down to D. M. Magie, of Butler County, Ohio, who
ultimately claimed to have originated the breed.[17] By 1870 a considerable
number of strains of closely-related pigs were available under a variety of
names. At this point the editor of the *National Live Stock Journal* suggested
the name "Great Western" only to withdraw it in favor of "Polyonomous"
by which was to be understood "the Miami, Miami Valley, Magie, Moore,
Poland and China, Poland and Big China, Poland and China or Magie,

[14] James W. Thompson, *A History of Livestock Raising in the United States, 1607–
1860* (U.S. Department of Agriculture, "Agricultural History Series," No. 5 [Wash-
ington, 1942]), p. 136.
[15] Russell, *op. cit.*, pp. 194–96; For a general review of all the breeds see Charles
S. Plumb, *Types and Breeds of Farm Animals* (Boston, 1906), pp. 467–554.
[16] Towne and Wentworth, *op. cit.*, p. 180.
[17] Plumb, *op. cit.*, pp. 484–96; See also Donald F. Malin, *The Evolution of Breeds:
An Analytical Study of Breed Building as Illustrated in Shorthorn, Hereford and Aberdeen Angus Cattle, Poland China and Duroc Jersey Swine* (Des Moines, 1923), *passim*.

Spotted China, Improved Poland and China, Butler County, Warren County, Gregory's Creek, Dick's Creek, Shaker, etc., until further notice." [18]

Most active of the prairie breeders was A. C. Moore, of Canton, Illinois, who took a stock of the Butler County hogs with him when he moved to Illinois from Ohio. On Moore's four farms a visitor in 1870 found 18 boars, 190 breeding sows, and nearly 900 pigs. Here, too, was "King Moore," winner of the Pork Packer's premium of $700 at the St. Louis fair, "over hundreds of the finest hogs that could be got together." [19] Moore's breeding program, he claimed, was designed to produce a "good gently arched back, with an entire absence of any falling in back of the shoulders, deep well sprung ribs, deep thick hams and fine short heads." [20] Moore's aggressive salesmanship infuriated his competitors, who called him "offensive and pretentious" and accused him of using "questionable means" to win premiums. [21] In a struggle over the premium list of the Illinois State Agricultural Society during the early 1870's, the breeders of "spotted hogs" aligned themselves in pro- and anti-Moore groups. [22]

After 1880 the Poland China suffered somewhat for its earlier successes. As the packers sought leaner hogs, they faulted the breed for excessive fat. The proportion of "hot-bloods" was high among the Poland Chinas and fecundity suffered. Some breeders, indeed, returned to the Butler County region in search of stock descended from the discards of the past so that they could out-cross to a rangier and more vigorous stock. But, writing in 1906, Professor Plumb believed the cross-bred or grade Poland China to be the most popular pig of the day. [23]

During the 1870's the number of hogs in Illinois and Iowa increased rapidly as the number of prairie farms increased, and price relationships made hog production relatively profitable. Interest in purebred hogs increased at the same time. "This year," wrote the secretary of the Iowa State Agricultural Society in 1871, "is signalized as the epoch of a mania for hogs. Every county rings the changes on fancy breeds of every description." [24] The breed associations and registers of a number of the improved breeds of swine date from this decade.

Both Woods in 1820 and Oliver in the early 1840's reported that the hogs of the Illinois settlements along the prairie margins were expected to forage for themselves in the woods. Looking to their masters for little but salt, these pioneer porkers fared indifferently during much of the year but luxuriated on a variety of wild nuts in the fall. Such mast-fed pigs produced

[18] *National Live Stock Journal*, March, 1871, p. 223.
[19] *Iowa Homestead and Western Farm Journal*, September 16, 1870, p. 1, (see also March 18, 1870, p. 2).
[20] *Prairie Farmer*, March 19, 1870, p. 81.
[21] *National Live Stock Journal*, August, 1871, pp. 409–11.
[22] *Ibid.*, March, 1872, p. 89.
[23] Plumb, *op. cit.*, p. 493.
[24] I.S.A.S.R., *1871*, p. 13.

a sweet but greasy pork.[25] When Oliver wrote, however, it was customary, in the late fall and early winter, to pen the pigs marked for slaughter and to feed them corn for some weeks. This not only brought them to a more prosperous state, but the corn-feeding firmed the flesh and produced a meat that was superior in quality to that found in mast-fed hogs.

The woods hog of the 1820's seldom reached a weight of more than two hundred pounds, even when kept until the age of three years. By the early 1850's the proprietors of Rome Farms at Peoria were calling in the *Prairie Farmer* for hogs that would fatten young and weigh 400 pounds when ready for market.[26] They argued that packers would pay a premium for such animals. Writing from Neponset, famous at this time for its hog-breeders, Ezra McIntire reported that in a month and a half during the winter of 1870–71, nineteen farmers had shipped 932 hogs weighing well above 400 pounds each.[27] The average weight of one lot of thirty-five hogs, indeed, was 556 pounds. McIntire admitted, however, that many hogs shipped did not approach these weights. In 1871 the editor of an Iowa paper, the 'Vebster City *Freeman*, reported admiringly that a local farmer had killed a nineteen month-old "McGee" hog that dressed out at 602 pounds.[28] These were extreme cases, of course. A correspondent reported in the *Iowa Homestead* in 1867 that the 1,000 hogs in the heaviest drove ever to leave Jackson County, Iowa, averaged 274 pounds each.[29] The heavy hog was still the ideal in the late 1870's, but by this time the demand for fresh pork was producing a market for younger stock that weighed between 175 and 200 pounds. The growing export market at the time and the changing taste of American consumers were also pushing hog-breeders in the same direction.[30]

As late as the 1860's agricultural writers severely criticized the methods of western hog-raisers. Particularly in the earlier days farmers often kept fattening hogs in small rail pens without shelter and dumped ear corn on the dirt floor of the pen where it was soon trampled deep into the mud.[31] On occasion, they turned the swine into a portion of the cornfield and allowed them to "hog down" their feed.

The historian of agriculture in the Illinois Military Tract has suggested that the better farmers there by the early 1850's were pasturing their hogs during early spring and summer on clover, turning them into oat fields in early July for an interval of a month or six weeks, and then feeding them on corn, the green stalks at first and later the ripe grain.[32] Such an elaborate

[25] Oliver, *op. cit.*, p. 77; Towne and Wentworth, *op. cit.*, p. 164.
[26] Clapp and Butler in *Prairie Farmer*, November, 1853, p. 414.
[27] *Prairie Farmer*, June 4, 1870, p. 169.
[28] Webster City *Freeman*, January 4, 1871.
[29] *Iowa Homestead*, November 27, 1867, p. 373.
[30] I.S.A.S.R., *1880*, p. 41.
[31] *Prairie Farmer*, February, 1848, p. 52, July, 1849, p. 218, January 28, 1865, p. 51.
[32] Theodore L. Carlson, *The Illinois Military Tract: A Study of Land Occupation, Utilization and Tenure* ("Illinois Studies in the Social Sciences," Vol. XXXII [Urbana,

regime was probably quite rare at that time. Replies to a questionnaire of the swine committee of the Iowa State Agricultural Society in 1866 show that many Iowa farmers still allowed their pigs to roam freely in the summer, slaughtering them at sixteen to twenty months after a period of corn-feeding.[33] As settlement thickened in any area, and particularly after the sheep and swine provisions of the herd laws came into effect, farmers had to confine their swine and to provide summer pasture for them. The transition was not always a simple one. Herbert Quick has told how the farmers of Grundy County, Iowa, became increasingly dependent on their hogs during the 1870's and soon lost great numbers from disease because they had failed to provide pasture.[34] Although the columns of the *Prairie Farmer* in the early 1870's did indeed recommend clover runs for pigs, their use was probably not general.

On the farms of the cattle-feeder, the hogs followed a somewhat different regime. Here they followed the steers in the fattening period, finding their sustenance in the droppings. Large feeders drew upon the farmers of a considerable area for stocker hogs. Joseph G. McCoy has left us a pungent description of the "heroes" who scoured Egypt for stocker pigs to sell to the cattle-feeders of south-central Illinois.[35] Those who specialized in feeding the slop from stills and breweries to hogs provided another market for stockers.

Decade by decade the number of hogs rose in Illinois and Iowa. Illinois farmers reported just under 2,000,000 swine in the agricultural census of 1850 and something more than 6,000,000 in 1900. Iowa farmers owned only some 300,000 hogs in 1850 but almost 10,000,000 in 1900. Marketing patterns changed drastically, of course, during the period. Before the coming of the railroad, farmers might band together to drive their pigs to market, but more frequently they sold their fat hogs to dealers who drove the hogs to packing centers. Although more celebrated as a cattle king, Isaac Funk dealt largely in hogs in central Illinois, bringing many droves of 800–1,200 head to Chicago.[36]

A Des Moines paper noted the beginning of the droving season in late December of 1850 by describing a drove of 750 fat hogs assembled in Mahaska County, Iowa, that was to be driven to Keokuk some eighty miles away. Farmers along the route had engaged to sell additional hogs to the

1951]), p. 124. This statement was based on a letter from Peoria County to the Commissioner of Patents, which was requoted in Robert Russell, *North America: Its Agriculture and Climate Containing Observations on the Agriculture and Climate of Canada, the United States, and the Island of Cuba* (Edinburgh, 1857), p. 116.

[33] I.S.A.S.R., *1866*, pp. 188–91.

[34] Herbert Quick, *One Man's Life* (Indianapolis, 1925), p. 214.

[35] Joseph G. McCoy, *Historic Sketches of the Cattle Trade of the West and Southwest* (Kansas City, 1874) (reprinted Washington, 1932), p. 237.

[36] Helen M. Cavanagh, *Funk of Funk's Grove: Farmer, Legislator and Cattle King of the Old Northwest, 1797–1865* (Bloomington, 1952), p. 67.

drover so that the herd would number 1,000 on arrival in Keokuk.[37] In 1858 a Monroe County correspondent of the State Agricultural Society remarked, "So many different persons are engaged in the trade — frequently non-residents of the county — that any estimate of the number would be mere guess work."[38]

The hog was much harder to drive to market than the steer, and the improved breeds, particularly, suffered when forced to walk to market. For these reasons the early packing industry was widely distributed. Most Iowa towns along the Mississippi, and Illinois centers on both the Mississippi and the Illinois participated in it.[39] Packing started in Chicago during the early 1830's, but this city gained its pre-eminent position among packing centers only after it became the railroad hub of the upper Mississippi Valley. With the coming of the railroad, greater concentration developed. At the end of the late 1860's the hogs of northwestern Iowa still might face a considerable drive to the nearest railroad station; but, as the railroad grid of that state filled in rapidly during the 1870's, the "long drives" ended.

Encouraged by the difficulty of moving live hogs to market, many farmers slaughtered considerable numbers at home before the coming of the railroad. After the killing season in late December and January, they hauled the carcasses to nearby towns where they sold them to merchants and packers.[40] Packers complained, however, that home-slaughtered pork was often improperly cut, poorly cleaned, and even tainted because of careless cooling methods. On occasion too, farmers allowed the carcasses to freeze. Discrimination against home-slaughtered pork and the building of the railroads convinced most farmers that it was unprofitable to slaughter more than enough hogs for home use. Although Chicago packers were using ice by the 1850's, the market for fat hogs was generally restricted to the winter months until the 1870's, except, perhaps, for a modest demand from local butchers.[41] With the development of improved refrigeration techniques that allowed the shipment of fresh meat, the packing industry could operate on a year around basis. By 1880 this development was largely completed.[42] Combined with the demand for smaller and younger hogs, it encouraged the farmer to arrange his breeding program so that some, at least, of his sows farrowed in the fall.

The market for prairie pork was a varied one. Midwesterners themselves consumed great quantities. It became a staple item in the diet of canal hands, railroad construction workers, and lumberjacks. Before the Civil

[37] *Prairie Farmer*, January, 1850, p. 38.

[38] I.S.A.S.R., *1858*, p. 335.

[39] U.S. Commissioner of Patents, *Agricultural Report, 1847* (Washington, 1848), p. 655; *1849*, p. 496; *Iowa Homestead*, February 26, 1863, p. 37.

[40] Oliver, *op. cit.*, pp. 77–80 contains a classic description of hog-killing in Illinois.

[41] A writer in the *Prairie Farmer*, March 17, 1866, p. 173 noted, for instance, that the packing season was now over.

[42] I.S.A.S.R., *1880*, p. 41; Towne and Wentworth, *op. cit.*, p. 179.

War great quantities went to the southern plantations, some to the West Indies, and some to Europe. During the mid-1840's England became a major destination for American pork. With the coming of the railroads to the Middle West, the eastern domestic market became highly important. During the 1870's increasing quantities moved into the markets of continental Europe as well as England. Food, preservative, lubricant, and, in the form of lard oil, illuminant, the lard that he rendered from waste meat and offal was as important to the early midwestern packer as the meat which he pickled or cured. England's decision to lower tariffs during the 1840's, the disruption of the southern market by the Civil War, the later actions of a number of European countries in barring American pork because of the threat of trichina — all had their effect upon the price level of pork, and this, in turn, influenced the decisions of prairie farmers.[43] As early as 1844 the editor of the *Prairie Farmer* lectured his readers on the short supply of pork and concluded, "The time to go out of business, *is not, when everybody else is quitting it.*"[44]

Crucial in the decision of the farmer to raise more or fewer hogs was the relationship between the prices of hogs and corn. Certainly by the 1840's many farmers knew how much corn they must feed a thrifty hog to produce 100 pounds of gain.[45] If they could purchase considerably more than this quantity of corn for the price of 100 pounds of live pork, it was obviously profitable to feed hogs. If the crucial quantity of corn cost more than 100 pounds of pork, the farmer did well to sell his corn rather than to feed it. A later generation would call this relationship the hog-corn ratio and generally consider that ten to twelve bushels of corn should produce 100 pounds of pork.

The size of the corn crop, of course, had much to do with its price. Prior to the 1880's most hogs lived through two corn crops. Farmers' plans might change drastically between farrowing and fattening time in deference to changes in the supply of corn and in the prices of both corn and pork. Hogs, as a result, sometimes reached market at very modest weights. A multitude of farmers, trying to accommodate their production of hogs to the fluctuations in the corn crop and in the price relationships between corn and pork, caused the number of hogs to rise and fall in short cyclical swings. But long run production trends and price relationships underlay the hog cycle. The numbers of hogs in Illinois and Iowa increased greatly between the Civil War and 1900, while during most of the period the over-all trend of hog

[43] Charles T. Leavitt, "Some Economic Aspects of the Western Meat Packing Industry, 1830–1860," *Journal of Business*, IV (January, 1931), 79–82; Russell, *op cit.*, pp. 188–97.

[44] *Prairie Farmer*, November, 1844, p. 251.

[45] *Prairie Farmer*, January, 1848, p. 11; February, 1848, p. 54; U.S. Commissioner of Patents, *Agricultural Report, 1851* (Washington, 1852), p. 443. There was, however, considerable speculation about this relationship in the agricultural press during the 1870's, and unquestionably there were great variations from farm to farm. See Towne and Wentworth, *op. cit.*, p. 201.

prices was downward. Hog production, however, was relatively profitable, in part, because the prices of other farm commodities fell to a greater degree.

Complicating the calculations of the individual hog-raiser, of course, was another imponderable — disease. Hog cholera struck regions of Illinois and Iowa repeatedly during the nineteenth century, sometimes almost wiping out the stock of a farmer or even a neighborhood. The farm journals of the time passed along many "sure" cures, but, apart from the effort to raise healthy weanlings and to keep them in relative isolation, no satisfactory answer was discovered until the development of vaccine after 1900.

After traveling in Illinois, Patrick Shirreff prophesied in the 1830's, "The time will . . . soon arrive when much of the unsold prairies will be covered with sheep, and then perhaps almost the whole surface of occupied farms will be devoted to providing winter-food for the flocks." [46] Shirreff's prophecy was far from the mark; neither the Illinois nor the Iowa farmers ever became as enthusiastic about sheep as they did about swine and cattle. Still, they made their contribution to the regional economy both during and after the days of raw pioneering. In 1840 there were 395,672 sheep in Illinois and flocks totaling 15,354 in Iowa territory. George Flower's pioneer flock of the 1820's in Edwards County, Illinois, evidently numbered between 400 and 1,000.[47] But most of the sheep of this period, apparently, were in very small flocks, which supplied the wool for household manufactures. The age of homespun, however, was drawing rapidly to a close as farmers moved into the prairies. Cyrenus Cole's suggestion that "practically every pioneer farm or claim in early Iowa had its own flock of sheep" is open to some question.[48] As late as the 1870's, however, some farmers did trade the wool from small flocks at local woolen mills in return for flannels, woolen cloth, and yarn.[49]

With the coming of the early 1840's, sheep made their first major onslaught on the prairies of Illinois and Iowa. "If representations made [to] us are correct," wrote the editor of the *Prairie Farmer* in 1844, "the rush of sheep to Illinois, Wisconsin, Iowa, and Missouri is a perfect tornado." [50] Ovine immigration to Illinois was directed mainly to the southern or the central portions of the state. At about this time Sangamon and adjacent counties received their pioneer flocks. Soon this region was the stronghold of the sheep industry in Illinois.[51] In Iowa, flocks grew most rapidly at this time

[46] Patrick Shirreff, *A Tour Through North America; Together with a Comprehensive View of the Canadas and United States, as Adapted for Agricultural Emigration* (Edinburgh, 1835), p. 457.

[47] Woods, *op. cit.*, p. 284; Oliver, *op. cit.*, p. 109; George Flower, *History of the English Settlement in Edwards County, Illinois, Founded in 1817 and 1818 by Morris Birkbeck and George Flower* (Chicago, 1882), p. 305.

[48] Quoted by Edward N. Wentworth, *America's Sheep Trails: History, Personalities* (Ames, 1948), p. 141.

[49] I.S.A.S.R., *1871*, p. 489.

[50] *Prairie Farmer*, September, 1844, p. 204.

[51] *Ibid.*, March 7, 1863, p. 147.

in the southeastern and southern counties. So eagerly did buyers seek stock for the West among the flocks in Ohio during these years that prices reportedly rose there by 100 per cent in the course of a few weeks in 1844.[52]

Unrealized, however, was the hope of the editor of the *Prairie Farmer* that the flock-building of the early 1840's would open a "new era," by giving farmers a staple so valuable that transportation would "not eat up all the profits of its production."[53] The price of wool remained below the levels of the 1830's until the early 1850's, medium wools seldom bringing prices above 40¢ a pound. Despite an upward tendency in prices during the 1850's, the number of sheep in Illinois actually declined during the decade. The eager grain market of the time, no doubt, gave many farmers profitable alternatives to wool production, but possibly problems of adjustment to the prairies and lack of satisfactory market outlets played some part. By late 1862, however, Prince Wool was profiting from the tribulations of King Cotton. In 1864 the price of fine Ohio wool soared above $1.00 per pound.[54]

Renewed interest in sheep — some called it a mania — developed in the prairie states as the price of wool rose during the Civil War. The federal census figures reflect this development very inadequately. Iowa flockmasters, for instance, sheared 259,041 sheep in 1860, and 855,493 in 1870. But the state census showed that almost 1,600,000 sheep were shorn in 1867.[55] As wool prices plummeted after the war, prairie sheepmen liquidated their flocks very rapidly. Although sheep had commanded prices of $2.00 to $3.00 apiece or even more during the war boom, some owners now sought to sell their animals for as little as 90 cents a head.[56] "OUR FLOCKS MUST GO TO THE PLAINS!" wrote one sheepman. "Southwest Missouri, Kansas and Nebraska, are rapidly filling with the sheep of Illinois and Ohio," reported another observer in early 1870.[57]

In both Illinois and Iowa the numbers of sheep declined during the 1870's, stabilizing in the next decade. There was renewed interest in sheep in Iowa during the 1890's, but the enumeration of 1900 was still more than half a million short of the 1867 census figure. The sheep boom of the 1860's affected all regions of the prairie states, but in the days of adversity afterwards, the flocks retreated to those districts where the terrain was rougher or the soils less fertile. In the old sheep-raising centers of central Illinois the "golden hoof" gave way to fields of golden corn. Southern and northern Illinois and southern Iowa became the centers of sheep-raising.

[52] *Ibid.*, September, 1844, p. 204.

[53] *Ibid.*

[54] Price data in this and following paragraphs are taken from L. G. Connor, *A Brief History of the Sheep Industry in the United States* (American Historical Association, *Report, 1918*, Vol. I), 193–95.

[55] *Census of Iowa for 1880 . . . with Other Historical and Statistical Data . . .* (Des Moines, 1883), p. 364.

[56] I.S.A.S.R., *1869*, p. 242.

[57] *Prairie Farmer*, January 8, 1870, p. 1.

In the early 1840's William Oliver pronounced the sheep of southern Illinois to be "nondescript" but usually somewhat affected by Merino blood.[58] The sheep of Van Buren County, Iowa, in 1849, however, were of the "common, coarse, long wooled kind." [59] During the 1850's and 1860's Merino blood worked a very considerable improvement in western flocks. Until the debacle of the late 1860's the prairie flockmaster usually regarded his sheep almost solely as a source of wool. William Oliver reported that mutton seldom appeared on western farm tables unless it were in the household of "some person from the old country or from the eastern states." [60] But the railroad-building of the 1850's and 1860's brought urban mutton markets closer to Illinois and Iowa farmers. The demand for coarse wool quickened, and prices improved. Sheep that were coarser-wooled and heavier than the Merino stock became increasingly popular. Southdowns and Cotswold sheep had won admirers in Illinois and Iowa even before the fine-wool boom of the Civil War years had ended. Such interest increased greatly after the war and extended as well to the Lincolns and the Leicesters.[61]

Foundation flocks made their way to the prairies of Iowa and Illinois under a variety of auspices. Immigrants from eastern sheep-raising areas, particularly Ohio and Pennsylvania, brought flocks west with them during the 1840's and in later years. Fired with the vision of a prairie sheep industry, westerners went east to buy flocks. Eastern flockmasters, on occasion, sent flocks west for sale or lease to resident farmers. Assisting in the transfer of sheep, also, were western men of capital, stock-dealers, in some instances, who capitalized on the sheep booms by bringing flocks to their home communities and selling them to resident farmers.[62] Although Ohio and Pennsylvania were the favorite recruiting grounds during the 1860's as in the 1840's, Michigan, Wisconsin, and Missouri also supplied sheep to Illinois and Iowa during the war years.

Flockmasters who were particularly eager to improve their stock imported a few choice animals, particularly rams, from Vermont. The tyro did well to be cautious in his efforts at improvement. "Sheep peddlers" frequented the fairs and other agricultural gatherings, each with a "*choice lot* of bucks to sell to the green ones, at high prices." [63] Often of dubious lineage, such animals might display luxuriant fleeces, accumulated over two seasons, and — to the practiced eye — show other evidence of "Vermonting" or fraudu-

[58] Oliver, *op cit.*, p. 108.
[59] *Prairie Farmer*, January, 1850, p. 23.
[60] Oliver, *loc. cit.*
[61] U.S. Commissioner of Agriculture, *Report, 1862* (Washington, 1863), pp. 256–58, 293; *Prairie Farmer*, March 22, 1873, p. 93.
[62] *Prairie Farmer*, March 7, 1863, p. 147; I.S.A.S.R., *1858*, pp. 11, 39, 1866, p. 220; *Hamilton Freeman*, June 7, 1862; July 2, July 9, August 13, 1864; July 29, August 12, 1865.
[63] *Prairie Farmer*, September 17, 1864, p. 177; *Iowa Homestead*, February 3, 1864, p. 13. The term "Vermonted" was used by "Wool Grower" in the *Prairie Farmer*, May 19, 1866, p. 338.

lent fitting. As interest turned somewhat to coarse- and medium-wooled mutton sheep, sheepmen often imported animals from Canadian flocks, built on the foundation of stock imported from England.

Most of the foundation stock brought to the prairies came on foot before 1860, and even after that date some sheepmen preferred to drive their flocks west rather than to ship them by railroad. Typically, the drives began in the late spring or early summer as soon after shearing as the condition of the lambs in the flock and the growth of grass allowed. The sheep-drover needed no elaborate equipment nor organization. A team and wagon loaded with supplies, one or two men, and a boy and a dog were quite adequate. Five hundred sheep was an optimum flock for driving, although a larger number was satisfactory if the weather remained dry. Sheepmen believed that ten miles was a good day's drive, although they might add a few miles to this total if all was going well. When driving through settled regions, the herders rented bed-grounds from farmers along the way and might purchase a little hay or grain in addition if the browse had been scanty along the route. Some drovers carried a long strip of burlap with them from which they constructed a fold each night.

The cost of driving sheep to Illinois from Ohio or Pennsylvania during the early 1840's seems to have amounted to less than 30¢ a head on sheep valued at 50¢ to $1.00 in the East, depending on the proportion of wethers and ewes and other characteristics of the droves.[64] In 1861 flockmasters of central Iowa could purchase sheep in the Kalamazoo area of Michigan for prices ranging from $1.00 to $1.50 per head and drive them west for approximately 50¢ per animal.[65] Four years later a resident of Jefferson County in southeastern Iowa estimated that it would cost between $1.00 and $1.25 per head to bring sheep by rail from Ohio, Michigan, or Pennsylvania but that the expense of driving sheep from these states would be only some 80¢ per head.[66] By this date correspondents from some Iowa counties were reporting to the State Agricultural Society that good ewes were worth $3.00 and even $4.00 each.[67]

The western farmer did not always have to purchase animals to make a start in sheep-raising. Eastern or western sheepmen sometimes offered farmers the opportunity of handling flocks on shares. Prior to 1862 the usual terms of leasing in central Illinois called for equal division of the wool and the natural increase, with the owner standing the loss of dead sheep, although receiving the pelts or pulled wool from such unfortunates. During the Civil War sheep boom, owners improved their bargaining position and commonly asked lessors to replace losses in the original flock from their

[64] *Prairie Farmer*, September, 1844, p. 205, May, 1845, p. 120, August 20, 1864, p. 114; U.S. Commissioner of Patents, *Agricultural Report, 1845* (Washington, 1846), pp. 341–42.

[65] *Iowa Homestead*, August 28, 1862, p. 242.

[66] I.S.A.S.R., *1865*, p. 170.

[67] *Ibid.*, pp. 162–81.

share of the weanlings.[68] We cannot know how common such sharing enterprises were. Iowa's most famous sheepman of the day, Josiah B. Grinnell, who owned 4,000 sheep during the late 1850's, was offering to sell farms in 1863, supplying a flock to each buyer and taking his pay in wool.[69] In his reminiscences Grinnell recorded that he scaled down the wool rent of his tenants in the postwar debacle when these men faced ruin.[70] Another prominent Iowa agriculturalist John Scott, of Story County, also had a number of sharing contracts with local farmers in those same years.[71]

Opinion differed on the degree to which the prairies were suitable for sheep production. Heavy losses among the flocks of the early forties convinced some that the prairie triangle was anything but a shepherd's paradise. The prairie grasses, they believed, were too coarse for sheep. What was more, they claimed, the wool of sheep became coarser over time on the prairies, and might become darker in color.[72] By the 1850's western flockmasters had shown that sheep could thrive in the prairie environment. A zealot like Grinnell, indeed, praised the prairies to the point of arguing, quite erroneously, that foot rot never appeared in western flocks.[73] Although most sheepmen evidently agreed that tame pastures provided better grazing in early spring and late fall, the prairie grasses, in the main, supported the early wool industry of central Illinois and Iowa.[74] The sheep, however, flockmasters agreed, should not be expected to forage for themselves until the prairie grasses had a good start, and their rations must be supplemented in the fall when the natural vegetation became dry and unpalatable.

The early western flocks received considerably different treatment from that given to the flocks of Pennsylvania or Vermont. Although some flocks never left the boundaries of their master's land, there was much daily herding by boy and dog on the open prairies. The sheep frequently found the most rudimentary of improvements awaiting them on the western farmstead, and winter shelter might consist of straw-covered sheds, used mainly in lambing time, and a simple feed yard with a windbreak of stacks or perhaps boards along the northern side. A western writer of 1862 drew a sharp contrast between the feeding practices of East and West:

The difference between eastern and western winter management arises partly from our keeping, as a general thing, larger flocks, partly from our having less inside fencing, but mostly from the different kind of feed and different manner of feeding. . . . Eastern authorities tell us not to winter over one hundred sheep in a flock, which is good advice; but with lumber at western prices it

[68] *Prairie Farmer*, July 15, 1865, p. 22; also September, 1843, p. 207.

[69] *Iowa Homestead*, July 23, 1863, p. 207.

[70] Josiah B. Grinnell, *Men and Events of Forty Years: Autobiographical Reminiscences of an Active Career from 1850 to 1890* (Boston, 1891), p. 308.

[71] I.S.A.S.R., *1866*, p. 220.

[72] *Ibid.*, *1857*, pp. 398, *1863*, p. 441.

[73] U.S. Commissioner of Agriculture, *Report, 1862*, p. 311.

[74] *Prairie Farmer*, October, 1845, p. 235.

would cost too much to fence off a sufficient number of lots for two to six thousand sheep. In the east the principal feed is hay; in the west corn. They (eastern men) think it a good plan to feed a little grain with the hay; we think that perhaps it might be well to feed a little hay with the grain. They feed hay twice a day and grain once, the kernels being counted out of a peck measure into little three-cornered troughs; we feed, twice a day, as much shock corn as the sheep can eat, or herd on standing corn two hours in each half day. . . . They are inclined to believe corn to be 'most too heating;' we think the want of it most too freezing.[75]

Despite a heavy dependence on corn, western flockmasters did feed quantities of oats and hay, and occasionally some roots, to their flocks as well.

The prairie style of sheep husbandry during the Civil War years evidently flourished most impressively in central Illinois. The *Prairie Farmer's* "Wool-Grower" maintained in early 1863 that many men there clipped between 2,000 and 6,000 sheep. Here the smaller flocks of Merinos numbered some 500 head and sheepmen considered flocks of 1,000 and 1,500 only "fair sized." [76]

When John Scott liquidated his sheep interests after the Civil War, he remarked that he could "find more men who can appreciate a hog or bullock, than understand sheep." [77] Actually, this had always been the case on the prairies. Where most farmers owned cattle or hogs, only a minority had maintained commercial flocks. Unquestionably, the boom of the 1860's drew many novices into the sheep business. Complaints of sheep diseases and the ravages of dogs upon the flocks marked the days of liquidation. We can trace losses from these sources largely to inexperience and disinterest after profits from the flocks began to decline.

Although midwesterners established a number of carding and woolen mills before the outbreak of the Civil War, most western wool passed through the hands of commission merchants to the markets of the northeastern seaboard. As early as 1850 John S. Wright established a wool depot in Chicago, where he hoped to sort and grade wool so that it would bring the best possible price on the eastern market.[78] Shortly after the Civil War one firm of commission merchants tried to explain why western wools did not command top prices in the wool market. Western wool, they pointed out, was often poorly washed and contained burrs and cotted wool. Also, the staple often showed weak spots due to sudden changes in feeding practices.[79]

[75] U.S. Commissioner of Agriculture, *Report, 1862*, p. 295. The Reports of the Iowa State Agricultural Society during the 1860's are particularly helpful, especially the reports of the standing committees on sheep, *1865*, pp. 162–81, *1866*, pp. 192–223, *1868*, pp. 300–319. The columns of "Wool Grower" in the *Prairie Farmer* during the same period are informative. See also *Iowa Homestead*, August 28, 1862, p. 242 and January 1, 1868, p. 413.

[76] *Prairie Farmer*, March 7, 1863, p. 147.

[77] I.S.A.S.R., *1866*, p. 220.

[78] *Prairie Farmer*, March, 1852, pp. 150–64.

[79] *Ibid.*, March 31, 1866, p. 208.

Although westerners disputed the criticisms of their product, there were many inexperienced western flockmasters whose wool merited the strictures of the commission men. During the mid-sixties wool-growers organized a number of local and regional associations in both Illinois and Iowa that sponsored sheep-shearing festivals and encouraged improved practicies as well as lobbying for higher tariffs against the "mestizo" wools of South America. Had not the boom caused both the industry and these organizations to go up "like a rocket, and . . . [come] . . . down like a stick," as one writer put it, prairie wool would soon have won respect.[80] But given the superior talents of hogs and cattle for carrying middle-western corn to market, the vision of a shepherd's empire in the prairie triangle had never been more than a delusion.

The prairie farmer maintained two classes of livestock on his farm. From his cattle, hogs, and sheep he raised each year a crop of fiber and stock for sale. But essential to farming operations of any scale were also the animals of a secondary category — the workstock. The dividing line between the two, of course, was not completely hard and fast. After several years before the plow, the ox was frequently fattened for slaughter. When pioneer farm-makers had accumulated some capital, they often kept several broodmares and reared enough colts so that they might sell one or two animals each year, as well as providing replacements for their own teams.

The federal census of 1850 showed that horses outnumbered oxen on Illinois and Iowa farms by roughly three to one. In Iowa the ratio was actually less than two to one. If the census of 1840 had included comparable figures, they would probably have shown that oxen were even more important in that year. A full grown ox of five or six years and of common stock outweighed the average horse, was powerful in the yoke, and usually docile. Stronger than many of the farm horses of the mid-nineteenth century, oxen were also hardier, with less need for grain during the seasons of heaviest farm work. But if oxen had some advantages as draft animals, they were also slower and much less nimble and maneuverable than were horses.[81] The harvesting and mowing machines worked a revolution in which there was little place for the ox, for these must be drawn at a fast clip to cut grain or hay properly and must be swung neatly at the corners of the field. Cultivating in the expanding cornfields was also a task for light-footed and speedy animals rather than the slower ox. Where Illinois farmers had reported 112,168 oxen in 1850, they listed only 6,579 in the agricultural census of 1890. The numbers of oxen declined in Iowa from a peak of 56,964 in 1860

[80] The simile is found in I.S.A.S.R., *1868*, p. 18. For notes on the organizations and shearing festivals see *Prairie Farmer*, September 24, 1864, p. 197, October 28, 1865, p. 324, February 24, 1866, p. 115, March 3, 1866, pp. 130–31, June 2, 23, 1866, pp. 369, 431; *Iowa Homestead*, May 4, 1864, p. 117; *Hamilton Freeman*, June 2, 1866; Mildred Throne, "A History of Agriculture in Southern Iowa, 1833–1890" (unpublished Ph.D. dissertation, State University of Iowa, 1946), pp. 140–43.

[81] *Union Agriculturist*, March 1842, 22, January, 1843, p. 11.

to 2,367 in 1890. In Illinois the ox lingered longest in the southern portion of the state where the mechanization of agriculture moved most slowly. The ox also made a stubborn stand in pioneer communities, where it represented a smaller capital investment than did a horse and where its power was still prized on the breaking plows.

William Oliver described the horses of west south-central Illinois in the early 1840's as "mostly small, barelegged, durable animals, and more adapted for the saddle than for the heavier kinds of agricultural labour." [82] The horses of northern Illinois in the same years were "scarcely any breed of horses — but a pell-mell mixture, occupying all the intermediate grades between a zebra and an elephant." [83] The horses of southern Illinois were believed to be considerably superior to the stock in the northern part of the state. Quite clearly, the prairie farmers of the 1840's and 1850's preferred light animals that would take them and their produce to the village or other market at a speedy clip. The stallions which horsemen traveled through the farming districts or "stood" at the livery stables in the prairie villages and towns were light animals, whose owners usually boasted of bloodlines tracing to the Morgan stock or other trotting horses. A Cedar Falls horseman informed the readers of the *Northwestern Farmer* in 1858 that he proposed to put Young Morgan Eagle into stud in the west; this stallion was only fifteen hands high and weighed but 950 pounds. [84]

If harvesting machinery ran best when pulled by horses, it also demanded more powerful horses than the light horse-of-all-work so common during the 1840's. Thus the same force which helped to discredit the ox as a draft animal also worked to change the type of horse commonly found in the draft teams of the prairies. Powerful horses, too, were not out of place, farmers found, on the wagons in which they hauled wheat or corn to shipping points over prairie roads that became quagmires during spring or rainy autumns. The market which developed for heavy dray horses in the growing cities of the Middle West also influenced farmers to grow larger and more powerful horses. But the transformation took place slowly. As late as 1872 the *Prairie Farmer* lamented:

. . . the millions [of horses] that tug at the city trucks, at the plows, at the reapers and mowers and threshing machines, and at the wagon-loads of grain on the way to market, are 'too light in the poop.' They lack avoirdupois. Instead of weighing 1300 to 1500 lbs., and walking easily and gracefully along with a ton and a half, or, on a good road, with two tons, they weigh from 900 to 1100 lbs., and wriggle and twist and pull and tug and sweat before one ton or less. [85]

Percheron or Norman blood played a major part in transforming the horses of the West. Although numbers of draft animals from France had

[82] Oliver, *op. cit.*, p. 101.
[83] *Prairie Farmer*, January, 1845, p. 24.
[84] *Northwestern Farmer*, April, 1858, p. 134.
[85] *Prairie Farmer*, July 27, 1872, p. 237.

arrived in America before 1850, this new chapter in the history of prairie livestock did not truly begin until A. P. Cushman brought the imported gray stallion, Louis Napoleon, to Illinois in 1856. Others soon followed. Although large in comparison to the ordinary western horse, the first Percheron stallions were often of a small type, weighing around 1500 pounds. By the 1870's the interest in Percherons had become widespread, and importations were common in Iowa and Illinois. With Michigan and Ohio these states became the centers of Percheron-breeding in the United States.[86]

Certainly by the mid-1870's it should have been easy for any farmer to mate his broodmares with stallions showing heavy Percheron influence, if not imported full bloods. By this time, too, breeders had become interested in the larger type of Percheron stallion weighing as much as a ton or more. During the 1870's also, importers began to bring in numbers of hairy-legged Clydesdales from Canada or Scotland as well as the English Shire horses. Although the Clydes, particularly, won many supporters, they never attained the popularity of the trim-limbed, free-gaited Percheron. Although horsemen in Illinois and Iowa established a number of famous studs during the 1870's and 1880's, most farmers were apparently content to grade up their stock by taking their mares to improved stallions.

If horses fared somewhat better on pioneer farms than did other varieties of livestock, they still received treatment that a later generation of farmers would have considered rude indeed. A resident of Polk County, Iowa, reported in 1865:

> There is no established method of raising horses. They really 'come up' till three years old, except it be a little care in winter, and this care consists mostly in feeding them a moderate amount of corn, and a majority of cases, giving them the *privilege* in winter of standing on the *leeward* side of an Iowa barn, or stable, or straw stack. This is what is called *raising them hardy*. . . . In summer, they run on the prairies, and are usually broken at the age of 2½ or 3 years.[87]

One writer has emphasized that farm-making was particularly hard on teams of horses brought by settlers from their old communities.[88] During the first couple of years on a new farm, the teams must work at times on the breaking plow and draw other machinery in fields not yet reduced by continued cultivation to a state of smoothness and good tilth. These unusual demands came at the very time when the farmer was most apt to be short of grain with which to feed his work animals.

The farmer who raised a few more horses than he needed for his own use found a variety of markets for them. While pioneering continued in Illinois and Iowa, there was a demand for horses from the regions where

[86] Alvin H. Sanders, *History of the Percheron Horse* (Chicago, 1917); Plumb, *op. cit.*, pp. 98–110.
[87] I.S.A.S.R., *1865*, p. 192.
[88] Mrs. George Sprague in the instalment of her reminiscences, published by the *Iowa Homestead*, June 9, 1876, p. 182.

farm-makers were in the majority. Since raising colts involved a greater capital investment than raising other types of livestock and demanded its own peculiar skills in the bargain, some farmers preferred to buy replacements for their teams from neighbors. Prior to 1870 the plains-country freighters provided a market for workstock in the Missouri Valley, although the demand there was more largely for oxen and mules than for horses. The government bought many horses for army use, particularly during the Civil War, but before and afterwards as well. From the 1860's onward the lumbering industry of Wisconsin and Minnesota absorbed many of the excess horses of northern Iowa and Illinois. With the exception of the war years, southerners, too, bought midwestern horses. As middle-western cities grew, they, also, drew horses from prairie farms.

Since horses were consistently worth from $50 to $125 each in the years from the 1830's to the 1880's, a minor horse-raising enterprise appealed to many farmers. But except for the few proprietors of studs or purebred horse farms, farmers considered the major role of the horse to be that of a work animal. No other kind of farm animal showed such a consistent distribution from county to county through the period of this study as did the horse.

Particularly in the southern portions of Illinois and Iowa, some farmers used mules rather than horses. One writer has suggested that German farmers especially liked the mule.[89] Inured to heat and a thrifty keeper, the mule was lighter in weight than many horses and possessed a personality that excited respect rather than affection. It was never as strong a competitor of the horse in the prairie triangle as the ox had once been. The Civil War apparently gave considerable impetus to mule production in southern Illinois, but the major domain of these animals under ordinary conditions was the South.

[89] I.S.A.S.R., *1866*, p. 270; *Prairie Farmer*, August 12, 1865, p. 108.

CHAPTER VII

The Crops in the Field

The commercial farmer has always tried to find the combination of crops and livestock that would give him the greatest return on his investment of labor and capital. The pioneer farm-makers of the prairie triangle must experiment to discover whether familiar crops would prosper in the region. If a crop failed quite generally, they had to ask themselves whether this reflected a basic incompatibility between crop and region, or whether the failure stemmed solely from an unusual season. If the crop of one pioneer farmer failed, while those of his neighbors flourished, this unhappy fellow was obliged to ponder whether local differences in soils, in cultural practices, or just bad luck explained his misfortune.

The ever-shifting relationships between the prices that the farmers received for the various crops and animals complicated the process of decision-making. Transportation problems added to the difficulty of these calculations. There was a limit beyond which the farmer could not draw grain to market profitably. Some have placed this at forty miles. But we must remember that the farmer decided among alternatives, rather than on the basis solely of labor cost. If the pioneer farmer had nothing more remunerative to do, he might haul grain considerably farther than forty miles, provided, of course, that spring or fall pasturage was available for his workstock along the way. Yet, there was a definite limit to the amount of time that could be spent on long trips to market or shipping point. At least one historian has argued that commercial agriculture could not develop in many districts of Illinois before the railroad age because they lay isolated from shipping points on river or canal. Actually, there was no district of Illinois so isolated in 1850 that farmers there could not market their grain in the form of pigs or cattle. And farmers in new communities with few transportation outlets might find a considerable market for some years in supplying newcomers who proposed to settle there. Pioneer farmers deep in central Iowa discovered buyers long before the railroad came, among the members of the Mormon migration, the gold seekers, and later settlers bound for the plains or the Far West.

Since many pioneer farmers had little capital, they found grain production for sale to be their most profitable enterprise when market outlets were available within traveling distance of a day or two. No major investment in livestock or farm improvements need be involved; no intermediate stage of feeding the grain to livestock was necessary. Excellent in its keeping qualities and used both at home and abroad as a bread grain, wheat was usually the favorite of the pioneer in such circumstances. An initial period of heavy dependence on the wheat crop was not universal, however, in Illinois and Iowa. If the pioneers of northern Illinois during the 1840's and 1850's, and the farm-makers of northern Iowa during the 1860's and 1870's were deeply committed to the wheat goddess, those of central Illinois and southern Iowa were considerably less so when they laid the pioneer foundations of these regions. Markets and transportation facilities accounted in large part for the contrast. The settlers of southern Iowa and central Illinois developed a corn-and-livestock economy early. Specialization, of course, is the essence of commercial agriculture, but even today many Corn Belt farmers hate to put all of their eggs in one basket. Despite the occasional story in the agricultural periodicals, the pioneer wheat-grower was seldom a monoculturist. The early farming patterns should be visualized in terms of more or less of wheat, corn, oats, barley, rye, flax, and hay, and few or more of cattle, swine, sheep, and horses.

Were the prairie soils good wheat soils? Discussion of this question went on for almost two generations. During the early 1830's John M. Peck proclaimed winter wheat to be "a good and sure crop, especially in Morgan, Sangamon, and other counties north." [1] But on the basis of his observations in the mid-1830's, Edmund Flagg decided that the "*worst*" soil of the prairies was best adapted to wheat. In general, prairie soils were too fertile, he believed, for this cereal. Illinois, he argued, could never become a celebrated wheat region, although he believed that it was already unequaled for corn and coarser grains.[2] William Oliver was somewhat of the same mind a few years later and pointed out that the best crops of wheat were harvested from the timber and ridge lands rather than from fields on the open prairies.[3] A writer in the *Prairie Farmer* of 1851 presented an analysis of western soils in terms of their capabilities and proper management for growing wheat. On the uplands where the white oaks grew was a pure wheat soil, that supporting yellow and red oaks differed somewhat, and where the bur oaks and hazels grew was "perhaps the richest soil." Least adapted

[1] John M. Peck, *A Guide for Emigrants: Containing Sketches of Illinois, Missouri, and the Adjacent Parts* (Boston, 1831), p. 147.

[2] Edmund Flagg, *The Far West: or, A Tour Beyond the Mountains. Embracing Outlines of Western Life and Scenery: Sketches of the Prairies, Rivers, Ancient Mounds, Early Settlements of the French, etc., etc.* (2 vols.; New York, 1838) (reprinted Reuben Gold Thwaites [ed.], *Early Western Travels, 1748–1846*, Vols. XXVI, XXVII [Cleveland, 1906]), XXVI, p. 302.

[3] William Oliver, *Eight Months in Illinois; with Information to Emigrants* (Newcastle upon Tyne, 1843) (reprinted Chicago, 1924), p. 88.

to wheat culture, he maintained, was the soil of the open prairies.[4] Other writers of the period were less elaborate but often suggested that wheat grew best on the soil of the timbered stretches or of the barrens, stretches of alternating timber, hazel, and prairie. Newly broken prairie, they suggested, was far superior for wheat-growing to old prairie fields.[5]

Do we dismiss these comments simply as the imaginative theorizing of a generation that had no systematic soil science at its disposal? These suggestions probably did stem in part from accurate observation. Although some spring wheat was grown in these years, mainly in northern Illinois, winter wheat with its superior milling qualities was usually preferred. In some years intermittent thawing and freezing during the winter and early spring heaved the winter wheat plants from the ground and killed them. The remnants of woodland cover as well as the topographic and climatic conditions which originally encouraged the development of the barrens and prairie groves may well have sheltered winter wheat crops from the climatic extremes that faced them on the open prairies. As for the suggestion that winter wheat on new breaking was less subject to winter-killing than that planted in older prairie fields, it is possible that the rough surface and partially decomposed root mass of the breaking gave the roots of the wheat plants more protection and purchase than did the smoother and more friable soil of older breaking.

Writers suggested that farmers might prevent winter-killing by spreading light coverings of straw over their wheat fields during the late autumn.[6] Some farmers recommended planting winter wheat between the corn rows so that the husked stalks would provide protection for the wheat plants and trap snow during the winter. Advocates of the grain drill argued that use of this implement prevented winter-killing because it deposited the seed wheat in small trenches. Alternate freezing and thawing simply acted to shift the earth from the intervening ridges down into the trench, thus giving the plants additional protection.[7] But the merits of the grain drill were not striking enough to convert great numbers of farmers.

Winter-killing was not the only problem which the farmer faced during the late 1840's and early 1850's in trying to grow winter wheat. Unfavorable seasons, rust, blight, Hessian fly, and, to a lesser extent, chinch bugs, all contributed to a series of poor winter-wheat crops between 1847 and 1852.[8] In the face of these tribulations the wheat-growers of Illinois and Iowa planted larger acreages of spring wheat. Although some farmers in central

[4] W in *Prairie Farmer*, April, 1851, pp. 166–67.

[5] *Ibid.*, February, 1854, p. 56, June, 1854, p. 205; *Northwestern Farmer*, January, 1857, p. 7; Iowa State Agricultural Society, *Report, 1857* (Des Moines, 1858), pp. 256, 434, *1863*, p. 481, *1866*, p. 186. Hereafter this series will be cited as I.S.A.S.R.

[6] *Prairie Farmer*, August, 1853, p. 304, August 4, 1866, p. 70; I.S.A.S.R. 1858, p. 7.

[7] I.S.A.S.R., *1870*, p. 483.

[8] *Prairie Farmer*, August, 1846, p. 245, August 1847, p. 244, October, 1847, p. 299, June, 1849, p. 196, September, 1849, p. 271, July, 1852, pp. 324, 328.

and northern Illinois and Iowa continued to grow winter wheat, it was considered to be an extremely uncertain crop in those regions through the 1860's and 1870's. During the late 1870's, however, favorable seasons brought renewed interest in winter wheat, particularly in southern Iowa and southwestern Illinois.

The crisis in winter-wheat culture during the late 1840's and early 1850's evoked a variety of reactions from farmers. To some the problem was an outgrowth of slovenly western farming. Probably few farmers of the late 1840's rode through their cornfields on horseback to sow wheat broadcast on uncultivated ground from a basket, a practice reported from the Illinois bottom during the early 1830's.[9] But western wheat culture was at times enough to make a farmer from the Genessee wheat regions of New York wince. Western farmers did often sow wheat after very little preparation of the soil. It was difficult to prepare a really satisfactory seedbed between rows of standing corn, but many farmers were still trying to raise wheat in this way during the late 1840's.[10] A resident of Davis County, Iowa, reported as late as 1865 that the usual mode of cultivating wheat there was much as in Illinois, "that is, to 'hog in' and 'hog over' a large number of acres at a half hammon gait, or a hop, step and jump, and trust to Providence for the result."[11] Some farmers believed that good crops of winter wheat would grow only on newly-broken meadow ground.[12] Some argued that the western soil had deteriorated in the wheat districts because of repeated cropping to wheat with no effort to restore fertility by manuring or rotation.[13] Others claimed that the pressure of western plows had created a hard pan some three inches below the surface that prevented proper drainage and deprived the roots of adequate supplies of plant food.[14] They proposed deep plowing or subsoiling.

Excessive reliance on wheat in various districts of Illinois and Iowa at times during the early period probably allowed the population of microparasites like rust, and pests like the Hessian fly and the chinch bug, to build up to the point where they seriously affected yields. Figures on crop yields before 1880 are scattered and untrustworthy, but pests and parasites may have played a larger role in any decline in yields than did soil depletion. Fighting such enemies directly was unrewarding. Some sought to avoid rust by sowing in mid-August, but soon they discovered that this practice provided ideal conditions for the ravages of the Hessian fly in the wheat seedlings during September.[15] Other farmers believed that they could ward

[9] Ibid., June, 1847, p. 189.
[10] Ibid., October, 1849, p. 345.
[11] I.S.A.S.R., 1865, p. 413.
[12] Prairie Farmer, August, 1850, p. 259.
[13] Ibid., March, 1851, p. 123.
[14] Viator in ibid., December, 1853, pp. 476–77.
[15] Ibid., October, 1843, p. 237, August 8, 1844, p. 188.

off marauders by steeping the seed wheat for a time in brine or other preparations.[16] This, too, of course, was futile.

Farmers tried to find varieties of winter wheat that were hardy enough to withstand the enemies of winter wheat. Those whose fields had prospered while the crops of others failed or faltered found their wheat in demand for seed. Some farmers imported varieties from other regions or from the east. Prairie husbandmen were cultivating a considerable number of supposed varieties during the late 1840's and the 1850's, including Mediterranean, Red Chaff Bald, White Chaff Bald, Red Chaff Bearded, Black Sea, Yellow Lamas, Soft Siberian, White Flint, Canada Flint, China, Early May, and Golden Chaff. As fall wheat regained some measure of popularity again during the late 1870's, farmers reported that they were planting Canada Swamp, Clawson, White Russian, and Odessa or Grass wheat.[17].

The prairie farmer decided during the early 1850's that the most satisfactory solution to the problems of winter-wheat growing was simply to shift to spring wheat. During the early 1840's this crop had primarily been a supplement to winter wheat, planted most broadly when farmers concluded that the fall planting had failed to withstand the winter. The large acreages of wheat planted through northern and central Illinois and in eastern Iowa in response to the favorable prices of the mid-1850's were mainly of spring varieties. This continued to be the case. When Iowa farmers produced a bumper crop of more than 44,000,000 bushels of wheat in 1875, only 850,889 bushels were winter wheat.[18] Farmers tested almost as many varieties of spring wheat as of winter wheat. Black Sea, Wild Goose, Hedge Row, Tea, Michigan White, Rhode Island, Canada Club, Red River, Scotch Fyfe, Scotch Spring Wheat, Crimean, and Galena all had their supporters.[19] Some wheat evidently doubled both as spring and winter varieties. This was certainly true of Odessa wheat and possibly true of Mediterranean, Siberian, and some of the "chaff" varieties. Farmers of different districts, too, may well have called identical grain by different names. One suspects certainly that Red River, Scotch Fyfe, and Scotch spring wheat may well have been the same variety.

By 1890 one could discern two widely separated districts in Illinois and Iowa where farmers placed considerable emphasis upon wheat culture. One

[16] *Union Agriculturist and Western Prairie Farmer*, December, 1841, p. 94; U.S. Commissioner of Patents, *Report, 1850* (Washington, 1851), p. 355.

[17] *Prairie Farmer*, January, 1847, pp. 22–23, July, 1847, p. 221; *Iowa Homestead*, August 14, 1862, p. 229, August 21, 1862, p. 237; I.S.A.S.R., *1858*, pp. 351, 352, *1859*, p. 167, *1879*, p. 382.

[18] *Census of Iowa for 1880 . . . with Other Historical and Statistical Data . . .* (Des Moines, 1883), pp. 278–364.

[19] *Prairie Farmer*, February, 1843, p. 26, September, 1845, p. 210, June, 1849, p. 198; *Iowa Homestead*, March 5, 1863, p. 42, February 26, 1869, p. 60, February 25, 1870, p. 4; I.S.A.S.R., *1857*, pp. 195, 225, 355, *1870*, p. 259, *1877*, p. 310, *1874*, pp. 320, 449.

included the counties of the lower Illinois Valley and the counties extending southward along the east bank of the Mississippi. On the northwestern perimeter of the district lay some seven counties in the southeastern corner of Iowa. This was a winter-wheat region. The second area lay in north-western Iowa where spring wheat still held position as a frontier staple.

It was a simple matter for a farmer to change the variety of wheat that he wished to grow. For less than half of the cost of a young purebred Short-horn he could purchase enough grain to sow fifty acres of wheat. If he had harvested a crop himself during the previous season, he need only sell what he would otherwise have set aside for seed and select a supplier. No doubt most farmers effected such decisions by buying seed from some neighbor who had harvested a particularly good crop. But new varieties evolved or entered the local community in a variety of ways. Farmers who were new to a region frequently brought supplies of seed grain with them from their old homes. If such seed proved more successful than that of their neighbors, it won converts among them. A Kane County, Illinois, farmer reported a new variety that "was selected by a farmer near Sycamore, Dekalb County, from a field of common hedgerow [wheat]." [20] Another Kane County man gave his version of the origins of Rio Grande wheat some years later. A local farmer Mr. Leonard selected a half dozen particularly choice heads from a field of Italian or soft Siberian wheat and planted the kernels in isolation. The first man to purchase a supply of seed from Leonard named it Rio Grande wheat and began to sell it as a separate variety at an ad-vanced price.[21] A resident of Muscatine County in Iowa reported that local farmers called a popular variety of spring wheat "Pigman wheat," because "a very successful farmer [of that name] in the northern part of the county" had developed it.[22] Obviously, there was little of science in such seed selec-tion, but these examples do explain why the editor of the *Prairie Farmer* replied, when asked to discuss wheat varieties in 1848, "The number is so great, and the new sorts succeed each other so fast, that it is well nigh impossible." [23]

Since many farmers believed that the varieties in their districts would "run out," would become infected with local diseases, or were less well suited to the locality than others might be, they imported seed wheat from other regions, particularly from the north. The Lee County correspondent of the Iowa State Agricultural Society reported in 1858 that he had just obtained a supply of Canada Club from northern Iowa and some Scotch spring wheat from Minnesota.[24] He reported that the Wild Goose wheat, then largely in use in Lee County, had come from Canada about twelve years earlier, brought back by a former Canadian who had revisited his old

---

[20] Thomas Judd in *Prairie Farmer*, February, 1849, p. 43.
[21] A. G. Wheeler, *ibid.*, January, 1850, p. 29.
[22] I.S.A.S.R., *1857*, p. 385.
[23] *Prairie Farmer*, September, 1848, p. 283.
[24] I.S.A.S.R., *1858*, p. 351.

home. Poweshiek County farmers of the same year owed their Fyfe wheat to a local farmer who brought a supply from Jefferson County, New York. Farmers there had imported this wheat earlier from Canada.[25] Such importations were on a minor scale. But after transportation facilities improved, they could be quite large. One of the granges in Bremer County, Iowa, for instance, imported two carloads of wheat from Minnesota in 1872.[26]

Although the seed-distribution activities of the Department of Agriculture drew much criticism, many farmers experimented with packets of seeds from this source. Agricultural society secretaries in Iowa reported that members had obtained Providence wheat, White Australian, and at least one variety of Turkish wheat from the Department of Agriculture.[27]

If the major expectations of many prairie farm-makers rested upon their wheat fields, another cereal ultimately stamped its name upon the region. From the earliest days of pioneering, corn seems to have dominated the agriculture of the settlers of the Ohio Valley and people of southern origins who settled in lower Illinois. "Verily," wrote Edmund Flagg from Greene County in the mid-1830's, "would a farmer of Yankee-land 'stare and gasp' to behold the prairie cornfield of the Western emigrant." [28] This was to be a favorite figure among writers on the West, but somewhat unfair to Yankees who knew more than a little about the maize plant, though it found the hillsides of the northeastern United States less congenial than the Illinois prairies. Writing a few years later of the Randolph County region, William Oliver wrote:

This grain is the indigent farmer's main dependence for without it, I do not see how he could live and support his stock. It affords the means of subsistence to every living thing about his place, particularly during periods of snow, or hard frost; for not only is everything, down to the dog and cat, fond of the grain, in some shape or another, but its very stalks, leaves, and husks afford a valuable fodder for cattle and horses. Then, who but must admire the facility with which it is raised; the small amount of labour required; the trifling quantity of seed; and the most abundant return. It is not like other grain easily injured; but once ripe, there it stands, setting at defiance rain, frost, snow, and avery [sic] vicissitude of climate, often through great part of winter.[29]

As the unique significance of corn in the prairie economy became increasingly clear, the encomiums became more florid. Read the words of a writer in the *Prairie Farmer* in 1864:

With a nominal cost of seed, a range of two months for planting it waits for the sick and the absent — may be harvested almost any time without expensive

[25] *Ibid.*, p. 384.
[26] Union Publishing Company, *History of Butler and Bremer Counties, Iowa . . .* (Springfield, 1883), p. 1142.
[27] See e.g. I.S.A.S.R., *1871*, pp. 18, 410, *1874*, p. 379; *Wisconsin Farmer*, February, 1856, p. 60; *Iowa Homestead*, July 23, 1869, p. 4.
[28] Flagg, *op. cit.*, p. 215.
[29] Oliver, *op. cit.*, p. 85.

machinery, is almost indestructable, destroys worthless plants, gives about as
much rough feed for all domestic animals, and is unequalled for fattening purposes. The buxom girls and stalwart sons of the West deem it the staff of life
when made into bread, and when made into whisky many think it life itself. It
supports the poor man's family, the rich man's flask and the merchant's trade.
It is the basis of an immense trade in beef, the main pillar of our national
prosperity, the golden fleece of America, the staple of the West, the pride of
Illinois.[30]

Despite its general use in the West for johnnycake, corn pone, dodgers,
and the like, or the demands of distillers, Indian corn, in contrast to wheat,
was primarily stock feed. Western farmers counted themselves fortunate
when the wheat crop returned yields between twenty and thirty bushels to
the acre; corn, by contrast, produced between forty and sixty bushels per
acre on the average, and the individual who harvested more than sixty
bushels per acre was probably far more common than the farmer who reaped
more than thirty bushels of wheat to the acre. Corn, however, was the
bulkier product in that its price per bushel was usually far less than that
of the breadgrain and would, therefore, not repay transportation for so
great a distance. As a result, prairie farmers concentrated much of their
corn by feeding it to swine and cattle.

Since cattle-feeding demanded considerable outlays of capital, many
farmers preferred to let more affluent neighbors handle the cattle and sold
their surplus corn to them. Particularly in the pre-railroad era, but later as
well, it was common for stockmen to drive feeders to interior districts where
the corn crop had been good and either purchase corn for feeding under
the direction of an employee or work out a feeding contract with a farmer
whom the stockman believed to be reliable. During the 1830's and 1840's
farmers in such a district might sell their corn in the shock for feeding at
$5.00 per acre. Sale at ten cents a bushel or contracts to winter steers for
$5.00 or $6.00 per head were alternate arrangements.[31]

The marketing horizon was always less restricted for farmers who lived
within easy hauling distance of navigable streams. Considerable quantities
of corn moved each year into the southern trade during the 1830's, 1840's,
and 1850's. Shipments went to Ireland in the famine years, and there was
some market abroad thereafter, but foreign interest in maize was usually
negligible in comparison with the foreign demand for wheat.[32] A writer in
the *Maine Farmer* estimated during 1849 that at least 3,000,000 bushels of
southern and western corn was entering that state yearly.[33] Two years later
the *Prairie Farmer* noted that much more corn was being sold as grain than

[30] *Prairie Farmer*, April 9, 1864, pp. 246–47.
[31] *Ibid.*, January 6, 1866, p. 2.
[32] *Ibid.*, October, 1846, p. 317, October, 1847, p. 305; I.S.A.S.R., *1859*, pp. 220, 249,
1865, p. 376.
[33] U.S. Commissioner of Patents, *Report, 1849*, p. 236.

had been the case five or six years earlier.[34] Completion of the Illinois and Michigan Canal particularly was responsible. Farmers along this route who had sold their corn for perhaps a third of the Chicago price, 8¢–12¢ per bushel, a few years previously were now selling it, at the river, shelled and sewn into two-bushel sacks, for prices only slightly below those in Chicago.

Many early Iowa farmers found a market among the emigrants moving across the state to the plains country, and those in the extreme western portions sold considerable quantities of corn, mainly to government contractors and freighting firms. As the railroad brought adequate transportation facilities within reach of most farmers in Illinois and Iowa, the structure of the corn market changed. Even when it was destined for local use, farmers sold a good deal more of their corn to local merchants, commission men, and elevator operators. During the 1860's and 1870's when the elevator system was developing, capitalists, sometimes non-resident, often bought large amounts of corn and cribbed it near the local railroad station, counting on the seasonal rise in corn prices to return them a profit.[35]

Occasionally a bumper crop, low prices of hogs and cattle, and adverse economic conditions generally, combined to frustrate the corn-grower. Such a year was 1872, when the secretary of the Iowa State Agricultural Society reported that "immense and unknown quantities have been consumed for fuel." He wrote that the price formula involved was figured at Council Bluffs as " thirty-three bushels make one ton of corn, which at seventeen cents is worth $5.61, and this is equal for heating purposes to a cord of hard wood, costing with cutting $8.50." [36] Even so, farmers ordinarily found corn the most satisfactory of the staples in these years, and it was during this decade that corn began to outstrip wheat production spectacularly in Iowa.

Prairie farmers seem to have argued and theorized about corn-growing much less than about wheat culture. Perhaps the greater reliability of the corn crop accounts for this fact. Yet differences of opinion did exist, and particularly as farmers came to accept the crop as the great staple of the prairies, they submitted their pet theories about corn-growing in the agricultural press. During the 1840's and 1850's some believed that the corn seed should be treated with saltpeter, tar or, ashes before planting. Such preparation, they argued, would repel the cutworms, gophers, and birds who viewed the seeds and crops of the settler with epicurean delight.[37] Ground squirrels and birds particularly plagued the pioneers who were opening up farms surrounded by wide stretches of unbroken lands. Treatment of seed had less effect, however, than a well-aimed shotgun and seldom saved the farm-maker from replanting blank hills.

[34] *Prairie Farmer*, July, 1851, p. 289, September, 1851, pp. 381–82.
[35] Webster City *Hamilton Freeman*, July 9, 1879.
[36] I.S.A.S.R., *1872*, p. 17; *Iowa Homestead*, December 20, 1872, p. 404.
[37] *Prairie Farmer*, May, 1845, p. 108; *Northwestern Farmer*, May, 1858, p. 175.

From Prairie to Corn Belt

When, in prairie lore, the oak leaves were as large as a squirrel's ear, the farmer could begin to plant corn. Early May actually was preferred, but planting might extend from mid-April in forward years to mid-June during particularly wet springs. By the 1870's particularly punctilious farmers had their own theories as to the methods of seedbed preparation which would yield the largest crops. But, actually, most well-worked fields would yield good crops under ordinary conditions. The need of careful marking when using horse-drawn planters undoubtedly encouraged the greater use of the roller and the preparation of smoother seedbeds generally after 1860.

Farmers in southern Illinois around 1820 were checkrowing their corn crops at intervals of four feet or slightly less so that they could cultivate the hills from two directions, and this remained standard practice thereafter.[38] With the coming of the two-horse, straddle-row riding cultivator, which could be used to cultivate very close to the corn plants, some farmers called for sowing in drill, arguing that two-way cultivation was now unnecessary and that drilled rows actually produced larger crops of corn.[39] Prairie farmers in general remained unconvinced, although much silage corn was drilled in the dairy regions to the north after the 1880's.

The sod corn of the pioneer was a special case. Farm-makers dropped kernels at intervals in the bottom of every third furrow behind the breaking plow or, more commonly, slashed the overturned sod with an axe, dropped a few kernels into the opening, and then stamped the earth together again. The pioneer could expect perhaps as much as half a crop in return from this rude husbandry.[40] Corn, however, was no more the universal sod crop than was wheat the sole staple of the pioneer. Farm-makers sowed fall wheat on new breaking at times, and flax was a remunerative sod crop on the Iowa frontier of the late 1870's.

The first six weeks after the corn plants appeared were crucial for the development of the corn crop on old ground. Now the crop must be kept as clean of weeds as possible. Some farmers began the process by harrowing the crop just as it peeped above ground; others preferred to remove the point teeth from an A harrow and guide it along so that the side teeth stirred the earth and covered young weeds on both sides of the rows. Soon the corn plows could be used, shearing in as close to the plants as possible at first and then throwing earth over the weeds so snugly positioned that they could not be caught by plow or cultivator tooth. The cultivators of the 1860's had removable guard plates designed to allow close cultivation and at the same time shield the young plants from the wave of soil falling off the cultivator shovels. Ideally the farmer had guided his plows or cultivators between the

[38] Solon J. Buck (ed.), "Pioneer Letters of Gershom Flagg," Illinois State Historical Society, *Transactions, 1910*, p. 162.

[39] See e.g. *Prairie Farmer*, July 22, 1865, p. 57, May 5, 1866, p. 302, May 9, 1868, p. 298.

[40] Oliver, *op. cit.*, p. 86.

corn rows three or four times before the Fourth of July. By this date the corn had outstripped the weeds and he could pronounce it "laid by."

In his final passage through the corn rows, the midwestern farmer threw a wave of dirt about the cornstalks, but he had no sympathy for the New England practice of hilling at this time with a hoe. In the 1830's "suckering" might precede laying-by, but the strains of corn that required this service evidently lost favor wth farmers.[41] Yankee farmers were appalled by the reluctance of the western farmer to use a hoe in the corn crop, although he might reluctantly resort to it on occasion. But John M. Peck reported that even the southern-born settlers most devoted to dog and gun realized the crucial importance of corn-plowing time and tended patches whose cleanliness often surpassed that of their self-righteous Yankee neighbors.[42]

Corn harvest was not a time of strenuous urgency like the small grain harvest, when failure to cut at the right time allowed the grain to shell out or when a few days lost might be the margin between a crop safely stacked and one lying sodden in the shock, the sheaves matted together by the roots and sprouts of kernels that had germinated during a spell of wet weather. The corn ears could remain on the stalks in the field until the following spring, with little loss in feeding value and, usually, little damage from wildlife. October and November, however, were ideal months for gathering corn; thereafter winter made it an unpleasant task.

Although the inventor gave the farmer little assistance in gathering the corn crop during the nineteenth century, harvesting practice did become more efficient. Writing of southern Illinois in the early 1820's, Woods wrote of the corn harvest:

> It is gathered in October and November, when they only take off the ears; but as the ears are covered with a large husk, they carry them as they are to the corn-crib, and then all the neighbors collect together to help to husk it, and put it into the corn-crib. This is a high day with the Americans, and is called a Husking Frolic; plenty of whiskey is generally to be found at one of these frolics.[43]

Slightly more than twenty years later, Oliver noted that corn was cut with a large knife or truncated scythe and then hauled home or placed in shocks. As we have seen, those cattle-feeders who followed the Virginia or Kentucky system of feeding, fed corn on the stalk. "Frequently," also, wrote Oliver,

[41] There are, of course, many descriptions of midwestern corn culture. For this account I have drawn particularly upon: John Woods, *Two Years' Residence in the Settlement on the English Prairie, in the Illinois Country, United States . . .* (London, 1822) (reprinted in Vol. X of Reuben Gold Thwaites [ed.], *Early Western Travels, 1748–1846* [Cleveland, 1904]), p. 298–99; Oliver, *op. cit.*, pp. 86–87; Peck, *op. cit.*, pp. 153–56; *Prairie Farmer*, July, 1842, p. 59, February, 1848, p. 130, April, 1850, p. 132, May, 1850, pp. 147–48, 162, January, 1853, p. 131, October 31, 1863, p. 276, February 27, 1864, p. 132, February 11, 1865, pp. 84–85, June 16, 1866, p. 409; *Hamilton Freeman*, January 8, 1873. References to corn culture are scattered as well through the I.S.A.S.R. series.

[42] Peck, *op. cit.*, pp. 153–54.

[43] Woods, *op. cit.*, p. 300.

"it is left uncut, the ear alone being pulled and stored in the corn crib till the proper season for a husking frolic."[44]

A writer from Wayne County, Illinois, discussing farming methods there in 1848 with some sarcasm, described "pulling time" as occurring from November to spring when "corn is pulled by sending a cart or wagon through the field with two to six hands, and pulling the ears, leaving the stalks for the cattle to pick during the winter."[45] Farmers there fattened hogs by feeding them corn in the shock. In early 1850, however, James Osborne of Brown County, Illinois, told the readers of the *Prairie Farmer*, "I husk my corn on the stalk."[46] In the next year the editor of the *Prairie Farmer* contrasted the "usual custom of the east," where corn was cut on the stalk, with the western system of "husking from the standing stalks." However, he cautioned, "It is not affirmed that this is the general routine of culture taking the Northwest together; nor is it set down as a pattern for any section, since particular districts follow, and will do so, courses peculiar to themselves."[47] A few years later, he suggested that it was common practice south of Springfield to feed cattle the whole corn plant, but that when it was intended to feed the crop to hogs, it "is frequently picked — sometimes husked — and fed to them by ears simply."[48]

Although corn might be harvested simply by turning in stock or by cutting and shocking the whole plant, it seems clear that by 1870 the most common method was to husk it from the stalk in the field. This method involved a minimum of handling and also prevented the spoilage that occurred when corn cribbed in the shuck became wet. A writer of that year maintained, "The manner of shucking and cribbing corn as practiced by our farmers, by driving a wagon astride every fifth row, shucking the corn and throwing it into the wagon, driving the wagon to the crib and unloading with a large scoop, is the most expeditious way known."[49] John Hopkins has suggested that Iowa farmers fed much corn in the shuck in Iowa after 1870 but "A Plain Farmer" maintained in the *Iowa Homestead* in 1872 that "all farmers in Iowa, so far as I have been able to learn, husk out their corn in the fall, and then turn their cattle into the stalk fields."[50] The going rental rate for stalk fields according to this writer varied from 50¢ to $1.00 per acre.

We cannot be certain when farmers began to raise an additional bangboard or throwboard on one side of the wagon box to make the picker's task easier. Donald R. Murphy, of *Wallace's Farmer*, believes the practice

[44] Oliver, *op. cit.*, p. 87.

[45] *Prairie Farmer*, February, 1848, p. 52. This item was reprinted from the *Maine Farmer*.

[46] *Prairie Farmer*, January, 1850, p. 29.

[47] *Ibid.*, November, 1851, p. 477.

[48] *Ibid.*, October, 1854, p. 362.

[49] *Ibid.*, March 26, 1870, p. 90.

[50] John A. Hopkins, Jr., *Economic History of the Production of Beef Cattle in Iowa* (Iowa City, 1928), p. 127; *Iowa Homestead*, March 15, 1872, p. 82; (see also I.S.A.S.R., *1857*, p. 241).

to have become general in Iowa during the early 1880's.[51] Herbert Quick's young Hawkeye, Fremont McConkey, however, was using one during the late 1870's in one of the classic accounts of husking:

His horses danced in the nipping air. He could hear in other fields other wagons driven across the frozen ridges of the corn-fields in successive spasms of rattle-te-banging, and from a mile off, so still was the morning, he heard the dull, 'clump, clump, clump' of the ears of corn against the throw-board, and the men talking to their prancing horses, left without any management save the voice. He began the mechanical operation of husking, the exercise of that knack which took the prairie farmers a quarter of a century to learn after they emerged from the forests into the region where corn became the great crop. The left hand is extended for the ear, which it grasps with the thumb toward the tip; at one sweep of the husking peg on the right hand, the shucks are ripped and with the ripping, the left hand slips them off, and another gesture of the right tears the ear from the stalk and throws it into the wagon-box by hurling it against the high throw-board on the opposite side. Never look at the wagon, there is no time for that; never look at the horses — one can tell what they are doing by the movement of the wagon, and the sound made by their hoofs; never stop to pick off the silks or the little clinging husks; they can go in with the ears. And forget the sky, the clouds, the blood drawn by rosebrier or the sharp tips of the kernels of the 'hackberry' ears; forget everything but the economy of movement, the making of every second count. Make sure that you do not fail to tear the ear from the stalk and throw it into the wagon by a single movement of the muscles; see to it that when the right hand returns from the throw, the body has moved forward if necessary to another proper position, and that the left hand has seized another ear and holds it ready for the husking peg; and do not fail to remember that if you husk your hundred bushels in a day, the steady 'clump, clump, clump' against the throw-board must continue hour after hour, even while the trained horses are making the turn at the end of the field.[52]

Plant scientists have recently suggested that the credit for developing the "common yellow dents" that dominated the cornfields of the Middle West by the late nineteenth century should go to the pioneers. These corns came from the crossing of "white southern dents, mostly of Mexican origin, and the long, slender northern flints" grown in the northeastern seaboard region well before the discovery of America.[53] Some of this hybridization was purposeful, much of it, undoubtedly, was quite accidental, as winds cross-pollinated the corn in adjacent fields.

[51] During the spring and summer of 1960, Donald R. Murphy of *Wallace's Farmer* solicited recollections about the introduction of the bangboard from old-timers in Iowa. Most of them believed that it came into use in the 1880's. In a conversation of July 29, 1960, Senator Earl Elijah of Clarence, Iowa, however, informed me that his grandfather had used a throw board in Cedar County, Iowa, during the late 1860's.

[52] Herbert Quick, *The Hawkeye* (Indianapolis, 1923), pp. 263–64.

[53] Edgar Anderson and William L. Brown, "The History of the Common Maize Varieties of the United States Corn Belt," *Agricultural History*, XXVI (January, 1952), 2.

The role of the individual farmer in this process varied, of course. Some paid little attention to the kind of corn that they grew, even using ears from the crib for seed. But the fact that the market distinguished between varieties particularly good for cattle, for hog feed, for distilling, and for grinding, no doubt, made many farmers variety conscious.[54] They wished also, of course, to grow a variety that would give large yields and ripen well before the usual date of killing frosts in their locality. If well satisfied with their crop, they picked the choicest ears for seed. If their crop fell short of their expectations, they looked elsewhere for seed or even consciously set out to develop a variety of corn that would meet their special needs. As early as 1835 the *Disseminator* of New Harmony, Indiana, published an article, based upon an item in the *American Farmer*, that explained how to hybridize corn varieties.[55] In 1841 the *Union Agriculturalist* described the successful efforts of Lewis Curtis of Galena to cross a small early-ripening variety of his district with a much larger but slow-ripening strain obtained from the vicinity of Peoria. This farmer's method consisted simply of planting the two varieties in alternate hills, and then selecting ears for three years with the desired characteristics.[56] An article in the same journal two years later, extracted from the *Farmer's Register*, provided a more satisfactory guide, recommending that the base or female stock should be detasseled.[57]

In 1842 a farmer described his efforts to find a satisfactory variety of corn after arriving in the West from Yankee land; his experience was, no doubt, common and more typical than that of the farmer who tried to develop his own varieties. In succession he tried the streaked and speckled Canada corn, then a so-called Hoosier corn, next the Baden, which failed to ripen, then the New Jersey, handsome but also too late, succeeded by the Dutton, highly recommended by the *Cultivator*, but "a burlesque on corn raising" in practice, and — to complete the catalogue of failures — the Chinese tree corn, on a small scale. Finally, he found corn that suited him in a field near Macomb, Illinois, "a beautiful yellow with red cob" that matured as many as two or three ears before frost and, so he said, produced from 80 to 100 bushels per acre.[58] Some farmers, on the other hand, liked to mix several varieties rather than to concentrate on any one kind.

So-called varieties of corn were legion. The number of rows of kernels, the shape of the kernel, the coloring, and the name of the last grower, all might produce different nomenclatures within the two major strains of flint and dent corns.[59] One hundred and fifteen types of Indian corn appeared

[54] Oliver, *op. cit.*, p. 86; U.S. Commissioner of Patents, *Report, 1849*, p. 239.

[55] Anderson and Brown, *op. cit.*, p. 6.

[56] *Union Agriculturist and Western Prairie Farmer*, April, 1841, p. 27.

[57] *Prairie Farmer*, May, 1843, pp. 112–13. These were not, of course, the sophisticated hybridization techniques of the twentieth century in which highly inbred strains were used in making crosses.

[58] *Union Agriculturist*, May, 1842, p. 43.

[59] Edward Enfield, *Indian Corn; Its Value, Culture and Uses* (New York, 1866), p. 60.

in the exhibit of the United States at the Paris Exposition in 1867, and individual farmers could range in their choices from the regal King Philip to the prosaic Bloody Butcher.[60] In the early 1840's flints, both white and yellow, were apparently grown over much of Illinois, but the dent varieties became increasingly popular thereafter.[61] The dent strains produced more grain than did the flints, and their softer kernels also attracted supporters. In 1866 a writer used "Western" and "Dent" as synonyms.[62] As the prairie farmers came to recognize the key role of corn in their economy, some profited by producing seed commercially.[63] By the 1870's this development had become clear, and thereafter the tendency for particularly good varieties to enjoy regional reputation increased. Leaming corn was a great favorite during the 1870's and 1880's. Reid's Yellow Dent became particularly popular after James L. Reid won a prize at the World's Fair in 1893 on ears of a variety that members of the family had developed by seed selections extending back to 1847.[64]

Writers have suggested that lack of early maturing varieties of corn slowed down the speed with which the farmers of northwestern Iowa gave corn a major role in the farm economy of that region.[65] Certainly there does seem to have been some opinion among the early settlers there that corn did poorly. But the farm-makers had largely solved the problem by the end of the century. During the late 1880's the Agricultural Experiment Station in Illinois published the results of tests with various varieties of seed corn and recommended strains that seemed particularly adapted to the various regions of the state.[66]

In selecting his cereal crops the western farmer was not, of course, restricted to the two staples, wheat and corn. Oats, barley, and rye were all alternatives, but the agricultural census statistics show that they were not serious competitors.[67] Of the three, oats became by far the most significant when we consider the prairie peninsula as a whole. Although Woods reported that the crop was an indifferent one in southeastern Illinois in the 1820's, it was generally distributed throughout both this state and Iowa at mid-

[60] *Prairie Farmer*, March 2, 1867, p. 132; G. E. Morrow, *Field Experiments with Corn, 1888* (University of Illinois, Agricultural Experiment Station Bull. No. 4 [Champaign, 1889]), pp. 37–127, contained references to more than eighty dent varieties.

[61] Oliver, *op. cit.*, p. 85; U.S. Commissioner of Patents, *Report*, p. 128.

[62] *Prairie Farmer*, June 23, 1866, p. 429.

[63] From this background came J. S. Leaming's interesting *Corn and its Culture, by a Pioneer Corn Raiser, with 60 Years' Experience in the Cornfield* (Wilmington, O., 1883).

[64] Anderson and Brown, *op. cit.*, p. 7; (see also Everett E. Edwards, "Reid, James L.," *Dictionary of American Biography*, XV, 477–78 and attached bibliography).

[65] See the conclusions in Clare C. Cooper, "The Role of Railroads in the Settlement of Iowa: A Study in Historical Geography" (unpublished M.A. thesis, University of Nebraska, 1958), pp. 136–38.

[66] U. S. Commissioner of Agriculture, *Report, 1890*, p. 512; *Field Experiments with Corn, 1888*.

[67] See chapter x for a more detailed discussion of crop statistics, farming types, and agricultural subareas.

century.[68] But in 1850 only two Illinois counties and one Iowa county produced more than three bushels of oats per improved acre. Interest in the crop increased somewhat, particularly in the northern portions of the two states, but not until the 1880's was there any sharp rise in oats production. In Illinois this took place particularly in northern and central Illinois; in Iowa it occurred especially in the northern counties where farmers were taking their land out of wheat. Oats provided another small-grain crop that did not interfere with the work peaks of corn production.

In large part, of course, farmers increased their acreage of oats because of a growth in demand for them. The horseman, particularly, esteemed oats as stock feed, and the urban market for them had reached considerable dimensions by the 1880's. By this time also the oatmeal industry was establishing itself. The secretary of the Iowa State Agricultural Society dismissed oatmeal in 1880 "rather as a luxury than as a staple article of food; rather as a supposed dietetic and sanitary dish than as a substitute for wheat and corn," [69] but he underestimated the hardiness of the American digestive tract. Oats are particularly useful, also, as a cover crop to protect seedling grasses and clovers. As farmers grew larger crops of tame grass and clovers and worked them into cropping rotations, they increased their acreage of oats. During the 1880's the farmers of northern Illinois and Iowa were placing greater emphasis on dairying, and this farm enterprise also called for larger acreages of tame grass and clover.

Barley usually was less popular among Illinois and Iowa farmers than oats, but the crop became a specialty in some counties, particularly where considerable acreages were grown for malting purposes. Such was the case in Scott and Muscatine counties, Iowa.[70] In general, farmers grew more barley in the northern counties of Illinois and Iowa than did those in the southern portions of these states. During the 1880's farmers in the northern portion of the second tier of counties from the Missouri River in Iowa, found barley to be a profitable crop, and the 1890 census showed production of more than three bushels per improved acre in four of these counties. Less desired as a bread grain than wheat, and having no advantages over the other grains of the region as stock feed, rye was never an important crop in Illinois or Iowa during this period.

Many of the settlers of Illinois during the 1820's grew small acreages of flax for home use.[71] With the decline of household industries and the general acceptance of cheap manufactured cotton goods, this practice became less common. In 1862 William Duane Wilson reported a great falling-off in the production of flax in Iowa during the previous ten years.[72] Very

[68] Woods, *op. cit.*, p. 295; Oliver, *op. cit.*, p. 89.
[69] I.S.A.S.R., *1880*, p. 31.
[70] *Ibid., 1858*, pp. 338–39.
[71] Woods, *op. cit.*, p. 296.
[72] *Iowa Homestead*, December 4, 1862, p. 356.

shortly, interest in the crop revived. During the Civil War the prices of linseed oil rose, and the war also stimulated the demand for substitutes for cotton fabrics. A number of firms established oil mills in northern Illinois and central Iowa during the war decade. During the early 1870's the farmers of Johnson County, Iowa, grew enough of the crop so that it became "a recognized element in the rotation of crops," and farmers in a number of nearby counties produced quantities as well.[73] The impetus for growing flax came, to a considerable extent in these years, from the proprietors of oil mills, who provided a market for the crop of seed and sometimes contracted with farmers to insure work for their mills. During the 1860's and 1870's, however, some tow mills purchased flax fiber, either retted or in the straw. When the farm-makers of northwestern Iowa learned that a crop of flax could be grown on early breaking, flax became a common pioneer crop there during the late 1870's and 1880's.[74] In 1880, however, the counties of central Iowa still produced most of the flax in the state, and the leader, Marshall County, reported only 12,562 acres.

In the twenty years between 1860 and 1880 sorghum received much attention in the agricultural press of the Middle West. Indeed, the discussions were out of all proportion to the actual importance of the crop. The seed of the sweet sorghum of China reached the United States from France in 1853 and was distributed by the seed division of the Department of Agriculture during the 1850's, as well, ultimately, as by commercial seedsmen. During the late 1850's a number of varieties of Natal cane, collectively called Imphee, reached the southern states.[75] From the late 1850's a sorghum patch was a familiar sight on prairie farms. Interest in the crop waxed and waned depending upon the price of sugar and economic conditions generally.

When sugar prices rose during the Civil War, middle-western farmers experimented with cane quite widely, although few succeeded in reducing the juice beyond the molasses stage. Even so, it was a useful crop. Although the cost of small sorghum mills and evaporators probably made the making of molasses an uneconomical process for the individual family, a number of neighboring farmers often used the same equipment. Some individuals or firms established larger reduction plants that they tried to operate on a commercial scale. Having set up an iron crushing mill and evaporation machinery in 1862, a Des Moines firm offered to make sorghum molasses

[73] I.S.A.S.R., *1871*, p. 21.

[74] This account of flax growing is based for the most part on: *Prairie Farmer*, January, 1852, p. 38, September 26, 1863, p. 194, November 28, 1863, p. 344, March 5, 1864, pp. 150–51, April 9, 1864, p. 252, April 22, 1865, p. 302, November 10, 1866, p. 304; *Iowa Homestead*, June 26, 1867, p. 197, May 2, 1873, p. 137; I.S.A.S.R., *1863*, p. 380, *1870*, pp. 433, 470, *1874*, p. 405, *1875*, p. 487, *1876*, p. 27, *1879*, p. 432, *1880*, p. 35.

[75] Liberty H. Bailey (ed.), *Cyclopedia of American Agriculture: A Popular Survey of Agricultural Conditions, Practices and Ideals in the United States and Canada* (New York, 1907), II, 574–82.

on shares from stripped cane or work on a custom basis charging 15¢ per gallon. As early as 1863 one firm had established plants in seven Illinois communities. Interest in sorghum culture diminished when sugar prices becames more reasonable after the Civil War, although the lean years of the 1870's set the sorghum mills to "squealing" again in the farming districts.[76] The feeling that there were commercial possibilities in the crop lingered into the 1880's. It is doubtful if sorghum ever dominated the enterprises of many prairie farmers. A patch of an acre or less satisfied the sweet tooth of most families.

Never a major crop, buckwheat deserves mention from anyone calling the roll of the prairie field crops.[77] Rank of growth, quick to ripen, and usable as either feed or food, buckwheat could save a field from waste after normal spring planting had failed. There were few western farmers who did not try to cut their losses at some time or other by planting buckwheat. Some, of course, grew a small patch under any circumstances for buckwheat flour or chicken feed; more usually, buckwheat was a crop that was conceived in failure.

Wrote Harvey Lee Ross:

Smith's Prairie was one of the most beautiful prairies mortal eyes ever beheld. It was covered with what was called blue-stemmed grass, a most excellent grass for hay. It grew from three to four feet high, and afforded hay enough for all the people of Lewistown and the settlers for many miles all directions. All the people had to do was to cut the hay and haul it home. At that time hay was cut with a scythe and raked together with a wooden hand-rake and pitchfork. . . . We had to haul the hay together for stacking on what was called a brush sled.[78]

Written of Fulton County, Illinois, this account introduces another prairie crop — grass. While the prairie verdure waved unscarred for miles beyond the limits of the timber belts and groves, the farm-makers had little incentive to develop meadows or pastures of tame grass. Their energies returned larger dividends when spent in enlarging their cultivated fields and raising ramparts of Virginia worm, Shanghai fence, or bristling hedge around them. Nor was the pioneer concerned with resting his land by returning it to grass cover for a time. So he turned most of his livestock onto "the range" provided by the unbroken and unfenced lands of the neighborhood. When haying time arrived, he took his scythe or later his mowing machine to the

[76] *Iowa Homestead*, August 14, 1862, p. 226, January 29, 1863, p. 5, February 13, 1867, p. 42; *Prairie Farmer*, September 5, 1863, p. 152, December 19, 1863, pp. 396–97, October 1, 1864, pp. 212–13, November 12, 1864, p. 306–7; I.S.A.S.R., *1865*, p. 514, *1871*, p. 478; *Hamilton Freeman*, December 1, 1860, December 8, 1860, April 12, 1862, November 18, 1865, September 18, 1872, October 31, 1872.

[77] Oliver, *op. cit.*, p. 89.

[78] Harvey Lee Ross, *The Early Pioneers and Pioneer Events of the State of Illinois Including Personal Recollections of the Writer of Abraham Lincoln, Andrew Jackson, and Peter Cartwright, Together with a Brief Autobiography of The Writer* (Chicago, 1899), p. 64.

lower stretches of prairie where late-lying water had fostered a particularly heavy stand of prairie grasses. Curing hay under these circumstances was a task for mid- and late August rather than the June and July days during which farmers cured the first growth of tame grasses and clover.

Ordinarily, as we have seen, it took some thirty years for settlers to occupy most of the farm sites in any particular county of the prairie triangle after the first considerable flow of immigration. Not until relatively late in this process was the farmer strongly pressed to develop enclosed pastures or meadows because the open prairie was disappearing. Farmers postponed this day still further by sending livestock in community herds to more distant prairie pastures.

Some prairie farmers did try at an early date to establish grasses and clovers on their acres. The breeder of improved stock typically wished to keep his stock confined. Such men argued sometimes that prairie grasses provided poorer grazing in the early spring and after the first heavy frost than did tame grasses and that the prairie grasses could not support as many animals as Kentucky bluegrass. The bluestems and supporting grasses, they maintained, died out after several years under heavy pasturing in enclosures. No doubt, the lush pasturage of Kentucky inspired some of the early stockmen of Illinois and Iowa to establish bluegrass pastures. Most of the early sheepmen of Illinois and Iowa pastured their flocks on the prairie, but some of them had even stronger reservations about prairie forage than did the cattlemen. It was common practice to try to convert wild pastures to tame meadows without breaking the sod by scattering bluegrass or timothy seed on the ground or harrowing it in during the late fall or early spring after first burning off the prairie vegetation.[79] By the early 1870's the soil-enriching properties of clover were known, but, in general, this service was not yet needed by prairie farmers.

Some prairie farmers evidently believed that it was difficult or even impossible to start tame grasses and clovers on the prairies. One suggested in 1843 that clover would catch more easily on worn land than on virgin soil.[80] Two years later the editor of the *Prairie Farmer* reported "considerable difficulty . . . in getting timothy from a class of our prairie soils."[81] In 1848 he was more explicit and described an "infected district" that was "bounded on the north by the line running between the first and second tier of counties in Wisconsin, or near that; west by a line running near Rock River to the mouth of that stream; south and southeast by the Illinois River; and east by Lake Michigan." But he concluded that the difficulty was actually "an imaginary one," which would "yield to good culture and manure."[82] Some

[79] Oliver, *op. cit.*, p. 95; *Prairie Farmer*, May, 1845, p. 122, March 5, 1864, p. 153; I.S.A.S.R., *1871*, p. 433, (see also chapters v and vi).
[80] Abraham Smith in *Prairie Farmer*, August 8, 1843, p. 178.
[81] *Ibid.*, August, 1845, p. 197.
[82] *Ibid.*, October, 1848, p. 324.

twenty years later, another editor of the same journal proclaimed, "Every succeeding year's experience is contradicting the generally conceived idea that prairie land is not well adapted to the production of the tame grasses." [83] Was the trouble "imaginary" as the editor of the *Prairie Farmer* suggested? Whether erroneous or not, the belief had its effect upon the decisions of the prairie farm-makers. Clover plants, of course, thrive best on soils where organisms that assist their root systems to fix nitrogen are present, a fact which ultimately led to the development of soil inoculation techniques. That lack of certain soil organisms might retard the growth of a grass like timothy is highly improbable.

We cannot chronicle the march of the tame grasses and clovers into the prairies of Illinois and Iowa with any accuracy. An Ohio farmer who traveled over "considerable portions" of Illinois in 1864 found few meadows of timothy or clover.[84] In some of the older areas this could hardly have been the case. Two years later a standing committee of the Iowa State Agricultural Society asked correspondents to report on the acreage of tame grass in their counties. Eighteen responded. Jackson County, an old county on the Mississippi, reported some 27,000 acres; Mahaska and other counties of central Iowa claimed only a few thousand acres. Farmers throughout the northwestern third of the state probably would have echoed the report from Wright County, "There is no tame grass to speak of in this county." [85] The greater part of the hay cured during the early 1890's in northwestern Iowa was still, undoubtedly, prairie hay.

When he did decide to make tame pastures and meadows, the prairie pioneer ordinarily restricted himself to one of a relatively small number of grasses and clovers. Some did experiment with new varieties. In 1858 a farmer of Appanoose County, Iowa, was testing a crop grown from seed that his son had sent to him from California. Understandably, he called it California grass.[86] More important was a considerable flurry of interest during the late 1850's and early 1860's in Hungarian grass, a kind of millet. Reputedly introduced by Hungarian refugees who settled during the 1850's in southern Iowa and distributed also by the Patent Office and seed houses, this grass won supporters because of its hardiness and abundant yields.[87] It soon lost favor when farmers criticized its coarseness and its dustiness as a feed and complained that horses sickened upon it. Once planted also, it showed an alarming reluctance to abandon the field to following crops.[88]

[83] *Ibid.*, November 3, 1866, p. 281.
[84] *Ibid.*, March 5, 1864, p. 153.
[85] I.S.A.S.R., *1866*, pp. 193–221. The quoted passage occurs on 221.
[86] *Ibid.*, 1858, p. 200.
[87] *Northwestern Farmer*, December, 1857, p. 457, June, 1858, p. 191.
[88] There are numerous references to Hungarian grass in the annual reports of the Iowa State Agricultural Society during the late 1850's and early 1860's. For a cogent analysis of its defects see: I.S.A.S.R., *1858*, p. 399.

Most important of the tame grasses as a hay crop, by far, was timothy. Scattered references to the use of red top — particularly adapted to wet lands — appear, and bluegrass was important, of course, for pasture. Farmers planted white clover in their pastures to a considerable extent at an early date, but there was evidently little red clover grown in Illinois before 1870 and not much harvested in Iowa before 1880. Timothy evidently filled the need for tame hay until the special soil-building properties of clover were needed. Although introduced in the Middle West during the late nineteenth century, alfalfa was of little importance until after 1900. "As with alsike clover," said Professor George E. Morrow of Illinois University in 1885, "I can not see . . . [alfalfa's] . . . great practical value as long as we have our 'Great Three' — clover, timothy, and blue grass." [89]

Although hay is a notoriously bulky product, farmers could often sell considerable quantities of it. One emigrant party traveling through Iowa in the early spring, indeed, reported buying the hay that a farmer had used to roof his stable the previous year.[90] In restricted districts of Iowa this emigrant trade was important until the 1870's. Farmers of southern Illinois and eastern Iowa were selling considerable baled hay by 1850, and others were hopeful of starting a similar trade along the Illinois-Michigan Canal route. During the early 1880's farmers of northwestern Iowa were shipping considerable quantities of baled hay to Chicago by railroad.[91] As the middlewestern towns and cities grew, farmers within hauling distance also found a market for unpressed hay among the urban residents.

No doubt, farmers with an itch to learn planted all of the cereals, grasses, fruits, and vegetables of the older states in some part of the prairie triangle at some time during the nineteenth century. Settlers of southern stock moving north in Illinois carried with them the crops that we ordinarily associate with southern agriculture. Small patches of cotton and tobacco for home use had their place on many a claim along the southern side of the Illinois prairie region and in southern Iowa.[92] The Civil War sparked a mild resurgence of interest in cotton. In 1846 "D.C.B." reported that hemp fever was prevalent in Sangamon County, Illinois, "very contagious, and sometimes . . . fatal." [93] Although the crop was never of great importance regionally, farmers in a few restricted areas raised considerable quantities of broomcorn.[94] Hopeful capitalists experimented with the sugar beet during the Civil War, and farmers in the Chariton area of Iowa were "going wild on the subject"

[89] *Prairie Farmer*, October 24, 1885, p. 694.

[90] Jerome Dutton in "Across the Plains in 1850," *Annals of Iowa, 3rd Series*, IX (July, 1910), 452.

[91] *Prairie Farmer*, January, 1851, p. 10, September, 1853, p. 357; *Hamilton Freeman*, July 2, 1884.

[92] Woods, *op. cit.*, p. 297; Oliver, *op. cit.*, pp. 89–90.

[93] *Prairie Farmer*, July, 1846, p. 205.

[94] *Ibid.*, November, 1844, p. 255, August 5, 1865, p. 88; *Iowa Homestead*, October 7, 1870.

of hops during 1867 and 1868.[95] During the same decade some optimists were convinced that the Jerusalem artichoke would revolutionize hog-raising.[96]

Most western families, of course, grew a wide range of garden truck for home use: potatoes, onion, beans, peas, melons, pumpkins, and squash. Even though the prairie triangle was not to become a great fruit region, the settlers, both Yankee and southern planted apple trees in considerable numbers, and most communities had indefatigable orchardists who proclaimed that the day was approaching when the prairies would have their seas of apple blossoms and oceans of cider. In the grape patches of German farmers along the Mississippi, others saw the beginning of a new Rhineland region of vineyards.[97]

While the pioneers opened up the farms of the Middle West, eastern observers, editors, and even some of their fellows, peppered them with criticisms. The middle westerner, said the critic of the 1840's, 1850's, 1860's, and 1870's, was a slovenly farmer. His plowing was too shallow, and he used other cultivation implements too little in preparing his ground for seed. He failed to manure his land and to use lime or other artificial fertilizers. He did not know the meaning of the word rotation. Finally, he tried to cultivate too many acres and ended by doing nothing properly.[98]

Such criticism came both easily and naturally to men who were acquainted with the rural decay found in regions of the northeastern United States or in the older South. Often, however, the critics failed to understand that there were actually very good reasons why western farming was as it was. Some observers were more acute. Contrasting British farming with the agriculture of the western pioneer Patrick Shirreff wrote:

In the one country the farmer aims to assist, and in the other to rob nature. When the results of capital and labour are low, compared with the hire of them, they are sparingly applied to the cultivation of the soil, in which case nature is oppressed and neglected . . . ; and when they are high, compared with their hire, she is aided and carressed [sic].[99]

A few years later William Oliver also tried to explain western farming: "It ought always to be kept in mind, that in a country where labour is so dear,

[95] *Iowa Homestead*, January 22, 1868, p. 21, February 27, 1867, p. 57. References to beet-sugar experiments are found in *Prairie Farmer*, April 27, 1867, p. 279 and August 31, 1867, p. 129.

[96] See chapter x.

[97] Mildred Throne, "A History of Agriculture in Southern Iowa, 1833–1890" (unpublished Ph.D. dissertation, State University of Iowa, 1946), p. 145.

[98] Mildred Throne, " 'Book Farming' in Iowa, 1840–1870," *Iowa Journal of History*, XLIX (April, 1951), 117–42.

[99] Patrick Shirreff, *A Tour through North America; Together with a Comprehensive View of the Canadas and United States, as Adapted for Agricultural Emigration* (Edinburgh, 1835), p. 341.

land so cheap, and nature so liberal, it is better to do a great deal in a middling way than to do a little well." [100]

But there was more involved here than either Shirreff or Oliver realized. The pioneer spent a great deal of labor in producing his crops, but much of it was applied to them indirectly. Breaking, fencing, and the motion wasted by the very lack of improvements demanded outlays of labor which must be met if the acreage of his cropland was to grow. Far more time-consuming than the upkeep of an improved farm, these alternative outlets for the farm-maker's labor dictated that crops be planted and tended as hastily as possible. Shirreff's description of the returns on capital in pioneer America is also somewhat misleading. Capital, judiciously used in the pioneer settlements, could yield handsomely indeed. Isaac Funk and his like were proving this point during the 1830's and 1840's. Usurious interest rates were in part — although only in part — a reflection of the same fact.

The movement of settlers into the Mississippi Valley far outstripped the flow of liquid capital into the region. There were few pioneer farmers who could not have put additional funds to good use. Those who were still using oxen during the 1850's, for instance, could for another $150, no doubt, have substituted a team of horses that would soon have paid for themselves in time saved or crops more carefully cultivated. Shortage of capital forced many pioneers to concentrate on grain-farming, because they could not initially afford the livestock for a more diversified type of farming. Where there was little or no livestock, there could, of course, be little or no manure. The shortage of fencing and use of the range, of course, also deprived the farms of manure, and here, too, a capital shortage was in part responsible. The pioneer must fence his broken land first. Quite properly this concerned him more than fencing in pastures.

If the farmer did keep stock in numbers through the winter in feedlot, barnyard, or stable, he probably put manure on his land, despite Hamlin Garland's story of farmers who moved their stables rather than the manure pile.[101] In 1861 the Savage family near Salem, Iowa, drew out forty-one loads of manure from the barnyard at a time when they were still breaking out new land on a portion of their farm.[102] Agricultural historians have been too willing to accept the strictures of the critics. Many western farmers believed that the western soils did not need manure initially, and there was much truth in this — enough, perhaps, to absolve the farmers who did not bother to use the refuse from their stables and barnyards. Agricultural scientists, testing corn varieties and yields at the Illinois Experiment Station during the late 1880's, admitted that manure and commercial fertilizers apparently did not influence the yields in their experiments sufficiently so

[100] Oliver, *op. cit.*, p. 100.
[101] Hamlin Garland, *A Son of the Middle Border* (New York, 1928), p. 130.
[102] See below, chapter xiii.

that farmers with fields in similar condition would have increased their profits materially. In a report of 1891 the Illinois research team confessed, "Good crops of corn have been raised during the past three years from land which has now been in corn for 15 successive years, and has received no manure of any kind." [103]

Modern agronomists place considerably less emphasis on tidy, trash-free seedbeds than was once the case, and rotation, too, was hardly necessary in the early days. Why bother to follow a regime that called for alternation of corn, small grains, and meadow when the farmer often had little need of the latter, either for hay or green manure? Yet a generation of haphazard farming could deplete even the prairie soils somewhat, particularly by reducing the content of organic materials. When this began to happen, farmers listened with new respect to the prophets of rotation, clovers, and manure. "The farmers have learned," wrote the secretary of the Union Agricultural Society at West Liberty, Iowa, in 1879:

That their lands need feeding as well as their cattle and hogs and that it does not pay to starve one any more than the other. This year ninety bushels of corn have been raised to the acre on old land, simply by plowing under a good strong growth of clover, while others on the same kind of soil without the clover have produced only forty bushels.[104]

The "dirt farmers" of the 1840's and 1850's called the apostles of improved farming "book farmers" and scoffed at their message. In part they were unfair, for at times the critics hit the mark. Business-like procedures or more livestock would indeed, as they said, have profited most farmers. The improvers failed to understand, however, why more animals were often, for the time being, out of the question or that in calling for more careful cultivation, intensive manuring, clovers, and rotation they were sometimes a generation ahead of the need. The obvious shortcomings in the message of the reformers compromised its virtues. No doubt also, some scorned the "book farmers" because they were often gentleman farmers, believed to

[103] G. E. Morrow and T. F. Hunt, *Field Experiments with Corn, 1890* (University of Illinois, Agricultural Experiment Station Bull. No. 13 [Champaign, 1891]), p. 392; see also G. E. Morrow, *Field Experiments with Corn 1889* (Bull. No. 8 [Champaign, 1890]), p. 274. By 1895 the Illinois corn-researchers were reporting a definite decline in yields on the experimental plots devoted to continuous corn cropping without the addition of manure or commercial fertilizers: Eugene Davenport and W. J. Fraser, *Corn Experiments, 1895* (University of Illinois, Agricultural Experiment Station Bull. No. 42 [Urbana, 1896]), p. 179. Photographs taken approximately a decade later show strikingly stunted corn on the unfertilized, unrotated plots: Cyril G. Hopkins *et al.*, *Thirty Years of Crop Rotation on the Common Prairie Soils of Illinois* (University of Illinois, Agricultural Experiment Station Bull. No. 125 [1908]), pp. 332–33. To this writer the impressive thing about this series of experiments was not that the soils were depleted, but rather the length of time which this process took, despite a regime of soil depletion so rigorous that it was probably equaled on very few prairie farms.
[104] I.S.A.S.R., *1879*, p. 518.

have more means than sense and captivated by methods that were of little help to smaller operators, although perhaps suitable for large operations.

Argument over the intensity with which the farmer applied labor and capital to his acres expressed itself in argument over the number of acres that a farmer should till. From the 1840's through the 1870's, correspondents in the agricultural press fondly recalled the aphorism that a little farm well-tilled was just as desirable as a little wife well-willed. Thirty acres was enough, said some, provided they were properly farmed. Nonsense, said others, it was on the larger farm that the farmer realized the greatest return from his labor. In an age when machinery was rapidly expanding the individual's productive potential, the "little farm" men flew their banner in the face of circumstance.

CHAPTER VIII

How To Farm Sitting Down

The farm-maker of the prairies lived in a whirl of technological change. As the first two generations of farmers tamed the grasslands of the prairie peninsula, the tools and machinery of agriculture changed drastically. This technological revolution was part of the general process of applying the achievements of the industrial revolution to agriculture throughout the United States. But to some degree, the changes were in response to the peculiar problems and opportunities of prairie farming. The farm equipment of the pioneer of the 1830's was both simple and limited in amount. A wagon or cart, a couple of plows, a harrow, axe, shovel, scythe, cradle, fork, and rake — these were the essentials. Add a pair of oxen, with yoke and chain, or a team of horses and their harness, and the farm-maker was "tolerably well fixed." He could purchase this minimum of equipment and farm stock in the 1830's for $300 or less. Now, indeed, he entered an era of mechanical innovation and increasing costs.

William Oliver was scornful of the plows in use in Illinois during the early 1840's. The breaking plows, he believed, did slovenly work and were "crazy, creaky things, which, not unfrequently, are converted, by one smash, into a bundle of sticks." On the land "reclaimed from a state of nature," the Illinois farmer used "light" plows, often manufactured at home.[1] These implements served interchangeably as field and corn plows, drawn by one horse in the corn rows and by a team of horses or yoke of oxen when preparing the land for seed. Although Oliver evidently did not sense it, the plows were changing when he visited Illinois. The western blacksmiths, mechanics, and foundrymen improved the earlier breaking plows by substituting long, twisted, iron moldboards or iron rods for the old style wooden or iron-faced moldboards. Because the steel-edged share of the breaker ran just below the major "rind" of grass roots, the soil in the furrow slice was bound firmly together and unlikely to stick to the moldboard. Scouring was not a problem for the breakers.

With his land broken, the western farmer still found plowing a problem.

[1] William Oliver, *Eight Months in Illinois; with Information to Emigrants* (Newcastle upon Tyne, 1843 [reprinted Chicago, 1924]), pp. 98, 97.

148

The fine textured prairie soils clung to the shares and the moldboards of the 1820's and 1830's, forcing the plowman to "follow the plow, paddle in hand, stopping at every turn and oftener, to remove the load of soil which . . . accumulated, fretting at the imperfection and slovenly appearance of the work, often from necessity burning off the stubble and litter." [2] The plows of these early years were of wood with a "wrought steel tipped share" or they were of iron cast, often illegally, in the pattern of Jethro Wood's improved plow of 1819, or of a style designed to improve upon it. The cast-iron plow of the "whittling Yankee" would not scour in the prairie soils because the blowholes, caused by gases and water vapor, and other flaws of the casting process prevented the plow-maker from achieving a surface on the mold-board that was hard enough and smooth enough so that soil particles would not adhere to its imperfections. [3]

Historians have praised John Deere for the development of a strong, light, steel plow, which would scour in the western soils. Like most prairie inventors, he was only one of many who were trying to solve a particular problem. The early historian of the agricultural implement business, R L. Ardrey, gave credit to John Lane, of Chicago, for constructing the first steel plow of record in 1833, facing the moldboard with steel from the blade of an old crosscut saw. [4] Quite possibly another blacksmith or mechanic had done the same thing somewhat earlier, only to be deprived of his credit by some fluke of history. Edward C. Kendall has recently argued that Deere's contribution lay in successfully uniting a one-piece, steel moldboard and steel share. He suggests, also, that most of Deere's plows of the 1840's and early 1850's were equipped with highly polished wrought-iron moldboards and steel shares. Discussing the history of the western plow in the mid-1840's, J. T. Gifford listed a number of early steel plowmen in the territory of the Union Agricultural Society in Northern Illinois. John Deere's first place of business, Grand Detour, lay outside the society's territory, but it is strange that Gifford did not mention him, if he was indeed considered the pioneer steel plowman of the prairies. [5] Others, no less than Deere, imported steel

[2] *Prairie Farmer*, November, 1844, p. 260.

[3] R. L. Ardrey, *American Agricultural Implements: A Review of Invention and Development in the Agricultural Implement Industry of the United States* (Chicago, 1894), pp. 5–20. A useful discussion of plow-making principles and problems is found in the "Report on Trials of Plows," in the New York State Agricultural Society, *Transactions, 1867* (Albany, 1869), pp. 385–656. The following are helpful studies that treat a variety of the topics to follow as well as plows: Donald P. Greene, "Prairie Agricultural Technology, 1860–1900" (unpublished Ph.D. dissertation, Indiana University, 1957); John J. Thomas, *Farm Implements and Farm Machinery, and the Principles of their Construction and Use: with Simple and Practical Explanations of the Laws of Motion and Force as Applied on the Farm* (New York, 1869).

[4] Ardrey, *op. cit.*, pp. 14–16.

[5] Edward C. Kendall, "John Deere's Steel Plow," *Contributions from the Museum of History and Technology* (United States National Museum, Bull. 218, Smithsonian Institution [Washington, 1959]), pp. 16–25. Gifford's story appeared in *Prairie Farmer*,

from the east and abroad to use in preference to the saw steel available during the late 1830's and early 1840's.

Deere's career certainly did differ from that of most western blacksmiths. From the first steel plow, which he made in 1837, there grew an industrial empire; by the 1850's his Moline plows were used as the yardstick of quality in much of Illinois and Iowa. Throughout his life Deere displayed energy, salesmanship, and the will to improve his products. These qualities, combined with a talent for selecting capable associates and wise foresight in moving his business to an excellent location at Moline, rather than priority in the field or exceptional inventive genius, explain John Deere's success.

Once the plow-makers had made the first major steps in solving the scouring problem, they could turn part of their attention to refinements that would lighten the draft of their implements, prevent them from clogging in stubble, turn a tidier furrow, and improve the tilth of the soil by pulverizing the overturned sod to a greater extent. Thus the plow-makers experimented with the angle and length of the moldboards, with the placement of the beam in relation to the body of the plow, and with a great variety of colter and skimmer arrangements. Ultimately, an enterprising mechanic even sought and won a patent on the drag-chain device long used by plowmen for sweeping weeds under the turning furrow slice.[6]

The early steel plows were much superior to a good cast-iron plow like the "Eagle" of Joel Nourse, but they still had defects. The steel plate of the 1840's and 1850's was difficult to shape properly. Farmers complained, too, of brittle shares and moldboards that broke easily or wore out rapidly. Searching for cheaper steel, the plow-makers sometimes made plows in which the steel was uneven in temper and would not scour uniformly. Perhaps, as Kendall has argued, many of the steel plows of the 1840's and 1850's were steel in share only. Farmers were still complaining of plows that would not scour during the 1850's.[7] Some, satisfied with the scouring properties of the steel plow, argued that it picked up stones in gravelly soils. The plow-makers solved the technical problems of the steel plow during the 1860's, first by casting the steel shares, landsides, and moldboards in iron molds and later by using soft-core-steel plate, patented by John Lane, Jr. in 1868.

For the prairie farmer there was one basic defect of the steel plow that the inventors failed to remove. This was its cost — almost double that of a cast-

February, 1846, p. 42. At least one John Deere executive has argued that John Deere constructed the first workable steel plow. In a patent-conscious age, however, Deere did not patent his plow: Charles E. Chapman, "History of Deere and Company 1837-1911" (unpublished M.A. thesis, State University of Iowa, 1949), pp. 11–13, 53; (see also: Neil M. Clark, *John Deere; He Gave to the World the Steel Plow* . . . (Moline, 1937); Carl W. Mitman, "Deere, John," *Dictionary of American Biography*, V, 193–94.

[6] Iowa State Agricultural Society, *Report, 1866* (Des Moines, 1867), p. 244. Hereafter this series will be cited as I.S.A.S.R.

[7] *Ibid., 1858*, p. 432.

iron plow. Shortly after the Civil War, James Oliver, of South Bend, Indiana, was selling cast chilled-iron plows for prices ranging between $8.00 and $10.00. At the same time, his firm was offering steel plows priced between $17.00 and $22.00. During 1867 Oliver applied for the basic patent on his process for chilling cast-iron moldboards. Oliver cast his iron moldboards against iron chills, filled with hot water, and then tempered them in hot sand or charcoal. The result was a moldboard with a very hard surface and scouring properties similar to that of steel. Improving his process by subsequent patents and ever alert to improve the engineering of his plows, Oliver, too, built his business into an industrial empire. With the introduction of the chilled-iron plow, the basic problem of the prairie plowman had been solved. The most recent student of James Oliver and his plow business has accepted the claims of the Oliver company that its plow metal was "the hardest substance used in plow making," and that a chilled moldboard would wear "as long as three of steel." Of the nine share types that the company sold during the late 1870's, however, two were still of steel.[8]

Other achievements of the plow-makers interested farmers during the early years of prairie agriculture. If they read the agricultural press, they noticed many references to subsoil plows.[9] Useful as these might be in the older states during the mid-nineteenth century, they were of limited utility in the deep and fertile prairie soils. The Michigan double plow and its various cousins were generally implements for experimenters or fadists rather than the average western farmer. Even more remote from the experience and opportunities of the ordinary farmer were the occasional efforts made to apply steam power to the plow. After a steam-plowing exhibition at the Illinois State Fair in 1858, the *Chicago Press* proclaimed that "steam has conquered the face of nature," but the wry reference to steam-plowing engines that "bury themselves inextricably in the ground," made by the superintendent of the 1860 Census was closer to the mark.[10]

However exciting the idea of taming the prairie with steam might be, it was a soggy failure. More practical and successful were the efforts of inventors to mount one or more plows on a wheeled frame or sulky and provide the driver with a seat. Inventors obtained patents during the 1840's, and farmers bought considerable numbers of sulky plows in the late 1860's. In 1868 a farmer from Howard County, Iowa, reported complete satisfaction after three years of using a sulky gangplow.[11] But the patents for sulky gangplows that Deere and Company and the Oliver firm exploited successfully date from

[8] This account of Oliver is based upon Douglas L. Meikle, "James Oliver and the Oliver Chilled-Plow Works" (unpublished Ph.D. dissertation, Indiana University, 1958). The quoted passages occur on p. 167.

[9] See, e.g., *Prairie Farmer*, May, 1843, p. 112, February, 1852, pp. 78–79, July 15, 1865, p. 28; *Iowa Homestead*, November 13, 1867, p. 357; I.S.A.S.R., *1858*, p. 338.

[10] Quoted by Reynold M. Wik, "Steam Power on the American Farm, 1830–1880," *Agricultural History*, XXV (October, 1951), 182.

[11] *Iowa Homestead*, March 11, 1868, p. 73; Ardrey, *op. cit.*, p. 19.

the mid-1870's. The reports of the county agricultural societies in Iowa do not show much use of the sulky plow until the late 1870's.

His land once plowed, the farmer of the 1830's and 1840's usually prepared it for seeding with the harrow. Sometimes square, but typically a wooden triangular or A-frame studded with iron teeth, this implement had changed little from colonial times. Lacking even so simple an implement, the pioneer farmer might use a rough drag of tree limbs or brush to crush the clods and level his field. Among the Yorker and Yankee settlers, no doubt, one could find the Geddes triangular hinged harrow at work by the 1850's. In this variant the arms of two A harrows were attached in tandem to a center beam by hinges. But square or rectangular harrow sections became increasingly the rule during the late nineteenth century.

The basic features of the straight-toothed harrow defied major improvement. The mechanics and machinery men, however, increased its breadth and flexibility by linking two or more sections together, varied the arrangements of the rows of teeth, and strengthened it by casting the frame of iron. Early in the 1870's an Iowa inventor patented a device for changing the tilt of harrow teeth. During the 1870's the adjustable spring-tooth and disc harrows with driver's seat attracted supporters, each having its special utility, depending on the condition of the soil and the amount of litter upon it.[12]

Increasingly after the 1850's the farmers used the roller in conjunction with the harrow as the use of mechanical harvesting equipment and mechanical corn-planters placed a greater premium upon smooth seedbeds. The roller, of course, was little more complicated than the harrow and could be made from a smooth tree trunk, if need be. The farmer could, by the 1870's, purchase an iron roller that was a more durable and efficient implement generally than its wooden cousin and that displayed either a smooth or a serrated surface, according to his preference.[13]

Although their allegiance to the small grains varied from district to district, the farmers of the prairie triangle consistently included them in their cropping programs. In some parts of Illinois and Iowa, wheat, of course, dominated the pioneer farm enterprise. Outwardly much more striking than the transformation of the plow, the changing technology of the small grains introduced the prairie farmer to the age of mechanized agriculture. Mechanization of grain culture did, it is true, begin in the wheat regions of the middle states rather than in the Midwest. As the western harvests grew, Cyrus McCormick and a legion of other inventors and machinery manufacturers found their major challenge on the prairies, but small-grain technology was a foster child there.

Western farmers did not adopt all the machines of grain culture with equal eagerness. It would be the late 1870's before the grain drill won the

[12] Ardrey, *op. cit.*, pp. 21–23.

[13] *Prairie Farmer*, June 6, 1861, p. 369; U.S. Commissioner of Agriculture, *Report, 1874* (Washington, 1875), pp. 286–87.

approval of most prairie farmers. Yet practical machines were available in the late 1840's. In the interim, the principles of operation remained:

The regular and measured distribution of the seeds, by means of revolving cylinders furnished with small cavities, or by the vibratory motion of perforated plates and the passage of the seed down into the mellow earth through a hollow coulter, where it . . . [was] . . . immediately buried by the earth falling back upon it as soon as the coulter . . . [had] . . . passed.[14]

Refinements, particularly in regulating the flow of seed, continued into the 1870's.

In 1848 the *Prairie Farmer* promised the farmer who used either the Pennock or Palmer's drill a substantial saving in seed wheat and in labor, as well as a crop that would stand firm on deep roots and be less apt to lodge. More important still, claimed the editor, drilled wheat was less apt to winter-kill because the seeds fell in shallow trenches into which the intervening ridges of soil slid during winter thaws, thus protecting roots that the frost might otherwise heave from the ground. The farmer who drilled his wheat could expect to harvest from two to eight bushels above the yield on fields sown broadcast.[15] The first major flurry of interest in drills among western farmers came during the late 1840's and early 1850's when a series of disasters struck the winter-wheat crops of Illinois and Iowa. Those who used the drill, unfortunately, had little more luck than those who sowed broadcast; winter wheat and the grain drill went into eclipse together.

Writers suggested that drills sowed unevenly, and that the seed-conveying tubes clogged all too frequently. At the heart of such trouble, undoubtedly, was the fact that the farmers of the prairie triangle frequently planted wheat on their old cornfields. As late as the 1860's, some of them sowed winter wheat between the standing corn rows. For this task they preferred a small broadcast seeder which could be attached to hand cultivators or plows. When many of the farmers of northern Illinois and Iowa began to plant spring wheat during the 1850's and 1860's, they failed to clear their fields of old cornstalks or work them into the ground deeply, and thus they prepared a seedbed where it was almost impossible for the drill to do its work properly. Under these circumstances, some farmers used broadcast seeders that simply sprinkled the small grains on the ground to be covered by a trailing harrow or cultivator in a second operation. Some of the seeders had their own covering attachments.[16]

In 1863 the editor of the *Illinois Farmer* reported that hand seeders were available that were much more economical for the small or medium-sized farm than the horse-powered broadcast sowers.[17] Indeed, a farmer could seed

[14] U.S. Commissioner of Agriculture, *Report, 1862*, pp. 418–19.
[15] *Prairie Farmer*, December, 1848, p. 362.
[16] *Northwestern Farmer*, January, 1857, p. 19.
[17] M. L. Dunlap in U.S. Commissioner of Agriculture, *Report, 1863*, p. 428.

his small-grain crops quite rapidly without any special machinery at all, unless his farm was a large one. In 1871 a Yorker, of Hamilton County, Iowa, "sowed broadcast, by hand, seventy-five bushels of oats in three and a half hours. He rode in a cart and scattered the seed with one hand. With a boy to drive the oxen, Mr. Carpenter . . . [said that he could] . . . sow twice the quantity in the same time," by sitting in the back part of the cart and sowing with both hands. The local editor concluded, "This is fast work — almost equal to any of our machine broadcast sowers." [18] For those with less adept hands than Mr. Carpenter, manufacturers had already provided an end-gate broadcast seeder that gained some popularity. Obviously the drill or broadcast seeder did not cut the labor costs of Illinois and Iowa farmers impressively enough to bring rapid adoption. [19] Slowly the even, economical seeding of the drill, unaffected by spring or fall winds, won a majority of midwestern farmers to its use. By 1890 most farmers used it.

Skeptical though he was of the grain drill, the prairie farmer was eager to use machinery in the small-grain harvest. Not only did machinery greatly cut the cost of labor, obtained by hire or exchange with neighbors, but the farmer believed that it would relieve him of many uncertainties. For the thought of harvest wages was always linked with the worry that it might be impossible to obtain enough helpers when the crop was ready for the sickle. Once good machinery was available in quantity also, the farmer could more closely restrict his work in the grain to the period when it was at exactly the right stage for harvesting.

The editor of the *Prairie Farmer* reported to his readers in November, 1845, that one of the proprietors of McCormick's Reaper had called and "informed us that he is endeavoring to introduce them in the West." [20] Young Cyrus H. McCormick assured the editor that his machine could cut an acre and a half in an hour and save a bushel an acre that would have been lost by cradling. For such a machine the western farmer must pay $120. The few lines in the *Prairie Farmer* prefaced one of the most spectacular chapters in the history of the American agricultural implement business. [21]

The steps by which the grain harvest yielded to the machines are easily traced. During the 1830's Obed Hussey and the members of the McCormick family produced wheeled platforms, armed with a projecting finger bar along the forward edge in which a serrated blade vibrated, run by gearing attached to a drive wheel. As horses drew the machine through the ripe grain, the

[18] Webster City *Hamilton Freeman*, April 5, 1871.

[19] For a discussion of drilling and broadcasting wheat in the 1870's, see U.S. Commissioner of Agriculture, *Report, 1874*, pp. 60–67, 287.

[20] *Prairie Farmer*, November, 1845, p. 275.

[21] William T. Hutchinson, *Cyrus Hall McCormick* (2 vols.; New York, 1930 and 1935) is one of the classics in the history of American agriculture. Charles W. Marsh left an insider's account of the Marsh Harvester in his *Recollections: 1837–1910* (Chicago 1910). See also Merritt F. Miller, *The Evolution of Reaping Machines* (U.S. Department of Agriculture, Office of Experiment Stations Bull. No. 103 [Washington, 1902]); John F. Steward, *The Reaper* (New York, 1931).

blade cut the grain stalks off a few inches above the ground, and they fell onto the platform, from where a harvest hand raked them onto the ground. McCormick considered the fundamental principles of his machine to be a "reciprocating sickle passing through double fingers, the divider, the reel, the platform, the power derived from one main wheel, and the side draft" that kept the horses out of the standing grain.[22] The cutting mechanism of the Hussey machine was superior to that of the McCormick machine, but a rotating reel on the latter laid some stands of grain on the table in more efficient style. During the 1840's the raker was given a seat on the machines.

With the 1850's inventors devised practical methods of having the reaping machine itself clear the platform with sweeps or rakes, and Atkins Automaton Self Raker and Mower caused more merriment in Walnut Grove, Illinois, in 1853 "than any thing that ever came into . . . [the] . . . Grove."[23] The major reaper companies, however, did not push the sale of self-rakers vigorously until the 1860's. During that same decade the dropper became popular. This was a variant of the reaper in which the driver depressed the rear of the table behind the cutting blades at intervals, allowing the grain to slide backward onto the ground. During these same years the Marsh brothers of DeKalb County, Illinois, were perfecting their harvester, which carried the cut grain from the table on endless canvas belts and elevated it above the drive wheel to a platform where binders rode. The culminating step for many farmers came a few years later when mechanical binders, using wire and then twine, replaced the harvest hands on the binding platform. As early as the 1840's a practical header, that of George Esterly, was available, but the tendency of headed grain to heat and spoil in the stack turned midwestern farmers against such implements.[24]

By the end of 1849 the McCormick brothers had sold fewer than 3,000 reapers in the West, and their competitors had not sold many machines as yet.[25] Seemingly the western harvest was far from mechanized, but the editor of the *Prairie Farmer* toured a number of northern counties of Illinois during the harvest of 1850 and philosophized: "Who would have thought the cradle so soon to be superceded in the harvest field? But judging from what I have seen it is already so. In the whole journey I have found but two cradles in operation, while the reapers of various sorts have been numberless."[26] One Illinois farmer described the first run of a reaper on his farm in a neighborhood hitherto unacquainted with the machine. "Cradles," he wrote, "could

[22] Herbert A. Kellar, "The Reaper as a Factor in the Development of the Agriculture of Illinois, 1834–1865" (Illinois State Historical Society, *Transactions, 1927*), p. 108.

[23] *Prairie Farmer*, September, 1853, p. 357.

[24] *Prairie Farmer*, July, 1845, p. 180, October, 1846, p. 305, December, 1846, pp. 376–77, November, 1848, p. 345, May, 1849, pp. 152–53, June 2, 1866, p. 371. Use of the word "header" to describe these machines evidently did not become common until around 1900, Greene, "Prairie Agricultural Technology, 1860–1900," p. 229.

[25] *Prairie Farmer*, July, 1849, p. 212.

[26] *Ibid.*, September, 1850, p. 267.

have been bought cheap that day afterwards." [27] Through the 1850's the agents of McCormick, Seymour and Morgan, Manny, and many less well-known reaper manufacturers served a market eager for their products. Writers have stressed the effect which the Civil War had upon the sales of an implement advertised as saving the labor of at least four and a half men, and it is true that reaper sales boomed during that conflict. But the makers of good machines could hardly keep pace with the demand during the 1850's.

In many cases farmers benefited from the reaper years before they themselves bought machines. The first purchasers often did custom work and cut the grain of neighbors in addition to their own.[28] In other cases the members of neighborhood rings purchased machines that they used to cut the grain of the half dozen or more farmers in the group. On the other hand, the cradle disappeared more slowly on farms where fields had been hacked from the timber and stumps still stood to plague the reaper-driver and to defy the vibrating sickle blade.

Yet the story of the reaper was not a continual march of triumph. Even the better machines had their weaknesses in the early days, and flaws sometimes compounded when inventors like Hussey sold shop rights to firms with more ambition than skill. The letters of Cyrus H. McCormick show that the models of some years were much less reliable and satisfactory than others. If this was true in one of the most successful of the reaper companies, it was much more of a problem in the case of firms whose product was basically less sound or still in the experimental stage. Machines varied widely in the extent to which the sickle clogged in weedy grain, in their performance on rough ground, and in the trimness of the gavels that they laid down. Inferior machines made many an Illinois and Iowa farmer look back nostalgically to the sober certainty of the cradle.

While the reaper was finding its place in the harvest fields, the threshing operation, too, was changing. Once the grain sheaves were in stack or mow, they were safe from most natural hazards. Threshing lacked the peculiar urgency of the harvest. It was, however, a laborious and time-consuming task when the grain was flailed or trod out by draft animals. In the latter case, also, it produced a dirty and inferior product, particularly if there was no wooden threshing floor available. Since capacious barns or threshing floors graced few western holdings in the pioneer period, inclement fall or winter weather also might hinder threshing.

British inventors had produced workable threshing machines during the eighteenth century, but such machinery was little used in the United States before the 1820's and early 1830's. Leo Rogin has described the Pitts thresher of the late thirties as the first "truly practicable" machine.[29] Farm-

[27] *Ibid.*, August, 1847, p. 259.

[28] In 1849 custom operators reportedly charged fifty cents per acre for cutting wheat, the owner to find two horses (*Prairie Farmer*, September, 1849, p. 285).

[29] Leo Rogin, *The Introduction of Farm Machinery in its Relation to the Produc-*

ers west of Ohio threshed little grain by machine before the 1840's. As in the case of the reaper, interest in threshing machines developed first in the wheat-growing regions of the eastern states. By the late 1840's J. I. Case was manufacturing threshers at Racine, Wisconsin, and Hiram A. Pitts had moved to Illinois, establishing himself first at Alton, and later in Chicago.[30] The reaper on the one hand and improved transportation facilities on the other allowed wheat production and sale on a scale that made the older threshing methods seem annoyingly slow.

Threshing is a three-fold process that involves beating the kernels of grain from the husks, separating them from the straw, and finally winnowing out the chaff and other litter. Manufacturers greatly improved the threshing machine between 1840 and 1880. They increased the strength and efficiency of the cylinder and concave arrangement into which the feeder threw the sheaves, most notably by using iron or steel throughout. The separation phase became more effective when the straw was routed through a "vibrator" in its passage through the machine. After 1850 most of the machines used for custom work also contained a fanning or winnowing device, although smaller machines, intended for the individual farmer, still lacked them. By the 1860's elevators to carry the straw away from the machine were in use;[31] application of a blower to that task came much later.

The first threshing machines were "ground-hogs" sitting flat on the ground while in operation, but soon manufacturers attached the moving trucks directly to the machine. Although many of the small machines of the 1830's were hand-powered, horsepowers were essential for larger machines. These were mainly of the sweep variety, using ultimately four or five teams, despite the popularity that one or two horse-tread powers enjoyed for small machines during the 1840's and 1850's. Although horses still pulled both separator and steamer from place to place, mobile steam engines began to replace the horse during the 1870's.[32]

Like most innovations, the threshing machine caused mixed emotions. A farmer described his experience in 1842 near Springfield, Illinois, when he contracted with the owner of a horsepower thresher who agreed to thresh his wheat at a rate of 200 bushels per day, the farmer delivering the wheat in the bundle to the machine and accepting the clean wheat in boxes at the tail, for a charge of eight cents a bushel. The thresherman, as it turned out, only furnished three hands and six horses, all with voracious appetites, and the machine proved incapable of threshing more than 120 bushels per day, despite the fact that the farmer furnished four hands and a horse and a boy

tivity of Labor in the Agriculture of the United States during the Nineteenth Century (Berkeley, 1931), p. 165.

[30] Ardrey, *op. cit.*, pp. 103–14.

[31] *Prairie Farmer*, March 12, 1864, p. 167.

[32] Leo Rogin quoted a farmer of Hardin County, Iowa, who reported that steam-power threshers did not come there until 1890. *Op. cit.*, pp. 184–85, fn. 170. This was late in comparison to some other Iowa communities.

to take the straw away. The disgruntled farmer finally figured his costs at 16 cents per bushel and reported four years later that there had been no more horsepower threshing in his district to that date.[33]

By the 1850's most farmers with considerable acreages of wheat did their threshing by machine, even while stark pioneer conditions prevailed. S. F. Shepard later described his entry into the threshing business in northern Iowa. Settling in Bremer County in 1851, when he had but a handful of neighbors, he was able to thresh his grain by machine in the very next year due to the enterprise of a "gentleman farmer" from Anamosa who brought his machine more than thirty miles up the Wapsipinicon River Valley, threshing for farmers as he came to them along the stream. When he reached Shepard's district in November, a thirty-inch snowfall interrupted the work. During the few days that elapsed before they could dig out the machine and resume threshing, Shepard improved his time by dickering with the proprietor, and ultimately bought the machine in partnership with a neighbor. Charging 4 cents a bushel for threshing oats and 6 cents for wheat, Shepard served much of Bremer, Butler, and Black Hawk counties until competitors began to narrow the range of his operations in 1856.[34]

Although small tread-power machines received favorable comment briefly in the 1850's, the threshing machine did not become standard equipment for the small or medium-sized farm.[35] To invest $350 or more in a machine that the farmer could use for only a few days was patently bad business. In the prairie triangle threshing was typically a service provided by custom operators.

If the harvest rites of earlier ages had dwindled by the nineteenth century to a perfunctory harvest service on a hot summer Sunday, the culmination of harvest with the arrival of the threshers had its own excitement, impressiveness, and even its own rituals. Herbert Krause has tried to write the epic of the middle-western thresherman in the somber story of Johnny Black, whose tormented life ended beside his flaming separator, his clenched hands still clutching a few grains of wheat.[36] But perhaps the best description of threshing operations in the 1870's before steam had become undisputed master, is that of Herbert Quick, who pictured the driver on his perch above the power sweeps as he spoke to his five teams, and the feeder on his platform facing the "Buffalo Pitts" while the sun edged above the prairie horizon and fired the low-hanging morning mist:

The ponderous cylinder before him . . . [began] . . . to revolve, trying to gnash its polished steel teeth against those of the concaves, but failing because they always passed each other by a hair's breath. A deep growl like that of a

[33] *Prairie Farmer*, August 8, 1846, p. 253.
[34] Union Publishing Company, *History of Butler and Bremer Counties, Iowa* . . . (Springfield, 1883), pp. 845–48.
[35] *Prairie Farmer*, January, 1850, p. 21.
[36] Herbert Krause, *The Thresher* (Indianapolis, 1946).

bulldog magnified fifty diameters, filled the air, and as the cylinder gathered speed it rose from a bass to a baritone, and then to a tenor of a volume which sang over four square miles of haze-obscured prairie. The feeder looked up at the pitchers, saw the man who pitched to the machine, with his next bundle ready to fall on the table, saw Frank with his band-cutter's knife ready to slice softly through the band of it, and then, he moved the first two sheaves gently over between the open lips, deftly twitched their butts upward, and the great operation was on. The tenor took a little lower note; the horses felt the sweeps holding them back; the driver's shouts rose to a higher and more peremptory tone; and if everything went well, they were off upon a half-day's run, during which the feeder's pride would be that he would feed those four great stacks through the thrasher so steadily that not once would the thrashed straw in the straw-carrier fail to pass in an unbroken stream, hiding the slats of the carrier; not once would an inexpert handling of a bundle choke the thrasher down, even to a baritone; to say nothing of a bass note; not once would the cloud of chaff cease to rise from behind the sieves; not once would the stream of wheat fail to flow into the half-bushel measures which would keep the measurer and the man who hauled off in a perspiring hurry.[37]

Although the prairie triangle became the heart of the Corn Belt during this period, the application of machinery to corn culture was less impressive than was the mechanization of the small-grain harvest, or even of haying. Although midwestern inventors failed to perfect either corn harvesters or pickers during this period, they did develop planting and cultivating implements that greatly increased the acreage of corn that one man could plant and tend during the growing season.

Down to the 1850's a basic part of the prairie lad's farming apprenticeship came during late April or early May, when he carried his bucket of seed corn across fields, checkered into four-foot squares by shovel plow or drag marker, and deposited from four to six corn kernels in the heart of each black cross. From behind him he heard the bite, crunch, and scuffle of his father's or brother's hoe as it sliced down at his heels and scooped dirt upon the kernels, to be packed a second later by the foot of the hoe man. But if this was the usual picture on the farms of the first generation of prairie farmers, there were inventors as eager to change it as were the bucket-carriers.

Some inventors tried, in a sense, to combine the corn bucket of the dropper and the covering hoe, by constructing a cane-high device, equipped with a seed chamber and shod with a metal blade. When the operator jabbed it into the ground, such a planter dropped a few kernels of corn in the cut, automatically or by trigger release. Mounting two of these planters on a light crosspiece produced a dual planter that allowed the farmer to seed two rows at a time. The hand planter men probably exaggerated the labor-saving that they had effected. The secretary of the Agricultural Society in Lee County,

[37] Herbert Quick, *The Hawkeye* (Indianapolis, 1923), p. 251.

Iowa, reported in 1859: "The different hand planters have been tried and entirely abandoned. The general prevailing opinion among farmers is that the best method of planting corn is to drop carefully by hand and cover with the hoe." [38] The future lay with those inventors who developed two-row planters that could be pulled by horses and ridden by the operator.

Through the 1840's the inventors of horse-drawn corn-planters tried to perfect the dropping devices on their machines. These were all unsatisfactory to farmers who wanted to plant their corn in check so that they could cultivate it from both directions and eliminate as much hand hoeing as possible. The first two-row planter to win general favor was that of George W. Brown, who built up a considerable business at Galesburg, Illinois, during the 1850's and 1860's. [39] Brown obtained a series of patents from 1853 onward, protecting his rights to a machine on which the drop was manually controlled. Released simultaneously from two seed boxes, or hoppers, the kernels of seed corn traveled to the ground in tubes set in the back of two metal shoes and came to rest in furrows opened by the convex leading edges of the shoes. Rollers placed behind the shoes tamped down the soil around the seed.

The farmer, using the Brown machine or a competitive machine built on the same general principles, marked out his corn ground in one direction with drag or wheel markers and then planted across the marks. Cuts of two-row planters during the late 1850's and 1860's show a smug little gentleman, on a sideways seat ahead of the driver, poised to work the dropping lever as the machine crossed each line left by the marker. The foot release featured on some planters placed undue demands upon the driver. The next major improvement in the planter was the check-row mechanism activated by a knotted wire that ran across the field and fed through the tripping device. Although patented in the mid-1860's, such devices were not satisfactory enough at first to become popular until late in the next decade. [40]

Corn-cultivating implements changed considerably during the first thirty years of prairie agriculture. The pioneers of the 1830's and early 1840's depended mainly on light, single-shovel plows pulled by one horse for work in the corn rows, although farmers also used plows with a flat landside to cut very close to the young corn plants. By the 1850's two smaller shovels might be mounted on opposite sides of the plow beam, making the double-shovel plow. [41] At the same time, the horse hoe or cultivator with five or more teeth set in a triangular frame was in use in Ohio and eastern states. Ultimately it

[38] I.S.A.S.R., *1859*, p. 302.

[39] Ardrey, *op. cit.*, pp. 30–35. There were at least three other two-horse corn-planters on exhibit in addition to Brown's machine at the Illinois State Fair at Springfield in 1854 (*Prairie Farmer*, November, 1854, pp. 405–6).

[40] See U.S. Commissioner of Agriculture, *Report, 1874*, p. 292, for a good description of the check-rower device.

[41] Percy W. Bidwell and John I. Falconer, *History of Agriculture in the Northern United States 1620–1860* (Washington, 1925), pp. 303–4; U.S. Commissioner of Agriculture, *Report, 1863*, pp. 424–25; I.S.A.S.R., *1857*, p. 266, *1859*, p. 375.

found its place in western cornfields as well. But the implements that revolutionized corn cultivation in the prairie triangle were the riding and walking straddle-row cultivators pulled by two horses.

The origins of the straddle-row cultivator are unclear. By the 1840's farmers of the New York and Ohio wheat regions were using a two-horse wheeled cultivator, preparatory to sowing wheat on fallow land. As we have seen, a variety of plows and hand cultivators were present in the Middle West to provide inventors with ideas about plow suspension and shovel shape. From these antecedents came the two-horse sulky or riding cultivator, to be driven with one horse and one wheel on each side of the corn row, while a shovel tooth, or teeth suspended on gangs attached to the frame or axle, cut close on both sides of the corn plants. One or more rounds per row had been the rule with the shovel plow; with the straddle-row cultivator, the number of rounds was halved. This was the implement that "promise[d] to work a revolution in corn raising" in the Union District of eastern Iowa in 1863.[42] In the same year the editor of the *Illinois Farmer hailed* "this new and valuable implement" with which a "young lady fond of driving, and who wishes to assist her father or brother, can do a full day's work."[43]

Evidently, George Esterly, of Wisconsin, obtained the first important patent in the evolution of the two-horse corn cultivator during 1856.[44] Competing machines were soon in the field, of course, boasting "superior principles of construction." The farmer of the 1860's and 1870's heard much of the ease with which the cultivator operator could manipulate the gangs with his feet, of the shields and other attachments designed to protect small plants, of the methods of coupling the gangs to the frame or axles, of the systems of adjustment for deep and shallow work or for throwing soil to or from the rows, of the break-away pins or springs that saved the shovels from breaking when they hit a buried obstacle squarely, and of the arched frame or axle that allowed thigh-high corn to pass below without damage. Although the two-horse sulky cultivator seemed to carry all before it, the two-horse, tongueless, walking cultivator found champions who argued that hand control allowed better work and that eliminating the tongue, necessary on the riding models, allowed a narrower turning space on the headlands.[45]

At first thought it seems strange that midwestern inventors failed to apply machinery successfully to the corn harvest during this period. Certainly they tried. Hopeful inventors took a great variety of pickers and harvesters to the cornfields, only to fail, defeated by the size and strength of the cornstalks and by fallen and tangled crops. The need was less urgent than in those areas

[42] I.S.A.S.R., *1863*, p. 473.
[43] Dunlap, *op. cit.*, pp. 424–25.
[44] Ardrey, *op. cit.*, pp. 36–39.
[45] For stories or cuts of the straddle-row cultivator see: *Prairie Farmer*, November 18, 1865, p. 372, March 31, 1866, p. 217; *Iowa Homestead*, November 13, 1862, p. 329, January 15, 1863, p. 402, July 8, 1870, p. 1, April 14, 1871, p. 8, March 8, 1872, p. 80, March 22, 1872, p. 89, April 30, 1875, p. 129.

of technology where great strides were made during the fifty years between
1830 and 1880. The farmer had only a few weeks in which to plant or cultivate corn, if the job were to be done properly, and these were weeks in which
other crops also demanded attention. He had several months of relatively
pleasant weather in which to pick corn, and if need be, the job could be carried well into the winter, or it could even wait until spring. By the late 1890's
the binder-harvester was close to perfection, but this machine was of more
use in the dairy regions where farmers fed cornstalk fodder and ensilage more
frequently than in the Corn Belt. A really successful picker-husker had to
wait for the added power and speed that tractors could provide.

Corn had been a staple in the American diet since colonial times, and
inventors patented corn-shellers during the early national period. Until the
1840's there was evidently little demand for shelled corn in Illinois and Iowa.
We need not be surprised, therefore, that many of the first generation of
prairie-dwellers trod off the grain with horses or used small, crude, hand
devices. The operator of the Sucker Cornsheller, described in early issues of
the *Prairie Farmer*, rotated a hinged wooden arm, studded with spikes, across
the cobs.[46] Another correspondent of that paper constructed a sheller by
boring a hole in a wooden bench and facing the hole on one side with a metal
plate backed by an iron spring. The user drove the cobs through the hole with
a mallet.[47] By this time the fundamentals of a successful sheller were well
known. In most machines spiked or ridged wheels or cylinders rotated within
a framework in such a way that they forced the cobs into an increasingly
constricted space.[48] Introduction of iron hand shellers in the West probably
came in the late 1840's. Already, custom operators were using large power
shellers in the western population centers as did merchants who bought
quantities of corn on the cob. By the 1860's the market offered efficient,
portable, horsepower shellers and itinerant custom operators were shelling
the corn of many farmers.

The corn planters, two-horse cultivators and power shellers were the
major exhibits of corn technology down to the 1880's. During the 1860's
and 1870's farmers experimented with a variety of cornstalk-cutters that
chopped the old stalks into short lengths that could be easily buried by tillage
in the spring, thus ending the nuisance of clogged planting machinery and
cultivators. Most of the stalk-cutters featured long blades mounted on revolving drums or axles. Some farmers still preferred to rake up the old stalks
and burn them.[49] The need for special equipment for disposing of stalks became less pressing when the disc harrow won general acceptance.

[46] *Union Agriculturist and Western Prairie Farmer*, January, 1842, p. 7.
[47] *Prairie Farmer*, July, 1850, p. 203.
[48] *Prairie Farmer*, March, 1851, p. 121, February, 1852, pp. 74–75; Ardrey, *op. cit.*,
pp. 120–26.
[49] For representative pictures or discussions of stalkcutters and rakes see *Northwestern Farmer*, April, 1858, p. 130; *Iowa Homestead*, October 2, 1863, p. 282, March
23, 1864, p. 71, March 6, 1867, p. 65, February 19, 1868, p. 49, March 22, 1872, p. 89.

While inventors shifted much of the labor in the grain and corn crops to horse-drawn machinery, a similar process was under way in the hay meadows. Where the New York farmer of the 1820's cut his hay with a scythe, his son on the prairies of Illinois or Iowa during the late 1850's might use the mowing machine. Actually the development of the moving machine was closely linked to that of the reaper, and from the 1840's to the 1870's many manufacturers marketed combined machines that the farmer could adjust to cut either grain or grass. It was no trick to remove the grain table, of course, but other adjustments posed a greater challenge to the manufacturer. For work in grass the cutting bar must operate much closer to the ground and adapt itself to minor variations in contour to a degree unnecessary in grain. Thick, green grass posed a much greater challenge to the sickle than did ripening grain, for the knife blade would clog unless it vibrated at a faster clip than in the small grains.[50] To an editor of the *Prairie Farmer*, the surface of meadows mowed by machinery in 1854 suggested that "it had been cropped by a bevy of ancient cows, wh[o]se teeth had all been long gone from their lower jaws." [51] Obtaining his first mower patent in 1844, William F. Ketchum, of Buffalo, New York, was apparently the first machinery manufacturer who succeeded in marketing a machine built solely for mowing hay — a one-wheeler. In the 1850's a definite trend began toward two-wheeled-drive machines, with flexible, easily-elevated, floating cutter bars that were mounted in front of the wheels. Thereafter, mowing equipment changed only in minor details, and in the greater use of iron and steel in construction, until the tractor age.[52] By the late 1870's the mower was in undisputed command of the hay meadows.

Apparently originating in the northeastern United States during the first quarter of the nineteenth century, the revolving horse rake was available to the western farmer of the 1830's and 1840's. This implement "consisted of two rows of wooden teeth set opposed on a beam which was so attached to shaft and handles that it could be tripped to drop and slide over its load of accumulated hay. When so tripped, the second set of teeth dropped into position to commence a new windrow." [53] A picture and description of this machine appeared in the *Prairie Farmer* in 1843, but it is difficult to tell the degree to which it had displaced the hand rake at this date or its popularity in the following years.[54] The next decade brought the development of the iron, spring-tooth sulky rake, tripped by a ratchet mechanism geared to the wheels, and for this the revolver was no competitor, even when provided with sulky and seat. Although Garret Brown's horse fork for unloading hay received publicity in the 1840's, such tools attracted little general interest for

[50] *Prairie Farmer*, October, 1849, p. 320, April, 1852, p. 194, June, 1854, p. 234.

[51] *Prairie Farmer*, August, 1854, p. 284.

[52] Ardrey, *op. cit.*, pp. 78–95.

[53] Clarence H. Danhof, "Gathering the Grass," *Agricultural History*, XXX (October, 1956), 170.

[54] *Prairie Farmer*, March, 1843, p. 58.

a generation.[55] Hay-loaders appeared during the 1860's and satisfactory models were available in the next decade.[56] Tedders and the side-delivery rake that provided the tidy windrows so congenial to mechanical hay-loaders would be even longer in development, coming into heavy use in the 1880's.

The first two generations of prairie farmers came to know and use, if not always to admire, a great variety of agricultural machinery. In some cases, notably corn culture, inventors made less progress than one might have expected; in other instances, they revolutionized husbandry. Some of their more bizarre inventions only amused the farming community. After limited success, a few, like Comstock's Rotary Spader, disappeared when their limitations or cost became clear. The need disappeared for the horse-drawn hedge-trimmers, devised for an economy fenced with Osage orange, when technology triumphed on another front.

Even the simplest of farm tools changed their character during the years of mechanization. The axe became a far more effective tool when axe-makers began to use a better quality of steel. Resilient, cunningly shaped handles and light, curved steel tines replaced the thick, straight handle and cumbrous iron tines of the 1820 fork. When field implements usurped the hoe's role as a clod-crusher and left it only the task of weeding, steel blade and graceful goose neck became the style.[57]

The economic and social implications of mechanization were great. Most obvious and most stressed, of course, was the saving of human labor or increase in productive potential that came from shifting work previously done by human muscle to iron hands and straining animals. The man who could sickle less than an acre of grain in a day could cradle at least two; place him on the seat of a Virginia reaper, and he could cut ten to fifteen acres per day, with the aid of one man to rake the grain clear from the table. By the 1860's the self-rake reaper had eliminated this helper from many harvest fields. Prior to the Civil War, slightly more than five field hands were required to bind after the reaper, and somewhat less than this figure immediately afterwards. The Marsh Harvester cut the number to two, and the self-binder eliminated even these men. With the flail, one man labored all day to separate some seven bushels of wheat from its straw. Using horses to tread the grain, he could raise his product to fifteen bushels. The horse-powered, custom threshing machine of the late 1860's more than doubled this output, and the figure rose still more during the succeeding decade.

The farmer could expect less spectacular savings of labor from the early seed drills than from the mechanical reaper or threshing machine. Indeed, Pennock's drill sowed little if any faster than could a man planting his seed broadcast. A man could sow ten acres by hand in a day, and the advoctes of the seed drill promised ten to fifteen. In this fact, undoubtedly, lies part of the

[55] *Ibid.*, January, 1847, p. 23.
[56] See cut in *ibid.*, May 12, 1866, p. 332.
[57] *Ibid.*, July, 1844, p. 169.

reason for the slowness with which use of the drill spread. The horse-drawn broadcast seeders of the 1850's and 1860's did better, sowing between twenty and thirty acres per day. But with the portable, hand, broadcast seeder of the 1860's and 1870's, the farmer could sow between forty and fifty acres per day. The end-gate seeder did somewhat better and allowed the operator considerably more rest in the process.[58]

In his excellent study of the impact of farm machinery upon labor in American agriculture, Leo Rogin was not primarily concerned with developments in the culture of corn. One observer suggested, somewhat generously, I believe, that the introduction of the steel plow, the corn-planter, and the two-horse cultivator allowed one man to bring sixty acres of corn through to picking in comparison to twenty acres under earlier methods of corn culture.[59] In the hay meadows the mower, no doubt, resulted in labor savings comparable to that provided by the hand-rake reaper, while an authority estimated that the horse hay rake saved the labor of six men.[60]

Cyrus McCormick and other farm-implement manufacturers emphasized the contribution that their machines made to the war effort during the Civil War years by freeing farm laborers. One manufacturer of spring-tooth sulky hay rakes advertised under a cut of a bouncy young lady riding his machine and commenting, "My brother has gone to the war." [61] But even in the 1850's the demand for agricultural machinery was growing with great rapidity. The McCormick firm could have sold many more reapers in 1860 than it manufactured, and its increase in output during the war years seems to show the projection of a trend established in the fifties, as well as an unusual response provoked by war conditions.

Although not all farm tasks yielded to machinery, the midwestern farmer's productive potential increased greatly during the last half of the nineteenth century. In American agriculture as a whole, productivity, defined as outputs in relation to inputs, increased by 32 per cent between 1870 and 1910. Such national figures reflected the addition of fertile new lands to the nation's farm acreage, the increased use of fertilizers, improvements in plant and animal strains, and transportation developments as well as the new horse-power technology. The farmers of the Illinois and Iowa prairies used the new machinery under extremely favorable conditions, and probably productivity there increased considerably more than in the nation as a whole. When

[58] In these paragraphs I have utilized the findings of Rogin, *op. cit.*, pp. 125–45, 176–82, 204–12. However, I entertain some scepticism about the figures given for the handbag portable seeder.

[59] *Prairie Farmer*, January 6, 1866, p. 2; John M. Peck, *A Guide for Emigrants; Containing Sketches of Illinois, Missouri, and the Adjacent Parts* (Boston, 1831), p. 150; in *Prairie Farmer*, March 14, 1863, p. 163, "Small Farmer" struck a more conservative note, arguing for 30 to 35 acres. Estimates of labor productivity in 1885 give 40 to 50 acres, *Prairie Farmer*, February 7, 1885, p. 82, February 28, 1885, p. 130.

[60] C. L. Flint in U.S. Commissioner of Agriculture, *Report, 1872*, p. 289.

[61] *Prairie Farmer*, May 27, 1865, p. 431.

converted to constant dollars, Frank T. Bachmura's estimates of gross returns per member of the agricultural labor force in nine Iowa districts showed an average increase in Iowa of 112 per cent between 1869 and 1900.[62] Unquestionably, too, the impact of the new machinery was felt in the Middle West considerably before 1870 as well as after that date.

Harvesting and planting machinery demanded reasonably level fields unmarred by grubs or stumps. Farmers trying to achieve such conditions undoubtedly put their fields in a better condition of tilth, and this, perhaps, increased yields slightly. The new machinery also helped to eliminate oxen as draft animals. If the cutting mechanism of the harvesting machines was to work properly, they must move at a faster gait than oxen favored. Other machinery demanded an agility in the draft animals that cattle refused to display. Farm machinery, too, contributed greatly to the education of farmers and farm youths. Simple though they appear in retrospect, harvester machinery or check-rowing devices seemed marvels of perverse Yankee ingenuity to farmers who had never used anything more complicatd than an A-harrow or a three-piece plow. The wide dissemination of knowledge about simple mechanical principles among the farm population was of considerable significance to a young industrial nation, which looked to its farms for much of the labor needed in the industrial centers.

Herbert A. Kellar has suggested that the reaper gave a sense of security to the farmer, since he could now be assured of cutting his crop in just a few days, whenever optimum conditions prevailed.[63] There is much truth in this observation, but the reaper could contribute to tension and insecurity too. If the farmer exploited his increased productivity and planted extra acreage so that the normal harvesting period was still needed to complete the job, as many did, the fear of inclement weather was still with him. Now, also, the farmer must worry about keeping the machine in running order, for a breakdown would be frustrating, at least, and perhaps costly. A farmer wrote to Cyrus McCormick in 1855, "I broke a finger after I had bought it [the reaper] and there was not a finger among all the liberal supply you had sent as extras without an experienced mechanic working on them at a cost of fifty cents and six hands lying in the shade of the shocks all afternoon." [64]

More significant than such minor annoyances, farm machinery greatly increased the capital costs of farming. In 1849 a McCormick reaper cost

[62] Ralph Loomis and Glen T. Barton, *Productivity of Agriculture: United States, 1870–1958* (U.S. Department of Agriculture, *Technical Bulletin* No. 1238 [Washington, 1961]), p. 6; Frank T. Bachmura, "Geographical Differentials in Returns to Corn Belt Farmers: 1869–1950" (unpublished Ph.D. dissertation, University of Chicago, 1953), pp. 70–72. One should remember that Mr. Bachmura did not intend that his figures should be used in this way. See also Wayne D. Rasmussen, "The Impact of Technological Change on American Agriculture, 1862–1962," *Journal of Economic History*, XXII (December, 1962), pp. 578–91.

[63] Kellar, *op. cit.*, pp. 112–13.

[64] A. L. Porter, Oquawka, Illinois, to C. H. McCormick, May 17, 1855. Cyrus H. McCormick Papers, Wisconsin State Historical Society, Madison, Wisconsin.

slightly more than $120. In 1865 a self-raking combination machine for two horses cost $265. During the early seventies a variety of McCormick reapers and droppers ranged from $175 to $200 in price. For the twine self-binder of 1881, the farmer must pay $350.[65] And the reaper, harvester, or binder was only one of a considerable range of machines that his father had not used at all during the 1830's. Table 13 shows the cost of the implements and tools that one farm editor believed necessary on a farm of 150 acres in 1862, midway through our period. We should, of course, remember that farmers seldom outfitted themselves completely at any one time, that some bought second-hand machinery, and that others evaded machinery costs by sharing arrangements with neighbors or relatives.

The list in Table 13 also includes a number of items that few western farmers purchased. Few of them, for instance, used subsoil plows, although the manufacturers of subsoil attachments claimed sales of 1,000 in Iowa during 1867.[66] Many farmers regarded circular saws or platform scales as

TABLE 13
FARM EQUIPMENT, 1862 *

3 ploughs fitted for work (steel ploughs are best)	$ 34.00
1 subsoil plough; 1 double Michigan plough	24.00
1 one-horse plough; 2 cultivators	22.00
1 harrow, $12; 1 roller, $10	22.00
1 corn-planter; 1 seed-drill	15.00
1 wheat-drill, $65; 1 fanning-mill, $25	90.00
1 root-slicer; 1 straw-cutter	20.00
1 horse-rake; 2 hand-rakes	10.00
2 farm wagons; 1 one-horse cart	190.00
hayrack, harness, etc., for cart	38.00
1 sled and fixtures, $30; 1 combined mower and reaper, $125	155.00
2 scythes; 1 grain-cradle	7.00
1 shovel; 1 scoop-shovel; 2 spades	5.00
2 manure-forks; 4 hay-forks	6.00
1 horse-fork for hay, $10; 1 pointed shovel, $1	11.00
1 pick; 1 crowbar	3.00
2 ladders; 2 sheep-shears	5.00
large and small steelyards, $3; half bushel, $1	4.00
1 maul and wedges; 1 axe; 1 wood-saw	4.00
1 wheelbarrow; 1 grindstone	8.00
hand-hoes, baskets, stable lantern, currycomb, hammer, etc.	5.00
1 endless-chain horse-power threshing-machine and separator	160.00
1 circular saw	30.00
platform scales for weighing cattle, hay, etc.	100.00
	$968.00

* U.S. Commissioner of Agriculture, *Report, 1862* (Washington, 1863), pp. 422–23.
[65] These prices are taken from lists and correspondence in the Cyrus M. McCormick Papers.
[66] I.S.A.S.R., *1867*, p. 235.

luxuries, although useful. Although a threshing machine costing $160 was a very small model, it still required a greater investment than many farmers wished to make. A machine owned jointly with neighbors or custom operated was the answer. On the other hand, the corn-planter listed here was not the two-horse planter of the West that sold for a price of $50 to $60. Nor does the two-horse straddle-row cultivator appear, representing an expenditure of some $40 or more, and a field stalk-cutter would have added another $50 or more to the machinery investment given here.

TABLE 14
FARM IMPLEMENT PRICES, 1867 *

Walking plow	$18–24, 24–27, 22–28, 26, 24
subsoil attachment	$10
2 sole gang	$75–96, 80
Walking cultivator — straddle row	$30, 38
Two-horse riding cultivator (Hawkeye)	$60, 50
Hand planter	$6–25
Two-horse planter	$60–65, 65, 70
Corn plow	$60, 65, 70
Seeder attachment for corn plow	$10
Roller	$45–85
Cornstalk-cutter	$55
Broadcast seed-sower	$75
Combined seeder, cultivator, and rake	$125
Adjustable steel-tooth rake	$45, 50, 55
Revolver rake (walking)	$10
Mowers	$110–80, 130–50, 135–55, 150
Kirby Combined Reaper	$155 hand rake
	195 self-rake
Cayuga Chief Harvester	$120–185
Excelsior Reaper-Mower	$130–190
Johnson Self-Rake Reaper	$175–200
New Yorker Reaper	$180–200
Buckeye Reaper	$170–210
Woods Self-Rake Reaper	$200
Esterly Harvester	$125–225
Case Threshing Machine	$500–640
Fanning mill	$32
Hand sheller	$20

* Compiled from I.S.A.S.R., 1867, pp. 213–67.

Table 14 shows the cost of the major farm implements and machines that were on exhibit at the Iowa State Fair in 1867. When the farmer purchased such machinery on credit, as was often the case with harvesting machinery at least, his sense of security was hardly increased, even though good crops and fine harvesting weather might make his investment a profitable one in the end.

CHAPTER IX

Three Production Costs: Money, Labor, Taxes

The pioneer farmer of the 1830's in Illinois and Iowa was still settling in the timber or on the margins of the prairie adjacent to wooded lands. Close at hand were his fuel, his fencing materials, and the logs for a cabin or for the rough siding cut at a nearby sawmill. Although he might hire his rails split, or even buy them, the prairie pioneer of the 1830's could purchase them with his labor if need be. The range of farm machinery was still limited; a wagon, a couple of plows, a harrow, and the hand tools of axe, shovel, scythe, fork, and rake constituted the essential minimum. In addition the pioneer must have a pair of oxen with yoke and chains or a team of horses and their harness if he was to farm seriously. Three hundred dollars or less would purchase this minimum of equipment during the 1830's. For another $100 the settler could buy 80 acres of government land. A few cows or other stock might cost an additional $100 to $150.[1] The total investment was a modest one.

Forty years later the prairie pioneers were purchasing much of their fencing and usually constructed framed houses of sawed timbers and boards for their first dwelling. Their plows were more costly and they regarded a far wider range of additional equipment as indispensable. Mowers, hay rakes, reapers, corn planters, seeder or drill, and custom threshing had all become part of the farming patterns of the 1870's. Where the farmer of the 1830's often carried his water from stream or spring, the pioneer of the 1870's must ordinarily dig a well, on occasion hiring a professional well-digger to do the job. Although the pioneer of the 1870's in Iowa might be fortunate enough to obtain a farm from the 902,000 acres of land distributed under the

[1] Clarence H. Danhof, "Farm-Making Costs and the 'Safety Valve': 1850–1860," *Journal of Political Economy*, XLIX (June, 1941), 317–59 is the basic study on this subject. For the earlier years I have depended mainly on: John M. Peck, *A New Guide for Emigrants to the West* (Boston, 1836), pp. 183–84; Patrick Shirreff, *A Tour through North America; Together with a Comprehensive View of the Canadas and the United States* (Edinburgh, 1835), pp. 446–48; William Oliver, *Eight Months in Illinois* (Newcastle upon Tyne, 1843), pp. 243–47; *Prairie Farmer*, February, 1843, p. 44; George F. Green Ledger and Diary, 1839–48; John Goodell (ed.), *Diary of William Sewall, 1797–1846, Formerly of Augusta, Maine, Maryland, Virginia and Pioneer in Illinois* (Beardstown, 1930), *passim*.

homestead laws in northwestern Iowa, he was much more likely to to pay several dollars an acre to speculator, railroad, or other large holder.

The Iowa Railroad Land Company estimated the cost of team and "outfit" to a small holder on the Northwestern Railroad Company lands in central and western Iowa as follows:[2]

Team (oxen or horses)	$150	to	$300
Wagon and yoke or harness	100		150
Two plows	35		50
Cultivator and harrow	20		45
Combination reaper and mower	200		252
Other tools	10		50
	$515		$847

The land company had set its prices at $3.00–$12.00 per acre, and only limited amounts were available at the lowest figure. Added, of course, to the costs of team, outfit, and land, were those for house, fencing, and well, plus the cost of other stock.

Undoubtedly the minimum investment necessary for farm-making had increased considerably between the 1830's and the 1870's. Of course, the new farmer of the 1870's, like his predecessor of the 1830's, might evade or defer his capital needs. He might work part time for others; he might farm as a tenant; he might borrow equipment or combine with a work ring to share equipment costs. He could, finally, purchase his land or equipment on credit, perhaps borrowing money from a third party to meet such expenditures, alternatives that bring us to the subject of farm credit.

Until 1820 the purchaser of government land could spread his payments over four years. So abused were the credit provisions of the land code that Congress approved the Revision Act of 1820, allowing cash sales only and a minimum price of $1.25 per acre. The implications of this congressional decision were far reaching. Now the pioneer farmer must depend solely on private enterprise for aid in meeting the cost of land. Hereafter the most urgent need of the middle-western pioneer for credit would come in the weeks immediately prior to the federal land auctions. If he could qualify under the limited pre-emption laws of the 1830's or the general pre-emption act of 1841, the settler's claim was safe until the day of the land sale, provided, of course, that he had filed the required pre-emption declaration. But he must pay for his land before the day of the sale or see it go under the hammer.[3]

[2] Iowa Railroad Land Company, *Choice Iowa Farming Lands: 1,000,000 Acres for Sale at Low Prices, on Credit or for Cash by the Iowa Railroad Land Company, in Tracts to Suit Purchasers* (Cedar Rapids, 1870), p. 23.

[3] Benjamin H. Hibbard, *A History of the Public Land Policies* (New York, 1924) contains excellent summaries of the various land laws; Roy M. Robbins, *Our Landed Heritage* (Princeton, 1942) is more helpful in understanding the pressures to which

Many of the settlers of Illinois and Iowa who purchased federal land could not qualify under the terms of the limited pre-emption laws of the 1830's, including as they did the provision that settlers must have been on their claims before a given date. Such men had to find their purchase money and hope as well that none appeared at the auction with more funds and an overpowering desire to buy improved claims. Historians have stressed that the squatters' club or claim association was designed to prevent greedy speculators from outbidding "actual settlers." They have written much less about its usefulness to the squatter who needed funds. Many of the speculators were just as willing to lend money to the squatters for the purchase of the claims as they were eager to buy land on their own account. The pressure of the claim clubs may well have induced capitalists to lend on more equitable terms than they otherwise would have been willing to do.[4]

We cannot, unfortunately, discover the extent to which settlers in any area turned to the speculator for credit at the land sales. The working of the time-entry system has hidden many such loans. Under this system, the money-lender purchased the land in his own name, giving the settler a bond for a deed that obligated the capitalist to deed all or a portion of the squatter's claim back to him if he paid the purchase price and substantial interest within six months or a year. Typically, the county records do not contain these bonds. Yet the system was at work at many land sales between 1830 and 1860, as the business records of land-speculators show. By comparing claim-club records and county records, we can also detect the time-entry system in operation. Shortly after the federal land sale a large purchaser of government land in Johnson County, Iowa—Morgan Reno, for instance—deeded a number of small tracts to members of the local claim club who had themselves failed to purchase at the auction.[5] The county records, of course, fail to show the number of squatters who resorted to the capitalist and the time-entry system and who failed to pay out. They drifted elsewhere; their shattered dreams or miscalculations found no place in the recorder's indexes and

legislators reacted; Roscoe L. Lokken, *Iowa Public Land Disposal* (Iowa City, 1942) contains the occasional slip, but is indispensable for the Iowa story.

[4] Allan G. Bogue, "The Iowa Claim Clubs: Symbol and Substance," *Mississippi Valley Historical Review*, XLV (September, 1958), 231–53. Use of the time-entry system was apparently quite general in the Middle West of the 1830's, 1840's, and 1850's. Paul W. Gates described the activities of the Virginia capitalists Easley and Willingham in "Southern Investments in Northern Lands before the Civil War," *Journal of Southern History*, V (May, 1939), 161–62, and the "Nathaniel Gordon Papers" in the Manuscript Division, Baker Library, Harvard University, show a smaller operation of the same sort during the 1850's. There are scattered references to time entries in local histories and recollections. See: Alfred Hebard, "Recollections of Early Territorial Days," *Annals of Iowa, Third Series*, II (July–October, 1895), 217; J. W. Merrill, *Yellow Spring[s] and Huron. A Local History Containing Sketches of All the People, Institutions, and Events, from the Earliest Settlement to Date of Publication* (Mediapolis, Iowa, 1897), p. 42; Joe H. Smith, *History of Harrison County, Iowa* . . . (Des Moines, 1888), p. 100.

[5] Bogue, "The Iowa Claim Clubs," pp. 251–53.

registers. If some settlers turned in their need to capitalists or their agents in the land-office towns, there were many others who sought aid from parents or other relatives in the older states.

The period of cash sale and pre-emption included the lean years of the early 1820's and the hard times following 1837 and 1857. At such times the shortage of cash, so usual in the newly settled regions, was intensified by the general stringency throughout the country, and settlers paid rates of interest on entry loans that were high by any standard. Alfred Hebard wrote in his recollections of the government land sales at Burlington, "Parties were on hand with a plethora of specie — to loan, generally at a rate of about one hundred per cent. for a year — and many a man went home with a Title Bond of Doctor Barrett or some other party in his pocket in place of his certificate of purchase." [6] *The Hawkeye and Iowa Patriot* of Burlington was more conservative than Hebard in estimating interest rates at the sales under way during October of 1839, reporting that speculators had been lending money to the squatters at rates of 20–28 per cent.[7] A Fort Madison lawyer explained to an eastern relative in 1840 that he could put money out on good security at rates ranging from 25 to 50 per cent. Territorial law in Iowa at that time allowed no contracts to specify a rate of more than 20 per cent, but he suggested that all could be done legally if deeds of trust were used.[8]

By the 1850's both Illinois and Iowa had adopted usury laws that set the maximum rate of interest at 10 per cent. The figure was unrealistic until at least the 1870's, and one must view interest tables based on the county mortgage registers with some skepticism as a result. Above the legal maximum stood the agent's commission, which might well be split with the lender, although state courts viewed such procedure as a patent evasion of the usury laws. Sometimes, no doubt, usurious rates were concealed by inflating the principal that notes and mortgages specified.

His saddlebags bulging with specie, land warrants, or sound bank notes, the eastern capitalist or his agent might appear before the land sales of the 1830's and 1840's in the land-office towns of Illinois and Iowa, prepared to lend to the settlers. His business ended, he would depart in a few weeks time, leaving a local attorney, perhaps, to oversee the loans and accept payment. At the same time local attorneys, real estate agents, and bankers managed to procure some funds from clients, relatives, or acquaintances in the older

[6] Alfred Hebard, *op. cit.*, p. 217. Another local historian identified Richard Barrett, of St. Louis, Alexis and S. S. Phelps, of Oquawka, and Lewis Benedict, of New York, as lenders at Burlington: J. W. Merrill, *op. cit.*, p. 42.

[7] Burlington *Hawkeye and Iowa Patriot*, October 24, 1839.

[8] Henry Eno, Fort Madison, Iowa, to William Eno, Pine Plains, New York. October 17, 1840. ("Eno Papers," Special Collections Department, State University of Iowa Library, Iowa City, Iowa). See also Cyrus Sanders, Iowa City, to Richard B. Sanders, Beeson's Store, Highland County, Ohio, August 28, 1841, December 16, 1842, ("Sanders Papers," Iowa State Historical Society, Iowa City, Iowa).

regions for similar use. By the 1850's the flow of such funds from the older states to the new Midwest was becoming more obvious, more widely disseminated, and much better organized than formerly..

From the late 1850's onward, more and more eastern businessmen, professional folk, and prosperous farmers came to cherish the midwestern farm mortgage as an investment. For some the mortgage business was a natural outgrowth of western land speculation or investment in tax titles. There still stands by the river in Bath, New York, a small two-room building from which members of the Davenport family directed the investment of more than $5,000,000 in midwestern farm mortgages between the 1850's and 1902. Over $3,000,000 of this sum was invested in Illinois and Iowa paper. A nucleus of capital amassed in merchandising by Ira Davenport, Sr., grew handsomely when invested in raw western lands, tax titles, and ultimately, farm mortgages.[9] To others the western mortgage was simply a new but lucrative avenue of investment. Not only were individuals involved. Casting about for investments that combined safety with profit, and sobriety with heady interest, the insurance companies turned eagerly to the farm mortgage of the Middlewest. The laws of New York barred the insurance companies of that state from such investments until late in the century, but no such restrictions impeded the Connecticut Mutual, the Aetna, the Travelers, and other New England companies, or middle-western corporations like the Northwestern of Milwaukee.

As the farm-loan business grew, the local agents and would-be competitors strove vigorously to increase the flow of capital from the older states. Establishing his loan business at Loda, Illinois, during the 1860's, the banker and loan agent, Addison Goodell, visited the eastern states frequently, singing the praises of mortgages that were "gilt edged; copper fastened and hot rivetted," investments that were "solid as The Rocky Mountains." [10] Satisfied patrons of the loan agents told their friends of their formula for obtaining returns on their savings that were substantially above the current eastern interest rates. If Stephen A. Foley, of Lincoln, Illinois, and John Weare, of Cedar Rapids, tapped the substantial coffers of the Davenport family, or Addison Goodell prospered from the investment of funds won originally in the thriving collar-and-cuff business of Troy, New York, there were many who built their lending businesses on the investments of professional folk, petty businessmen, and eastern farmers who counted their savings by the hundreds of dollars rather than by the thousands. By the 1880's the desire of eastern investors for western farm mortgages amounted to a mild mania; in the exhilarating environment of the great plains, the dreams and greed of investor, agent, and borrower fused in the great mort-

[9] Allan G. Bogue, *Money at Interest: The Farm Mortgage on the Middle Border* (Ithaca, 1955), pp. 7–43.

[10] Margaret B. Bogue, *Patterns from the Sod: Land Use and Tenure in the Grand Prairie, 1850–1900* (Springfield, 1959), pp. 185–222.

gage debacle of the late 1880's and 1890's.[11] This disaster had no parallel in Illinois or Iowa.

To the farmer, slightly bewildered by the speed with which his world was changing, the procedures of the loan agent may well have seemed an invasion of privacy. Well aware that investors would hold him responsible for foreclosures, the agent pried into the farmer's affairs. Why did he want the loan? At what stage of improvement was his farm? Was it bottomland or upland prairie? What type was the soil? (No sand-hill farmers need apply.) Was the farmer married, or was he a widower? (Single men and widowers were, of course, poorer risks than family men.) Was the title clear — no prior mortgages, tax liens, or anything of the sort? Had he, by any chance, brought along an abstract of the property? The agent would just like to glance at it. So far, so good — the moneylender would drive out and examine the security soon. This he did, and the farmer spent an hour talking about his plans to the agent while the farm team stamped their feet and tossed their heads on the headland, and the sleeker horse of the townsman fidgeted in the buggy shafts. Later, the farmer might discover that the loan agent had inquired of a neighbor whether the loan-seeker quarreled with his wife or — in a temperance-minded age — drank. After such preliminaries, the agent, if satisfied, drafted the note and mortgage and informed the farmer that he had the money on hand or expected it as soon as the lender had received the mortgage papers.[12]

The agent's eagerness to earn a commission on the loan might, of course, temper the quality of his investigation. Involved also in the negotiations was the bargaining power of the farmer. By 1870 at least, most county towns had several agents competing for the mortgage business. The farmer with good security and a fine personal reputation in the community might play them off against each other and win concessions on the interest rate, the amount of commission charged by the agent, or in the form and type of paper. He might successfully demand that a plain note and mortgage form be used rather than the sale mortgage or the trust deed, which allowed foreclosure without recourse to court action in Illinois during much of this period. Or he might refuse to waive the appraisal procedure, which provided a minimum valuation on property involved in foreclosure proceedings. Undoubtedly, there were efforts, at times, by local agents to set standard rates and terms and thwart the efforts of borrowers to encourage competition among them. Yet if the lenders of one town combined, they might find themselves undercut by the energetic agents of some nearby prairie center, as well as by petty lenders.

[11] Bogue, *Money at Interest*, pp. 77–276.

[12] This description is based particularly on the letters written by John Weare of Cedar Rapids, Iowa, and Stephen A. Foley of Lincoln, Illinois, to John and Ira Davenport, of Bath, New York, between 1869 and 1885 in the "Davenport Collection," Collection of Regional History, Cornell University, Ithaca, New York.

The mortgage study included in the 1890 census showed that in eight Illinois and Iowa counties, the percentages of mortgagees owning one to five mortgages varied in round figures from 38 to 70 per cent in Iowa and from 33 to 56 per cent in Illinois.[13] Local lenders undoubtedly were heavily represented in this group. In the area studies of farm-mortgaging in Illinois and Iowa, we find that more than half of the funds loaned on farm security came from within the state concerned in most years of the nineteenth century. The West generated much of the capital needed by its farmers. As many of the first generation of farmers left the land to retire to the county towns, they accepted mortgages for a portion of the sale price of their land. Local land-speculators, too, were willing to wait for their money, provided that the purchaser paid his interest. We can misunderstand the significance of these facts. Local loans often reflected land sales in which the seller was willing to wait for his money. Loans from eastern sources more frequently represented fluid capital channeled into the Middle West and had, therefore, a sharper immediate impact upon the western economy than did the local lending.

Some western lending did involve the transfer of actual funds from lender to borrowers. Under the laws of both Illinois and Iowa, county officers loaned the school funds, derived from sale of the school-land sections, to local borrowers.[14] At least one Iowa county used the proceeds from the sale of swamp lands in the same way. Substantial numbers of Illinois and Iowa farmers borrowed from the county funds in the 1850's and 1860's. When Croft Pilgrim, of Stark County, Illinois, wished to enlarge his farm in 1870, he arranged a loan from a widow who was living in Peoria.[15] When Pilgrim's mother-in-law died several years later, her estate included several small mortgages. The professional and business people of the local villages and towns frequently lent their savings on land mortgages. Active and retired farmers who had been more than usually successful did the same.

Western banks seldom loaned on the security of agricultural land. The National Banking Act of 1863 with its amendments forbade national banks to hold real estate mortgages for any length of time, and the proprietors and officers of private and state-chartered banks were much more likely to serve as agents for non-resident capitalists than to lend bank funds on farm security. Such individuals or institutions, however, might have numbers of second mortgages on record, representing the commissions on first mortgage loans.

Few economic historians have studied farm-mortgage debt at the county

[13] U. S. Census Office, *Report on Real Estate Mortgages in the United States at the Eleventh Census: 1890* (Washington, 1895), p. 294.
[14] Hamilton County, Iowa, loaned its swamp-land funds in the years between 1868 and 1875 (see the Hamilton County, Mortgage Registers in the office of the recorder, and the Board of Supervisors' Minute Books in the office of the auditor, Hamilton County Court House, Webster City, Iowa).
[15] Croft Pilgrim Diary, December 30, 1870. Iowa Department of History and Archives, Des Moines, Iowa.

and township level in Illinois and Iowa. Tentatively, we can say that the early farmers of the prairie triangle used the mortgage freely. The agricultural censuses of 1860, 1870, and 1880 give the names of 145 different farmers who were owner-operators in Hamilton Township of Hamilton County, Iowa.[16] Of the group, thirty-nine failed to appear as a mortgagor on at least one indenture during the period 1853-96.[17] Twenty-three appeared in six or more mortgage transactions. In those communities settled from the 1840's onward, landowners usually encumbered from one-third to one-half of the agricultural land during the first generation of occupancy. Mortgaging proceeded most rapidly during the settling-in period and during years of prosperity. As the settlement period came to an end, the proportion of land under mortgage stabilized and in some cases dropped off. In communities where tenancy was most common, the percentage of land under mortgage was lower than in comparable communities elsewhere.[18] Most loans were repayable at the end of five years or by instalments over a short term of years. The long term amortized loan was not common in this period. Nor should this be surprising. The tendency of interest rates in any particular community was ordinarily downward — not a condition which encouraged long-term financing.

TABLE 15

OWNER-OPERATORS AND MORTGAGES IN
HAMILTON TOWNSHIP, 1853–96

CENSUS GROUP	FARMERS	NUMBER OF MORTGAGES							MOST ACTIVE BORROWER
		0	1	2	3	4	5	6+	
1860	22	7	3	4	2	2	1	3	11
1870	57	16	9	8	8	3	2	11	10
1880	66	16	11	9	11	6	4	9	13
Total	145	39	23	21	21	11	7	23	

Many factors affected the interest rate on farm loans in this period. The age of the community, estimates of soil fertility, transportation facilities, and the persistence and skill with which local businessmen sought outside capital

[16] The manuscript rolls of the Federal Agricultural Census, 1860, 1870, 1880 are available at both the Iowa State Historical Society, Iowa City, and the Iowa Department of History and Archives, Des Moines, Iowa.

[17] Hamilton County, Mortgage Registers, 1853–1896.

[18] These generalizations are based on: William G. Murray, *An Economic Analysis of Farm Mortgages in Story County, Iowa, 1854–1931* (Iowa State College of Agriculture and Mechanic Arts, Agricultural Experiment Station, *Research Bulletin* No. 156, [Ames, 1933]); David Rozman, "Land Credit in Walnut Grove Township, Knox County, Illinois," *Journal of Land and Public Utility Economics*, IV (August, 1928), 305–12; Margaret B. Bogue, *op. cit.*, pp. 185–222; A. G. Bogue, *Money at Interest, passim*, and studies of farm mortgaging in Warren Township, Bremer County, Union Township, Davis County, and Hamilton Township, Hamilton County, Iowa, for the years 1852–96. Additional studies of mortgaging at the local level would be most helpful.

were all involved. Of importance, also, was the competition of other western communities for capital, the prevalent rates of return from other investments in older communities, and the stage of development of the financial channels along which eastern capital flowed westward. Business conditions, generally, had their influence; in depression years the flow of capital westward greatly diminished.

Table 16 shows the interest rates recorded in the mortgages on agricultural land in three widely scattered Iowa townships between the early 1850's and 1896. In general, the rates stayed close to the usury maximum during the 1850's, fell somewhat in the late 1860's, and then rose again during the very late 1860's and the early 1870's. A pronounced break occurred during the late 1870's; thereafter, interest rates fell fairly steadily until 1896. The lower rates of the 1860's were in part attributable to the 8 per cent rate allowed on school-fund mortgages for a portion of this period, but private lenders, too, were filing some 8 and 9 per cent paper. David Rozman discovered a similar dip in rates during the 1860's in Knox County, Illinois, as did William Murray in his analysis of mortgaging in Story County, Iowa.[19]

By modern standards the interest rates of the 1850's appear high, and they would continue to be so until the mid-1890's. The county records do not reveal the actual market rate when it stood above the 10 per cent maximum that both Illinois and Iowa had set by the mid-1850's. Lenders simply inflated the principals specified in the notes to compensate for the 10 per cent rate, or, more usually, their agents extracted a more generous commission than usual and passed along a portion of it to the lender. Of six mortgage notes filed from Union Township in Davis County during 1853, the year of the 10 per cent usury law, two called for rates of 20 per cent and one for a rate of 12 per cent.[20] Thereafter, lenders filed notes and mortgages that called for no more than 10 per cent. When John Weare, of Cedar Rapids, loaned the funds of John and Ira Davenport on Iowa farms during 1869 and 1870 at 10 per cent, however, he also deducted a 10 per cent commission and set half of it aside for the New Yorkers.[21] When, as in some cases, these loans were only for a year, the borrowers were paying 20 per cent for their money.

Table 16 shows that there were definite differences between lending rates in the three Iowa Counties represented there. Comparison with rates in some Illinois communities would have shown still greater differences. In general, Illinois rates fell sooner than did those in Iowa. The arithmetic-mean rate for the decade of the 1880's in a township of Knox County, Illinois, for in-

[19] Rozman, *op. cit.*, p. 308; Murray, *op. cit.*, pp. 396–97. Professor Murray, however, believed that school-fund loans alone were responsible for the lower rates of the 1860's in Story County, Iowa.

[20] The law is found in Iowa, *Acts, Resolutions and Memorials passed at the Regular Session of the Fourth General Assembly of the State of Iowa,*" (Iowa City, 1853), chap. xxxvii, Sec. 2.

[21] Bogue, *Money at Interest*, pp. 28, 37–40.

TABLE 16

MEAN MORTGAGE RATE IN
THREE IOWA TOWNSHIPS
1852–96 *

	WARREN TWP		UNION TWP		HAMILTON TWP	
	Loans	Rate	Loans	Rate	Loans	Rate
1852	..	...	4	8.7	..	...
1853	1	10.0	6	13.5	1	10.0
1854	4	10.0	5	8.7	6	10.0
1855	2	10.0	8	8.0	..	...
1856	9	9.5	4	9.0	2	10.0
1857	8	9.3	15	9.5	11	10.0
1858	10	9.5	8	10.0	11	10.0
1859	12	10.0	7	10.0	11	10.0
1860	6	10.0	8	10.0	8	10.0
1861	9	10.0	4	10.0	6	9.3
1862	5	10.0	2	10.0	5	10.0
1863	14	9.2	4	10.0	2	10.0
1864	21	9.3	5	9.2	8	10.0
1865	20	9.3	6	10.0	9	8.8
1866	22	9.6	1	8.0	12	8.8
1867	39	9.5	7	8.9	8	7.3
1868	40	9.7	7	10.0	19	9.4
1869	32	9.9	4	9.3	16	8.7
1870	21	10.0	2	10.0	23	9.8
1871	37	9.9	3	10.0	13	9.3
1872	25	10.0	8	9.8	28	9.9
1873	26	9.9	12	9.8	23	9.9
1874	25	10.0	12	9.5	28	9.7
1875	34	10.0	13	10.0	53	9.9
1876	28	9.9	19	9.8	44	9.8
1877	30	9.8	29	9.9	22	9.9
1878	30	9.9	18	9.7	29	9.7
1879	20	9.6	29	9.8	25	9.0
1880	23	8.8	17	9.1	45	8.5
1881	17	8.3	23	8.8	42	8.5
1882	23	7.3	30	8.7	55	8.1
1883	15	6.8	25	8.9	48	7.7
1884	18	7.6	18	9.3	31	7.7
1885	20	7.7	18	9.3	34	7.8
1886	27	7.2	32	8.1	31	7.6
1887	17	7.0	34	8.9	45	7.5
1888	16	7.1	42	7.6	31	7.4
1889	18	7.1	19	9.2	17	7.3
1890	21	6.4	26	7.8	24	7.3
1891	14	6.7	19	6.9	42	7.2
1892	18	6.4	37	7.4	33	7.2
1893	16	6.1	22	7.8	43	7.1
1894	19	6.5	29	7.3	58	7.2
1895	18	7.0	41	7.2	57	7.1
1896	9	6.4	37	7.0	32	6.9

* The three townships lay in Bremer County, Davis County, and Hamilton County. The Davis County rate must be discounted somewhat; after 1880 a couple of mortgage-brokers there concealed their lending rate, evidently for competitive reasons.

stance, was 7.1 per cent. In only one of the townships in Iowa had the rate fallen to this level by the end of the 1880's.

The farm has usually provided its operator with a home as well as a place of business. The foreclosure of a farm mortgage, therefore, has always held emotional implications for farm folk that are lacking in urban bankruptcies or business failures. If, on the one hand, a farm foreclosure was more than a business failure, farm foreclosure statistics on the other hand do not completely reveal the number of business failures by farmers. A few failing debtors always preferred to deed their property to the mortgagees on the best possible terms rather than to wait for formal proceedings. The foreclosure rate, as a result, does not include all of the operators who failed to clear their land of debt. Even so, it is probably the best single index of agricultural distress in the nineteenth century that we can find. Of 2,649 mortgages negotiated in three Iowa townships between 1852 and 1896, 3.2 per cent ended in foreclosure proceedings. Table 17 shows the percentage of unsuccessful loans negotiated by five-year periods in these townships. Clearly the mortgagors of the years between 1865 and 1879 had the most difficulty in repaying their loans. Typically, foreclosure followed some years after the date of the original loans; in our three townships the courts were most active in foreclosure cases between 1870 and 1884. William Murray's findings in Story County, Iowa, in general support the township studies. Although there are no comparable studies of foreclosures in Illinois areas, the records of the Davenport family and Addison Goodell show that mortgage debtors found the 1870's particularly trying in that state also.

The suggestion that the very act of mortgaging was an indication of agricultural distress is, of course, quite erroneous. When George K. Holmes and John S. Lord prepared a special report on real estate mortgages for the census of 1890, they included a colorful catalogue of reasons for mortgaging, which ranged from alimony payments to the defense of wayward sons in-

TABLE 17

FORECLOSURE PROCEEDINGS IN
THREE IOWA TOWNSHIPS

Years	Loans Negotiated	Foreclosures	Percentage
1852–1854	27	1	3.7
1855–1859	118	3	2.5
1860–1864	107	3	2.8
1865–1869	242	10	4.1
1870–1874	286	15	5.2
1875–1879	423	22	5.2
1880–1884	430	12	2.8
1885–1889	401	7	1.7
1890–1896	615	11	1.8
1852–1896	2,649	84	3.2

dicted for murder.[22] The statistical record was more prosaic. More than 83 per cent of the mortgages in force in four Illinois counties represented expenditures for the purchase of real estate or its improvement. In four Iowa counties the percentage of mortgages filed for the same reasons ranged from 68 to 89 per cent. The categories of mortgages that could have included distress mortgages ranged in total from 3 to 14 per cent in the eight counties.[23] More research on the reasons underlying mortgaging in earlier years is needed, but most mortgages reflected real estate purchases or other productive enterprises. Indeed, it was characteristic of the credit system of the period that money was extremely difficult to obtain in periods of depression when borrowers might have sought credit to meet living expenses or personal debts.

County records give little indication of the amount of credit that farmers obtained on land contract; usually neither buyer nor seller felt compelled to record land contracts at the county seat. Although many large holders of unimproved lands sold on contract because these agreements could be canceled without court proceedings, the land-grant railroads and their land-company subsidiaries undoubtedly did the greatest amount of contract business.

The executive officers of the Illinois Central Railroad Company correctly realized in the 1850's that they must offer credit if they were to sell the lands of the road to farmers rapidly. Because the company had designated some of the lands in the grant for use in meeting specific obligations, credit terms varied somewhat on Illinois Central lands. On the so-called construction lands, the purchaser of the mid-1850's need pay down only two years of

---

[22] U.S. Census Office, *Report on Real Estate Mortgages in the United States at the Eleventh Census*, p. 280.

> People mortgage their real estate to get married, to obtain divorces, and to pay alimony; to pay their taxes, their rent, and to pay interest to the money lender. They raise money by mortgage in order that they may travel, and that they may spend it in extravagant living; they speculate with it and they relend it. Politicians pay the expenses of their political campaigns by means of mortgages. The guileless are deceived into buying worthless patents, wives pay the debts of their husbands and educate them for the ministry. Men mortgage their real estate to pay their physicians, their undertakers and their lawyers, to help their friends and relatives, to make good their defalcations, to educate their children and to support their parents.

> The weather and the elements are related to mortgages; rain and hail, the lightning that descends from the clouds, drought and heat, all affect the wealth of men so as to make them mortgage. Mortgages follow plagues of grasshoppers and epidemics of hog cholera. They erect tombstones to the memory of the dead, buy pianos and organs, provide daughters with dowry, and make wedding presents. By means of them young lawyers and physicians are able to keep from starvation, fathers to defend their sons for murder, housewives to get sewing machines, workingmen to travel in search of work, and men to pay their gambling debts. Fathers raise money on mortgages to throw away on prodigal sons, owners of race horses to pay entrance fees for races, husbands to buy gowns for their wives and to celebrate wedding anniversaries.

[23] *Ibid.*, pp. 282–83.

interest at 2 per cent on the cost price, commencing annual payments of one-fifth of the principal, plus advance interest on the remainder at the beginning of the third year. For the unencumbered or free lands of the grant, the buyer must pay down 25 per cent of the cost in cash and retire the balance in one, two, and three years with interest at 6 per cent. The Illinois Central executives modified these credit terms later, but they established precedents in land disposal that all of the middle-western land-grants roads or their sales agencies followed.[24]

In 1871 the Rock Island line was offering land-buyers a choice between short-term contracts calling for four equal instalments of principal with interest at 6 per cent or long-term contracts specifying two advance payments of interest at 6 per cent, followed by six annual instalments of principal and interest at 10 per cent starting on the second anniversary of the sale. The cash purchaser received a discount of 10 per cent from the list price of the land. Other Iowa roads offered similar terms.[25]

The courthouse vaults of the Corn Belt bulge with deed and mortgage indexes and registers containing information that will answer many questions about land tenure and credit. This is not true of chattel credit, however. State legislators saw little need to preserve a permanent record of chattel mortgages, concerned as these indentures were with security that was short lived and, on occasion, highly mobile. County recorders, therefore, have never been required to preserve a copy of chattel mortgages for more than a few years. I have found but one complete set of chattel books, covering an extended period of time in the nineteenth century, although more may, of course, exist. These records are in Lucas County, Iowa.[26] Preliminary research in them shows that chattel mortgages most frequently served to protect the vendor of plows, wagons, and other farm machinery, as well as the seller of draft animals. Frequently, too, farm tenants bound themselves to pay rent to their landlords by mortgaging their growing crops. Interest rates on chattel mortgages were similar in trend to those on landed security. Typically, the chattel mortgage was the resort of the less well-to-do farmer. Local vendors seldom bothered to demand a mortgage from the farmer with abundant assets.

[24] Paul W. Gates, *The Illinois Central Railroad and Its Colonization Work* ("Harvard Economic Studies," XLII, Cambridge, 1934), chaps. viii and xii; Richard C. Overton tells a part of the Iowa story in *Burlington West: A Colonization History of the Burlington Railroad* (Cambridge, 1941). I have some reservations about Professor Overton's comment, "In so far as possible, the B. & M. was determined to exclude speculators," (p. 314), a policy sometimes ascribed to other land-grant roads as well. I suspect that the railroad executives were determined to exclude only those speculators whose desire for land outran their capital resources.

[25] Iowa Railroad Land Company, *op. cit.*; Chicago, Rock Island and Pacific Railroad Company, *Description of Six Hundred Thousand Acres of Choice Iowa Farming Lands, for Sale by the Chicago, Rock Island and Pacific Railroad Company* (Davenport, 1871).

[26] Lucas County, Chattel Mortgage Registers, 1856–1900, in the office of the recorder, Lucas County Court House, Chariton, Iowa.

II

Most agricultural historians have ignored the farm laborers on middle-western farms during the nineteenth century, other than to suggest, perhaps, that the Civil War depleted the labor force and encouraged the use of agricultural machinery. Paul W. Gates and Lawanda F. Cox are exceptions. They have both emphasized that agricultural laborers were certainly present in considerable numbers during the last half of the nineteenth century. Both, too, have suggested that the lot of the agricultural worker became less satisfactory during the latter part of this period. Dealing with the prairie states alone, Gates linked the declining status and prospects of farm laborers to the system of federal land disposal. Concerned with farm labor in the country as a whole, Mrs. Cox stressed the disparity in returns to industrial and agricultural workers and detected a growing class consciousness among agricultural laborers.[27]

One need not look far for the reasons why historians have said so little about agricultural labor. No systematic compilations of farm-wage data cover the years prior to the mid-1860's. The federal census-takers of 1870 did ask farmers to estimate the sums paid out for labor during the previous year, but, unfortunately, the cost of board was included within the estimated figure. The 1870 manuscript census, however, does reveal the number of farmers who hired labor and gives some indication of the relative amount. But not until 1880 did the census-takers ask for the number of weeks during which farmers had hired labor. Agricultural periodicals and the reports of the agricultural societies say little about hired men and their cost.

How much did farmers pay their workers? Writing of Illinois, just prior to the crash of 1819, Fordham estimated that the lowest price for labor with board was $13.00 per month.[28] Patrick Shirreff found in the mid-1830's that a good "farming help" could command a wage of $10.00 a month.[29] But wage data are scattered, difficult to find, and hard to interpret (see Table 18). Apparently, the increasing productivity of agricultural labor after 1850 was not reflected in agricultural wages to any degree. Real wages were possibly lower in the 1880's and 1890's than during the late 1850's.

For day labor, of course, the farmer must pay a somewhat higher wage than by the month. When wages with board ranged from $8 to $10 in the 1840's, the farmer paid the day laborer from 37 to 50 cents per day.[30] During the late 1860's day laborers in harvest sometimes asked and obtained

[27] Paul W. Gates, "Frontier Estate Builders and Farm Laborers," in Walker D. Wyman and Clifton B. Kroeber, *The Frontier in Perspective* (Madison, 1957), pp. 143–64; Lawanda F. Cox, "The American Agricultural Wage Earner, 1865–1900: The Emergence of a Modern Labor Problem," *Agricultural History*, XXII (April, 1949), pp. 94–114.

[28] Elias P. Fordham, *Personal Narrative of Travels in Virginia, Maryland, Pennsylvania, Ohio, Kentucky; and of a Residence in the Illinois Territory: 1817–1818* Frederick A. Ogg (ed.) (Cleveland, 1906), p. 210.

[29] Patrick Shirreff, *op. cit.*, pp. 250, 449–450.

[30] George F. Green Diary; John Goodell (ed.), *Diary of William Sewall*.

TABLE 18

FARM WAGES PER MONTH IN ILLINOIS
1840–92 *

| | WITH BOARD | | WITHOUT BOARD | |
	Current Dollars	Constant Dollars	Current Dollars	Constant Dollars
A †				
1840	8.00	13.33	11.76	19.60
1845	9.00	16.66	13.33	24.50
B ‡				
1841	13.00	21.66	19.20	32.00
1842	9.50	17.27	13.96	25.38
1844	9.00	17.30	13.23	25.44
1845	9.00	16.66	13.23	24.50
C §				
1859	16.00	25.39	23.52	37.33
1860	17.00	27.86	24.99	40.96
1861	15.00	23.80	22.05	35.00
1862	18.00	26.08	26.46	38.34
1863	20.00	25.64	29.40	37.69
1864	22.00	23.15	32.34	34.04
1865	25.00	24.50	36.75	36.02
D ‖				
1859	....	....	16.50	26.19
1860	....	....	15.00	24.59
1861	....	....	19.00	30.15
1862	....	....	21.00	30.43
E #				
1866	18.72	18.17	28.54	27.70
1869	17.69	18.63	27.32	28.75
1875	16.87	19.61	25.20	29.30
1879	13.01	16.47	20.61	26.08
1882	17.14	19.93	23.91	27.80
1885	16.60	22.13	23.50	31.33
1888	16.00	20.51	23.20	29.74
1890	16.35	20.96	23.25	29.80
1892	16.50	21.42	24.25	31.43

* Numerous objections may be made to this table and the conclusions derived from it. Its internal contradictions reveal, as can nothing else, the problems of work in this field. Constant dollars were obtained by dividing the current-dollars column by the Federal Reserve Bank of New York cost-of-living index as given in *Historical Statistics of the United States Colonial Times to 1957* (Washington, 1960), p. 127. Some, no doubt, will consider this index more relevant to the position of industrial laborers than to that of Illinois farm laborers. It may seem unrealistic to weight the wages-with-board column by use of a cost-of-living index that assumes purchases of food on the part of the laborer. Current-dollar cash wages in A, B, and C were derived from wages with board by assuming that the average relationship of the two columns was the same as in the years 1866–92. In all cases wages are "per month for year or season."
† U.S. Department of Agriculture, *Wages of Farm Labor in the United States* (Division of Statistics, Misc. Series 4, [Washington, 1892]), p. 65; U.S. Commissioner of Patents, *Report, 1845* (Washington, 1846), p. 1152.
‡ Cass County, Illinois. John Goodell (ed.), *Diary of William Sewall, 1797–1846, formerly of Augusta Maine, Maryland, Virginia and Pioneer in Illinois* (Beardstown, 1930).
§ Champaign County, Illinois. *Wages of Farm Labor in the United States*, p. 66.
‖ Champaign County, Illinois. Ledger and Day Book of Benjamin F. Harris, First National Bank, Champaign, Illinois.
Wages of Farm Labor in the United States, pp. 16–17; (also given in United States Industrial Commission, *Report, XI* [Washington, 1901], 140–41).

as much as $3 per day for their services.[31] Undoubtedly, a disparity between farm and industrial wages did exist in the post Civil War years, working to transfer labor out of an occupation where would-be farmers were increasing in numbers faster than the number of farm units.

No less interesting to us than the wage level, of course, is the length of time which midwestern farmers actually employed laborers. Concerning this we have little definite information. We know, of course, that there were some large farms, a section or more in size, in almost every county of Illinois and Iowa from 1850 onward and others that utilized between a half and a full section. The operators of such units seldom had families large enough to provide the labor needed. The occasional gentleman farmer, like John Wentworth, must needs depend to a considerable extent on hired help also. The cattle kings of central Illinois and other large holders experimented, on occasion, as we have seen, with bonanza farms. Such men discovered that it was difficult to hire able and trustworthy laborers who were content to remain in that role for any length of time. Many of these large operators decided that they would do better to rent their lands to tenants than to try to farm them with hired labor.[32] This was not always the decision. Indeed, one Iowa landlord decided about 1880 that he would abandon tenancy on his several farms and, instead, hire laborers at a fixed wage to work under his personal direction.[33] On the large farm units there were undoubtedly year round jobs available for those who wished to work as farm laborers.

Those who farmed the average-sized farm of Illinois and Iowa seldom needed a hired man on a year round basis. Particularly in the early years of pioneering, the midwestern farmer could not afford, nor actually did he need, a full time hired man. And this might remain the case for a considerable number of years, particularly if he emphasized grain production. Unless he developed a dairy operation or had the capital to become a cattle-feeder on a considerable scale, the midwestern farmer needed much less help during the winter months than he did during the period between mid-June and mid-August when the last rounds of corn-plowing, the harvest of the small grains and the haying season all pressed upon him. Even the farmer with but 40 acres might find himself pressed to harvest his grain in season or cure his hay properly unless he hired a few days of labor. During 1869, in Poweshiek County, Iowa, 932 of 1,634 farm owners hired farm labor ranging in value from $5 to $2,000, including the cost of board. The average amount was "over $150," representing, no doubt, four to six months of labor.[34]

[31] Webster City Hamilton Freeman, July 28, 1869.

[32] Paul W. Gates, Frontier Landlords and Pioneer Tenants (Ithaca, 1945).

[33] Hamilton Freeman, September 21, 1881. "J. M. Funk is going to try a new plan of farming the coming season. He will hire men by the month to do the work, instead of renting the land."

[34] Gates, "Frontier Estate Builders and Farm Laborers," p. 146. Professor Gates sometimes lumps tenants and laborers together in this work pp. 150–51. It is true that tenants on some large frontier estates were little better than laborers, but, in

Farmers obtained their help from a variety of sources. Most importantly, they looked to the members of their family. By the age of ten, at least, the farm boy was of considerable help to his father; and by the time that he was fifteen, he was usually performing a man's tasks during most of the year. The family was not a perfect reservoir of labor by any means. Some farmers had no sons at all. For those who had sons, there were ordinarily a number of years of early married life, at least ten, before the growing lads were of much aid. Then came a period of from ten to twenty years, depending on the size of the family, in which the farmer had an abundant supply of labor in his own household. As the family matured, he once more found himself alone or perhaps assisted by one son who had elected to stay on the home farm in the expectation of inheriting it. In the middle period of the family cycle, when a farmer's sons were in their teens or early manhood, he might be tempted to enlarge his holdings in order to use the available labor fully or to prepare for the time when the sons would want farms of their own. During the first and third phases of the cycle he often had to hire considerable labor.

Family labor was typically cheap labor. The percentage of farmers who paid their sons set wages during the nineteenth century, particularly before they reached the age of twenty-one, was probably very small. Indeed, in some cases, middle-western farmers collected the wages that minor sons earned elsewhere when they were not needed at home.[35] In turn, however, the sons often expected their father to aid them in acquiring their own farms after they had married.

In times of work peaks, farmers turned also to their neighbors. Throughout this whole period, middle-western farmers typically traded work in harvesting and threshing — and sometimes haying — tasks where groups of five to ten workers allowed the most efficient division of labor. The more punctilious farmers measured their labor contributions against those of their neighbors with great precision and "settled up" in cash during the fall or winter for any surplus or deficit that they had accumulated.[36] Sometimes, farmer's sons or small farmers hired out by the day during part of the busy periods.

Farmers could turn also to the artisans, mechanics, and tradesmen of the neighborhood or nearby hamlets or towns in the periods of their greatest need, as well as to the families of such individuals. In 1869 the editors of a central Iowa paper exhorted the residents of the county seat. "As the grain in this section of country seems to be ripening all at once, many of our

general, the middle-western tenant enjoyed a degree of management control that made him closer in outlook and attitude to owner-operators than to farm laborers. It seems clear that many did climb the agricultural ladder in the Middle West of the nineteenth century. It is also clear that the farm operated by one owner-operator, Professor Gates' ideal, was an inefficient operation in a mechanical age, where many operations could be most effectively performed by two men.

[35] Croft Pilgrim Diary, July 10, 1871.

[36] There are numerous references to such settlements in *ibid.*

farmers are apprehensive that it will be hard work to get hands enough to harvest it as fast as necessary. Every man in town who can spend the time, and has the 'bottom' to stand the pressure, ought to turn out and help the farmers save their crops." [37] In the postwar years and particularly during the 1870's, itinerant harvest workers became common; "bummers, with a few rags tied up in bandana handkerchiefs and tar on their fingers, which are liable to stick to things without a moment's notice," an unkindly editor described them.[38]

Table 19 shows the male work force, fifteen years of age and over, found by census-enumerators in 550 farm households in Iowa and Illinois during 1850 and 1880. From so small a group we cannot, of course, draw any hard conclusions. But some trends appeared consistently in both the Jones County sample and in the three groups of one hundred householders that I have combined in the left half of the table. In both cases the total working force increased. Owner-operators were a smaller percentage of the working force

TABLE 19

MALE WORK FORCE SAMPLES
FOUR CORN BELT COUNTIES

| | 300 FARM HOUSEHOLDS IOWA AND ILLINOIS | | | | 250 FARM HOUSEHOLDS Jones County, Iowa | | | |
	No.	1850 Per Cent	No.	1880 Per Cent	No.	1850 Per Cent	No.	1880 Per Cent
Owner-operators	242	45.1	216	35.6	198	51.8	193	43.3
Tenant householders .	14	2.6	42	6.9	...	...	34	7.6
					45	11.8		
Laborer householders	36	6.7	33	5.5	...	...	17	3.8
Additional males .... (family)	187	34.9	200	33.0	98	25.7	134	30.1
Additional males .... (non-family)	57	10.7	115	19.0	41	10.7	68	15.2
	536	100.0	606	100.0	382	100.0	446	100.0

* This table is based on data from the manuscript agricultural and population censuses of 1850 and 1880. The 300 households included 100 in Clarion Township, Bureau County, Illinois, 100 in Center Township, Cedar County, Iowa; and 100 in Dutch Creek Township, Washington County, Iowa, taken in order from the census-enumerator's rolls. In Washington County in 1850 it was actually necessary to follow the enumerator through several townships to obtain 100 families. I made no effort to obtain the same households in 1880; because of turnover, this would have been a hopeless task. These selections of "neighbors", of course, were not random samples. To check the work, a 10 per cent random sample was taken from Jones County, Iowa, in 1880, and the same number of households, 250, was taken at random from the 1850 Jones County census, amounting in that year to almost half the far.n households. I used a standard set of random-number tables in this process. I did not exclude households that were headed by women, but I did not include the ladies in my final table. Among the 250 farm households of Jones County, there were seven women householders in 1850 and six in 1880; among the 300 households there were eight in 1850 and nine in 1880. Census-enumerators did not list tenants in 1850, but by comparing the property returns in the population census with the farm returns of the same year, it was possible to designate men who listed no real property but reported a farm business, as tenants. Since farm returns were in part based on the previous year's production, some new tenants may have been missed. Evidently, a number of the Jones County enumerators' return sheets were not included in the final agricultural census compilation of 1850, I did not, therefore, attempt to separate tenants and householders who were simply farm laborers in that year. The number of householders designated as laborers may be too large. I placed men in this category if they designated themselves as farmers or farm laborers and reported neither real property nor farm production. Some farmers who had just arrived in the community but had not purchased a farm may, therefore, have fallen into the group; some tenants who had not farmed in the community in the previous year may also have been placed erroneously in this category.

[37] *Hamilton Freeman*, July 15, 1868.

[38] *Ibid.*, July 15, 1874; See also *Iowa Homestead and Western Farm Journal*, August 25, 1876.

in 1880 than in 1850. To a considerable degree this was due to the increase in the number of workers who were not members of the operator's family. Their ranks increased 5 to 8 per cent. If this last development reflected the growth of a permanent farm-laborer group, we could also expect an increase in the average age of the non-family workers. This was not the case. The average age of the Jones County farm laborer in 1850 was 26.6 years in comparison to 24.9 in 1880. In the sample of 300 households the equivalent figures were 30.6 and 27.3. Males fifteen years of age and above did not, of course, represent the total labor force of the farms on which they worked. Still younger sons, farm wives, daughters, and hired girls assisted in the farmyards and even in the fields. We must remember, also, that the census enumeration ordinarily occurred in early June before the summer work peak. Transient labor or workers from non-farm households swelled the labor force somewhat in that period. It is worth noting, too, that the total of male labor in the 550 households did not decrease between 1850 and 1880 despite the increase in labor productivity that took place in the intervening years.

III

When describing taxation in Illinois and Iowa, historians have usually tried to evaluate its success in producing revenue for the state or territorial governments. We are mainly interested here in taxation as a production cost faced by midwestern farmers in the years between 1830 and 1900. Although legislators often succumbed to the temptation to improve the tax laws, the major outlines of the taxation structure had become clear in both states by the early 1850's. The county was always the basic administrative agency in tax assessment and collection — passing funds onward to the territorial and state governments and back, for a variety of purposes, to the smaller agencies of local government. Although small poll taxes on able-bodied males appeared in the tax systems of both Illinois and Iowa during much of the period, the general property tax was the major instrument of taxation. Farmers in both Illinois and Iowa knew that a county or township officer would assess their personal and real property each year,[39] that they must pay taxes on the basis of such assessment, that the county government would put their land or goods to tax sale if they failed to do so, and that the county treasurer would issue a tax deed on delinquent land if the owners failed to clear the tax lien within a limited period — never more than three years. Although state policies varied from time to time, the penalties for redemption were ordinarily high — above 30 per cent at times. If property owners wished to challenge the assessor's appraisals, their usual resort was to the county board of equalization and finally to the courts.[40]

[39] The actual assessment figures were not always revised annually, of course.

[40] John E. Brindley, *History of Taxation in Iowa* (Iowa City, 1911); Robert Murray Haig, *A History of the General Property Tax in Illinois* (University of Illinois "Studies

Tax burdens were by no means uniform throughout Illinois and Iowa. They varied over time and from county to county, township to township, school district to school district, and from road district to road district. Most writers agree that the period prior to the early 1850's was one of relatively light taxation in which county administraton was frugal, and the state or territorial governments levied on the people lightly and often ineffectively. The counties used their income for bridges, roads, schools, and to some extent, public buildings; the territorial and state governments used their tax revenue mainly to meet their payrolls and maintain the capitols.

By the late 1840's public officers at every level of government were finding wider uses for the tax levies. Debauched by a disastrous orgy of spending for public improvements, Illinois turned to taxation in order to retire the public improvement bonds, which the legislators of the 1830's had hoped to see repaid from the revenues earned by the projected canals and railroads. Through the 1850's, therefore, state taxes in Illinois went in part to debt retirement. By this time, also, the citizens of counties and townships were beginning to bond themselves to aid railroads. The interest payments and principal of these obligations, too, must come from tax funds. Railroad levies at both the county and township level were common in both Illinois and Iowa from the 1850's to the 1870's.[41] With the Civil War came other demands on the taxpayer. Taxes attributable to the war might be destined for state or federal use, as in the case of the direct federal tax of 1861, or be used by the county officers to pay soldiers' bounties or to provide relief for their families. By the late 1870's, drainage taxes were becoming extremely important in the communities of the wet prairie districts in Illinois.[42] A scant generation later this became true in Iowa as well.

Many pioneer farmers in Illinois benefited under the provisions of the Illinois Enabling Act, which forbade local agencies to tax land acquired from the federal government until five years had elapsed from the date of purchase, as well as military bounty lands in the possession of veteran patentees or their heirs during the first three years of ownership.[43] Many pioneers, of course, had occupied their farms some time before the date of the land sale. Periods of exemption from real estate taxation running to as much

in the Social Sciences," Vol. III, Nos. 1 & 2, [Urbana, 1914]). Margaret B. Bogue, *op. cit.*, pp. 223–31 has included a detailed description of the Illinois system of taxation and the more important changes in it from the 1850's to the end of the century. The Iowa system was much the same.

[41] Kathleen B. Jacklin, "Local Aid to Railroads in Illinois, 1848–1870" (unpublished M.A. thesis,Cornell University, 1958); Earl S. Beard, "Railroads in Iowa, 1865–1875, A Study in Attitudes," (unpublished M.A. thesis, State University of Iowa, 1950), pp. 53–69. The Iowa legislature forbade local bond issues for railroad aid in 1862 but allowed direct tax levies for the same purpose during the late 1860's and early 1870's.

[42] Margaret B. Bogue, *op. cit.*, pp. 152–56.

[43] Haig, *op. cit.*, p. 30. The exemption of bounty lands actually extended for three years past the date of alienation.

as seven years could not have been unusual, therefore, in pioneer Illinois. Not until 1847 did Illinois gain relief from restrictions that had long since become obnoxious to all landowners who held real estate on which the five-year exemption had expired.[44] Although farmers in Iowa enjoyed no such period of legal immunity, some early comers were able to develop their lands for five years or more before the federal land officers put it to sale. Farmers who settled on the railroad land grants, similarly, also enjoyed a tax free period when clear title did not yet rest in the road. Critics accused the Illinois Central of delaying final certification procedures until purchasers had paid up their contracts, but the Iowa roads did not provoke such criticism.[45] Of course, the farmers who obtained exemption from real estate taxes in these ways did not escape the tax-collector completely. They still must pay taxes on their livestock and other personal property, as well as poll taxes if they were of appropriate age and family status.

Table 20 shows the assessed value per acre, the mill rate, and the tax on a fine section of upland prairie in Muscatine County, Iowa, between

TABLE 20

TAXATION ON SECTION 6–78N–4W

MUSCATINE COUNTY, IOWA*

	Assessed value per acre	Mill rate	Tax per acre		Assessed value per acre	Mill rate	Tax per acre
1852	$ 5.11	7.5	4¢	1876	$11.75	21.0	25¢
1854	6.52	7.5	5	1877	12.72	25.0	32
1856	10.11	9.0	9	1878	12.68	14.0	18
1858	11.81	14.5	17	1879	11.83	15.5	18
1859	8.51	11.0	9	1880	11.84	18.5	22
1860	8.72	12.0	10	1881	12.69	16.5	21
1861	9.05	13.0	12	1882	12.69	18.5	23
1862	9.05	5.0	5	1883	13.84	22.5	31
1863	10.14	10.0	10	1884	13.85	19.0	26
1864	9.97	18.0	18	1885	17.00	15.0	26
1865	10.70	13.0	14	1886	16.99	17.0	29
1866	11.56	15.0	17	1887	15.07	17.0	26
1867	13.57	16.0	22	1888	15.07	18.0	27
1868	13.14	21.0	28	1889	14.77	17.5	26
1869	11.34	17.0	19	1890	15.91	16.0	25
1870	9.87	22.0	22	1891	15.28	16.0	24
1871	14.51	20.0	29	1892	15.73	16.75	26
1872	10.52	29.5	31	1893	15.54	17.5	27
1873	11.79	21.0	25	1894	15.54	18.75	29
1874	11.83	24.5	29	1895	16.73	18.0	30
1875	11.80	17.25	20	1896	16.96	19.0	32

* Compiled from data taken from the Tax Lists in the attic of the Muscatine County Court House, Muscatine, Iowa. Usually there were from five to eight owners of real estate in section six, which lies in the northwestern corner of Wapsipinoc Township.

[44] Haig, *op. cit.*, p. 92.

[45] Paul W. Gates, *The Illinois Central Railroad and its Colonization Work*, pp. 303–08; Leonard F. Ralston, "Railroads and the Government of Iowa, 1850–1872," (unpublished Ph.D. dissertation, State University of Iowa, 1960).

1852 and 1896. The taxes on 160 acres of land in this section in 1852 amounted to $6.40; twenty years later the tax on the same land was $49.60. In neither year did such land taxes constitute the whole tax bill of resident farmers in Muscatine County. Unless still minors, they must pay a poll tax of 50 cents and a few dollars worth of road district taxes, the latter payable usually in labor. More importantly they must pay taxes on their personal property at the same mill rate as that levied on real estate. The owner of land in Section 6-78N-4W in 1852 would have paid $3.75 on $500 worth of personal property; the tax on the same valuation of livestock, feed, and machinery in 1872 was $14.75.

Contrast the facts of Table 20 with the tax roll of 1838 in Johnson County, western neighbor of Muscatine. Here the assessor listed forty settlers with personal property ranging in value from nothing to $828.50. Land titles, of course, still rested in the federal government. The tax rate was five mills. The highest tax was $4.14, and in the end the settlers capitalized on the confusion involved in setting up a county organization and evaded payment altogether.[46] It is clear that taxes on personal property became relatively less important in the total tax bill of the Iowa farmer over time. The tax bills of the farmers in section 6-78N-4W show this in exaggerated fashion. During the early 1850's personal property amounted to almost half their total property; by the 1890's it was less than 20 per cent.

A few dollars did pay the taxes of most farmers in Illinois and Iowa in the years before 1850. But some writers have perhaps treated these small sums too lightly. The volume of cash business of the "average" farmer in the 1830's or 1840's was much smaller than was true a generation later. Nor had the inflation of the 1850's and the Civil War years yet pushed up the general price level of agricultural products. A farmer must sell a two-year-old steer or its equivalent if he was to realize $8.00 or $10.00 for the county treasurer in the 1840's; a similar animal would bring him $20 to $25 during the early 1870's. But in general the real tax did rise after 1850, and it rose very suddenly in some communities. The increase in the size of farm units after the mid-1870's would of itself have raised the tax bill of farm-operators regardless of changes in the mill rate or level of assessment. Then, as now, tax levels adjusted slowly to changes in the general price level. Increased levies for schools, railroad aid, or road construction during the late 1860's and 1870's fell doubly hard upon local taxpayers because of the currency deflation of those years. It was no accident that

[46] *History of Johnson County, Iowa* . . . (Iowa City, 1883), p. 270. Tax levies of the 1830's and 1840's in eastern Iowa are also discussed in: Western Historical Company, *History of Muscatine County, Iowa* . . . (Chicago, 1879), pp. 419–20; Union Historical Company, *History of Iowa County, Iowa* . . . (Des Moines, 1881), pp. 395–403; Western Historical Company, *History of Appanoose County, Iowa* . . . (Chicago, 1878), pp. 347–53; Western Historical Company, *History of Clinton County, Iowa* . . . (Chicago, 1879), p. 352; Western Historical Company, *History of Cedar County, Iowa* . . . (Chicago, 1878), pp. 383–89.

grumbling over taxes and tax fighting reached its peak in Illinois and Iowa during the 1870's.[47]

Even after most of the farmland in a county or region was on the tax roll, there were still possibilities of inequitable taxation of which most farmers were keenly aware. Granted that tax levels varied from place to place, depending upon local needs, assessment procedures might allow the farmers of one township to escape from paying their fair share of county and state expenses. Varying levels of assessment from county to county allowed one county to benefit at the expense of others in raising funds to maintain the state government. Early in the history of Illinois, appraisal procedures specified simply that lands should be categorized as first, second, and third class in quality and that a specified uniform valuation be given to all the lands in each classification. Illinois legislators abandoned this procedure and decided that property should be appraised at its true value, a procedure approved in Iowa as well.[48] So strong were local pressures, however, that the assessors never obeyed the law. Local classification systems were common; under-assessment was general.

By the 1870's the state auditors in both Illinois and Iowa were charging that assessed property valuations often fell from one-half to two-thirds below the sale value of property, with considerable variation from county to county. As early as 1858 Ogle County, Illinois, valued its horses at an average of $30.85 while Piatt County residents paid personal property taxes on horses valued at $77.93 on the average.[49] Almost twenty years later the state auditor of Iowa reported an average assessment of horses in that state ranging from as low as $16 in some counties to as high as $40 in others.[50] What was true of the counties within the state was also true of the townships within the counties. State and county boards of equalization wrestled manfully with the problem and manfully seem to have ended in agreement with the Iowa state auditor who wrote in 1879, "We have only patiently to wait the time, sure to come, when after free and full discussion of the whole subject, the quickened public conscience will demand a more rigid adherence to the letter of the law, which would inevitably tend to a more equal distribution of the public burden." [51]

Although taxpayers themselves often showed more concern about the problem of equalization than did the state auditor, local interest focused primarily on tax problems that were more personal than were discrepancies in assessment between counties. Were large landholders paying lower taxes than the small farmers who lived beside them? Were non-resident holders bearing an adequate share of the tax load? Were country folk paying more

[47] Margaret B. Bogue, op. cit., pp. 223–52; Iowa Homestead, January 3, 1873, p. 1, January 17, 1873, pp. 20, 24.
[48] Haig, op. cit., pp. 35–58.
[49] Margaret B. Bogue, op. cit., p. 227.
[50] Iowa State Auditor, Biennial Report, October 1, 1877 (Des Moines, 1877), p. 6.
[51] Ibid., 1879, p. 6.

taxes than urban residents? At any time, but particularly in years of depression, there were farmers willing to charge inequity on all counts. It is hard to evaluate the merits of their arguments. The answers to our questions lie behind the assessment figures, and we obviously cannot at this late date call for reappraisal of the property in Lime Creek Township in 1870.

In the years before 1890, land not only varied as always in productivity, it also varied in the degree to which it was improved. Ordinarily, the figures on the assessors' rolls did not show great variation in value from one piece of real estate to another or from Jacob Jones' horses to Samuel Smith's nags. In general, the rolls probably should have shown considerably more variation. The county officers came from among the most substantial farmers in the community, and assessors could have seen little personal gain in assessing the property of their colleagues in local government at high figures. The substantial farmers, too, were those with the resources to fight high assessments in equalization or court proceedings. Few large farmers were so happily situated that they could imitate Edward Sumner, who, it was said in 1878, had for twenty-five years switched his livestock back and forth between his Illinois and Indiana holdings to take advantage of the fact that the assessors called at different times in the two states.[52]

We cannot isolate the influence that tax policy and tax burdens had upon landownership and use patterns. Taxes were only one of a number of cash items that forced the "average" farmer of the 1880's to make a yearly cash outlay that his counterpart of the 1840's would have considered fantastic. When compared to the increase in the cost of land, however, or the outlay for farm machinery, the real increase in taxes was a small one. Certainly, however, the tax load of some farmers was onerous at times.

[52] Margaret B. Bogue, *op. cit.*, pp. 237–38.

CHAPTER X

Some Are Innovators

We can never completely understand, perhaps, the motivation that underlies the varied decisions of men. Indeed, the decision-maker may be moved by emotions and considerations that he hardly understands himself. With this saving formula stated, we can now face the fact that a multitude of farmers made a vast number of decisions about their farming operations between 1830 and 1890 and completely changed the character of agricultural life in the prairie triangle. From the very beginning, large numbers of settlers and farmers in this region had a strong commercial orientation. They sought to maximize the returns from their farming operations, and, if in the early years cash itself was scarce, they undoubtedly evaluated the material possessions that they accumulated — their lands and livestock — in terms of money.

Doubtless the deeper meaning of capital accumulation varied from farmer to farmer in Illinois and Iowa. For some it guaranteed that they could start their sons on farms of their own or give them an advanced education. For some the quest was security and a comfortable old age, visualized in a variety of ways ranging from curtailed activity while son or son-in-law shouldered the major burdens of the farm, to the massive white clapboard house on a shady street in the county seat. For others accumulation became simply an end in itself, an exhilerating game. Granted that the driving force was the desire on the part of individuals to improve their circumstances, the anatomy of agricultural change still needs much understanding.

The pioneer farmer of the prairie triangle was participating in at least two distinct processes. In a "settling in" process he acquired a farm and improved it while trying to adapt to local and regional peculiarities of environment that demanded different answers than those he had perhaps learned in his old home. At the same time he was caught up by changes in farm technology and in the marketing system for agricultural products that were almost revolutionary in scope. These processes provided the framework in which the prairie pioneer planned his farm business. Some of the decisions that he made involved the combinations of enterprises upon his farm — that it, the amount of emphasis to be placed upon certain crops or animals. Should the farmer concentrate on livestock production? If so, should he emphasize sheep, hogs, or cattle? or a combination of them? If a decision were made in favor of cattle, should the farmer make quantities of cheese, as many transplanted Yorkers would do? or butter perhaps? or even try to sell fluid milk in the county seat? Or should he concentrate rather, on the production of beef? Or on the production of grain for sale, perhaps? To what extent in any case should wheat be raised in comparison with corn, oats, and barley? Ought this wheat to be of spring or winter variety? Should our farmer add a new crop to his usual program — say flax? Should he follow the advice of the enthusiastic pomologist down the road and plant an orchard?

Another type of decision might stem from desire to improve the quality or quantity of production by substituting new varieties of the same field crops previously raised or by replacing mongrel animals with improved breeds of livestock. Should the settler purchase a purebred Shorthorn bull? and should he take his mares to the new Norman stallion recently brought to the county seat? Ought the seed oats be purchased from one of the farmers growing a new patent-office variety?

The technology of agriculture provided the pioneer farmer with another galaxy of decisions. With what materials should he fence? If he were on the prairie, and favored hedge, should it be Osage orange or willow? Would barbed wire really injure livestock if he decided to use it? Should he purchase one of the new McCormick mowers? or a reaper? or a header? or a binder? or a corn-planter? or a riding cultivator? or one of the considerable range of plows available? Should he follow the lead of his neighbor and start to tile the sloughs on his eighty acres? Such were the decisions that the pioneer farmer of the prairie triangle had to make, and some of them were faced not once but several times, as the economic weather blew fair or cloudy.

Decisions, one must remember also, were often of an interlocking sort. Most of the new machinery, for instance, gave the farmer time to till more acres. Must these be purchased? or might they be rented? How should these acres be utilized? A decision to drain would ultimately give the farmer land of a different character; how would this affect his combination of enterprises? A decision concerning livestock often affected a farmer's cropping patterns, particularly the amount of hay to be cured or corn raised. We can understand if he had trouble making up his mind.

We must remember, too, as we consider the decision-making of prairie farmers, that not all of them were alike in background or objectives and that their farming operations might differ considerably, even in the earliest days of settlement. Farm operators might be native-born or foreign-born, born to the English tongue or highly inept in its use. If continental-born they might have been raised among the Rhineland vineyards or trained to a mixed life of farming and fishing in Scandinava, been emigrants from the grain fields of eastern Europe or come from many other backgrounds. If native-born, they might be Yankee or Yorker, Kentuckian and Buckeye, Pennsylvanian or Sucker. They might be old or young or in between, well educated or illiterate.

The farm operation itself might differ drastically from its neighbor in scale, in purpose, and in method of control. In 1860 most Illinois counties had a number of farms of 500 acres or more; indeed, three central Illinois counties listed more than fifty operating units of this size. Such farms were less common in Iowa, but they were not uncommon in 1860 and would grow in number thereafter. The nonresident owners of some farms regarded them solely as investments. Such men might not participate at all in the managerial function, leaving this to their tenants. Others retained control of the farm business by using resident managers or limiting the range of decision exercised by renters. The non-residents might live in the East, in the next county, or be businessmen from the county seat. They could own one farm or many. When we consider the resident operators, we find some operating farms in conjunction with droving businesses of large scale, while others reaped an exotic harvest of agricultural copy by writing for the agricultural press. In the great majority, of course, were resident operators who looked solely to their land for home and living.

In making his decisions, the midwestern farmer could look for aid in a variety of directions. A number of agencies with varying degrees of impersonality sought to cater to his interests. These were the local press, the agricultural press, the agricultural exhibitions and — of little importance prior to 1880 — the agricultural colleges.

The farmers of Illinois and Iowa might find considerable about agriculture in the local papers of the county. By the 1840's, at least, editors were breaking away from the patterns of the early nineteenth century when the western papers carried little but political news. Farming was the occupation of a majority of householders in most western counties; it profited the editor to recognize this fact. Of course, the local editors varied in their preoccupation with farming matters. But if interested, they rendered the farm-operators among their readers a variety of services. In the first place an editor could try to guide the farmers along paths that he believed would prove most profitable to them. He could also open his columns to the opinions of others whose knowledge might assist the local farmers. Such writers might be local farmers who believed that they had worth-while information on crops and tillage to pass along, agricultural journalists, or writers in the exchanges that the editor clipped for the benefit of his own readers. Factual reporting of the activities of the farmers in the county also aided the individual operator, since he learned of developments outside his immediate neighborhood and gained vicarious experience. Implicit in the editor's factual reporting and in the selections from agricultural journals and exchanges were preconceived ideas of what the good farmer should be. These assumptions, too, might have a subtle influence in preparing the mind of the individual farmer for decision-making. Finally, the editor published market reports and notices, as well as bringing a variety of advertisements for agricultural machinery, blooded stock, nursery products, and stray animals to the attention of his farm readers.

Many of the agricultural items which appeared in the local newspapers covered the same subjects to which the agricultural periodicals devoted attention. Many faithful readers of the county paper did not bother to subscribe to an agricultural journal. And, since the topics were often linked in some way to the local scene and endorsed or evaluated by an editor who was known as a member of the community, they sometimes had greater impact than those presented by a "foreign" editor tailoring his offerings to regional dimensions. Because the local papers probably reflected the concerns of local farmers more accurately than the regional journals, we can profitably spend some time in considering the agricultural items that appeared in one midwestern county paper during its first thirty years. Published in Webster City, the county seat of Hamilton County, Iowa, the *Hamilton Freeman* began publication in 1857, shortly after county organization. Three able newspapermen, Charles Aldrich, V. A. Ballou and John D. Hunter succeeded each other as editor of the *Freeman* in our period.

In 1858 the editor of the *Freeman* made his most sweeping recommendation to the farmers of Hamilton County when he suggested that the most profitable branch of agriculture was stock-raising.[1] Corn had actually rotted during the previous fall and winter for want of livestock to eat it, and the prairies, he argued, provided unlimited pasture. "We have no doubt," he concluded, "that those of our farmers who devote their efforts to stock-raising will in a few years become our richest and most prosperous citizens." The editor showed real perception in this article, and in a sense his prophecy was borne out. Twenty years later, livestock did hold an important place in the farming patterns of the more prosperous farmers of Hamilton County. But livestock in any numbers represented a capital investment beyond the reach of many settlers who arrived in the sixties and seventies. For these a farming operation that demanded smaller investments of capital was essential, and this they found in growing considerable acreages of wheat as a cash crop.

The action of Aldrich in offering a ten-dollar premium to the farmer who raised the best acre of wheat and a similar prize to the settler who produced the best sample of sorghum sugar in the crop year of 1861 was undoubtedly much more in accord with the realities of agriculture in the Webster City district than was his admonition to concentrate upon the pro-

---

[1] *Hamilton Freeman*, July 15, 1858. Professor Thomas LeDuc has been suggesting for some years that the major point developed in this paragraph applies generally to pioneer farmers in the Middle West during this period.

duction of livestock.[2] By the mid-1870's Hunter was swinging toward Aldrich's original position, as the production of cash crops of wheat became less profitable and more emphasis was placed generally on livestock. Such stock, moreover, should be of high quality. It cost no more to raise a valuable horse than a "dunghill." [3] When Colonel John Scott, of Story County, proposed to sell fifty cattle "off the top of his herd," in the late seventies, the editor suggested that it would be worthwhile for Hamilton County farmers to bring home every animal.[4] Although the activities of the cattle-feeder drew more editorial comment than those of other agriculturists, the editor could, by the late 1870's, suggest that dairying was a more satisfactory kind of livestock operation for the man of small capital.[5]

Through the 1870's the editor's attitude toward the grain crops mirrored the change that was taking place in the county generally. When reporting the state of the crops during the previous decade, his primary concern had been with the wheat crop. But in 1873 he observed that "Iowa relies much on her corn crop," and four years later he wrote, "Farmers are fast learning that there is more real profit in the corn crop than in almost everything else." [6] Where Aldrich had offered premiums in 1860 for the best acre of wheat and the best sample of sorghum sugar, Hunter, twenty years later, offered a special premium of ten dollars for the best five acres of corn.[7] In 1885 he affirmed, "The soil of Hamilton county is pre-eminently fitted for the growth of corn and our farmers are each year paying more attention to this crop, which is the sure road to successful farming." [8]

In Hamilton County cutting prairie grass for hay was a task for the August and September days during the pioneer period. In the mid-1870's the editor admonished his readers to make their hay early before the grasses went to seed, so that a product of better quality might be obtained. As the unbroken prairies surrendered rapidly to the plow in the late 1870's and the early 1880's, Hunter, with support from Aldrich, devoted some attention to the tame grasses, particularly timothy and red clover.[9] "Prairie hay," he wrote, "will soon be a thing of the past. . . . There is nothing the West needs more than an extension of the varieties of grasses cultivated. Especially do we need varieties that will stand as pasture during the usual droughts of July and August." [10] In the spring of 1879 he noted that clover and timothy seed were in greater demand than ever before. To the embarrassment of both the *Freeman* and Aldrich, much of the red clover died during

[2] *Ibid.*, December 8, 1860.
[3] *Ibid.*, April 21, 1869.
[4] *Ibid.*, October 3, 1877.
[5] *Ibid.*, November 8, 1876.
[6] *Ibid.*, May 14, 1873; April 11, 1877.
[7] *Ibid.*, April 14, 1880.
[8] *Ibid.*, September 9, 1885.
[9] *Ibid.*, April 10, June 5, 12, July 3, 24, 1878; April 2, 1879.
[10] *Ibid.*, August 15, 1877.

the winter of 1880, and discussion of tame grasses vanished from the columns of the newspaper for a time.[11]

Aldrich, Ballou, and Hunter were inveterate champions of fruit-growing. Their Yankee heritage included a vision of pleasant countrysides where every farm boasted an orchard. The fact that Mr. Downing in Cass Township had a peach tree in bearing demonstrated to Aldrich that "peaches may be abundantly raised in North Western Iowa." [12] Ballou in 1864 maintained that "Iowa is the very paradise of small fruits," and hopefully forecast that "in a few years Iowa will become noted as a wine producing state." [13] Winter killing or the unfortunate experiences of local farmers with peripatetic nurserymen might silence the editors for a time, but they invariably returned to the subject.[14] Hunter differed with one of the local experts in 1880 at some length:

We have long believed that Hamilton county will be noted in the future for its large and excellent crops of apples; but now we hear that our venerable friend, Huitt Ross, avers that in ten years apples will be so plenty here that they won't be worth 25 cents per bushel! We rather differ with him in this regard. There will be an almost unlimited demand for Iowa apples, on the plains and in all parts of the Rocky mountains, from British possessions to Old Mexico. There will be improved methods of drying and preserving them for shipment everywhere. Hogs and cattle may be profitably fed upon them to almost any extent — if they ever get cheap and plenty enough. So, on the whole, without going into any argument about the matter, we are of the opinion that our farmers can do nothing more sensible than to keep right on planting apple-trees.[15]

Such premonitions on the part of the editor and his "venerable friend" earned neither of them a prize for prophecy.

If importing purebreds or planting fruit trees won the approval of the editor, certain practices inspired his censure. He showed little sympathy for the man who allowed a scrub bull to roam, nor for the beast either. On the latter, improvement-minded farmers were to "use the knife unsparingly" in what he called "heroic treatment." [16] A man who burned the prairies in September or October, the editor wrote in 1864, should be prosecuted.[17] Only a week later he supported his position with a story of local cattle badly burned or killed by a prairie fire.[18] Roughly a decade later he repeated his advice with the additional admonition that it was now a violation of the law to burn the prairies in the fall. Quite aside from all the risks of fall burning, the farmer could destroy young grasshoppers if he fired the old

[11] *Ibid.*, May 12, 1880.
[12] *Ibid.*, September 27, 1862.
[13] *Ibid.*, September 10, 1864.
[14] *Ibid.*, June 3, August 6, 1865.
[15] *Ibid.*, June 9, 1880.
[16] *Ibid.*, May 30, 1877.
[17] *Ibid.*, October 1, 1864.
[18] *Ibid.*, October 8, 1864.

grass in the spring.[19] As early as 1872 the local editor warned against using
the plow on steep slopes and deplored the water erosion that resulted from
such practice.[20] The editor of the *Freeman* served as a community conscience, but people often ignore the prompting of conscience.

The editor's ideal farmer seems to have been an industrious man, alert
to improve his agricultural practices by applying the ideas that he discovered
in the columns of the local paper and agricultural press or at the annual
fair of the agricultural society. At the same time he was cautious in expenditure. During the seventies the editor warned against increasing the size
of the farm unit unduly and echoed the aphorism that it was better to farm
a small farm well than a big farm poorly.[21] The editor believed that farmers
could help themselves by discussing mutual problems, and the farmers' club
organized in Cass Township during the early 1870's undoubtedly owed
something to his guidance.[22] At first he commended the Grange, but, as a
power in the local Republican party, he could hardly approve the interest
in politics that the members developed.[23]

Many of the agricultural items in the *Freeman* simply illustrated the
reportorial function of the paper. One category of items included discussion
of plant and animal diseases or pests. Periodically Hamilton County farmers
fought the potato beetle, chinch bugs, and grasshoppers, and the editor
printed battle communiques along with critiques of the war plans. In 1877,
for instance, "Uncle Jimmy Adams" was "making it red-hot" for the young
hoppers in his wheat by driving them into windrows of hay which he fired.[24]
Recurrently during the period blackleg struck the cattle, horses suffered
from pinkeye and epizootic, and cholera attacked the swine. The editor
passed along remedies to his farm readers with indeterminate success. Suggestions that burnt corn or jimsonweed tea would cure or prevent hog
cholera serve better, no doubt, as evidence of the level of veterinary science
in that day than proof of aid given by the local editor in solving a farm
problem.[25] But there were exceptions to this rule. In 1869 and again in
1871, he printed directions for applying Paris green to control the potato
beetle.[26] Although this successful treatment had been in use for only a few
years at the time, the frontier farmer was by no means isolated from improved farming techniques, if their worth had been proved.

At times the editor reported the text of state laws that he thought of
interest to the farmers. In the earlier days of the paper, such reporting
merely filled space, in part; by the 1870's much more selection was apparent.

[19] *Ibid.*, October 11, 1876.
[20] *Ibid.*, June 12, 1872.
[21] *Ibid.*, August 23, September 6, 1876.
[22] *Ibid.*, December 10, 1864; February 23, 1870.
[23] *Ibid.*, May 20, 1872; May 14, 1873.
[24] *Ibid.*, May 30, 1877.
[25] *Ibid.*, August 14, 1878; September 3, 1879.
[26] *Ibid.*, May 12, 1869; June 14, 1871.

At appropriate times of the year the editor reminded his readers that burning prairies in the fall was a crime or that the tumbling rods of threshing machines must be boxed under state law.[27]

Undoubtedly the editor was selective in reporting the activities of the farm population. He pandered to his readers' taste for the novel. When William Hook slaughtered a "McGee" hog that weighed 602 pounds at the age of nineteen month, the *Freeman* challenged anyone else in the region to "show better figures on the hog question." [28] The reading fare of Hamilton County citizens was liberally garnished with big cabbages, double-yoked eggs, and tall corn.[29] Unusual crops or innovations provoked comment, although they might be of little significance in the long run. On the other hand, farmers who followed progressive practices did receive mention some of the time, at least, as an item of 1877 shows clearly. J. A. Felt, the editor noted, was becoming a large stock-raiser and did not "propose to fool away his time raising wheat." [30] The editor reported that the Odessa wheat of W. H. Riley threshed sixty-two pounds to the bushel, and the plug, no doubt, helped Riley in his plans to popularize this variety of seed in the county.[31] Although community coverage in the *Freeman* improved somewhat during the late 1870's when the editor succeeded in building up a staff of local correspondents, these writers frequently took farming for granted and emphasized local social life.

The editors of the *Freeman* desired to make the paper a forum in which local farmers might discuss agricultural problems. If farm readers never swamped the editor with letters, they supplemented the plow with the pen rather frequently during the 1870's when low prices and the encroachment of settlers on prairies, hitherto used by the established farmers as commons, produced a period of bickering and readjustment. A number of writers attempted to lay down the philosophy that the farmer should bring to his work. Do things in season; always plan ahead; use good seed; do not try too much — these were the admonitions of "Aitch" from Cass Township.[32] His last bit of advice appeared in a variety of forms in these years, including simple repetition of "the old fashioned adage that 'a little farm well tilled' is the best after all." [33] Be honest, thrifty, and avoid both beer and agricultural implement salesmen was the counsel of others.[34] Although negative in tone, a letter written originally by Oliver Templer for the *Country Gentleman* reflects some of the more progressive attitudes of the time:

One of the roads to poor farming is well traveled but not generally acknowl-

[27] *Ibid.*, September 29, 1869; August 12, 1874.
[28] *Ibid.*, January 4, 1871.
[29] *Ibid.*, July 30, 1864; September 23, 1885.
[30] *Ibid.*, June 27, 1877.
[31] *Ibid.*, October 8, 1873.
[32] *Ibid.*, February 19, 1873.
[33] *Ibid.*, January 29, 1873; (see also, April 4, 1871; August 30, 1876.)
[34] *Ibid.*, April 12, 1871; April 17, 1878.

edged — invest all your capital in land and go in debt for more. Hire money at a heavy interest to run the farm; have very little faith in farming and always be ready to sell out; buy the cheapest and poorest kind of stock and farming machinery; feed poor grain and hay to your stock, and you will have less repairs to make on your rickety fences and farm machinery, as fine horses and fat stock make sad havoc with the old wagon, plow . . . and fences. Use the oil of hickory whenever your oxen need strength; it is cheaper than high feeding and keeps the hair lively, and pounds out the grubs. Never waste time by setting out fruit or shade trees, as leaves rotting around a place make it unhealthy. Sell the best calves, lambs and shoats, to the butchers, as they will bring a little more, and the thin and poor ones will do well enough to keep.[35]

Even Templer, however, subscribed to the "little farm well tilled" gospel, which the county census report of 1890 showed to have been overwhelmingly rejected.

Some farmers discussed the profit to be found in specific farm enterprises. Between 1870 and 1876 the returns to be expected from wheat were the subject of particular argument. Early in 1870 "Hamilton" was convinced that wheat acreage should be reduced sharply, that the proportion of other crops, especially corn, should be greatly increased, and that more and better stock should be raised. These points, he modestly suggested, constituted "*intelligent, discriminating, agricultural wisdom.*" [36] Three years later a number of the local farmers were challenging each other's figures on the cost of wheat production, and "A. G. N." charged "Prairie" with padding his accounts by including allowances for "poor plows, high-priced harvest hands, worthless machinery, worn out teams and wagons, gabbling, time killing teamsters, *etc.*" [37] Three years later "Alfo" concluded that farmers were "becoming satisfied of the folly of attempting to raise grain to ship," and the census returns of 1880 bore him out.[38]

Other letters ranged over a variety of topics, sometimes in polemical fashion. The manager of the River Bend Farm, owned by L. L. Estes, flayed Charles Aldrich for his support of the Jersey breed and argued that the Shorthorn was a superior animal for any local need.[39] In the mid-seventies those who opposed restraining stock under the terms of the state herd law submitted a series of strongly worded letters.[40] The most violent of these partisans hinted strongly that all of the advocates of the measure were selfish, if not dishonest, and divided them into a number of uncomplimentary categories that included land sharks, land-agents, and lawyers.[41] Less dramatic and also less numerous were letters in which the writer advocated

[35] *Ibid.*, March 18, 1874.
[36] *Ibid.*, February 16, 1870.
[37] *Ibid.*, January 22, February 12, 26, 1873.
[38] *Ibid.*, April 19, 1876.
[39] *Ibid.*, April 4, 1883.
[40] *Ibid.*, March 6, 1872; October 28, 1876; September 19, 26, October 3, 1877; October 8, 1879.
[41] R in *ibid.*, September 26, 1877.

improved tillage and feeding practices or discussed livestock or plant diseases and pests.[42]

A number of successful agricultural journals were serving the farmers of the seaboard states when the farm-makers turned their attention to the prairies. The Albany *Cultivator*, later the *Country Gentleman*, the *American Farmer*, the *Genesee Farmer*, and Moore's *Rural New Yorker* — all had loyal readers in the West during the mid-nineteenth century. In 1841 the prairies gained their own voice when John S. Wright established the *Union Agriculturist and Western Prairie Farmer*. A considerable number of other farm or horticultural papers appeared briefly before 1870 in Illinois and Iowa, but of the group only two lasted for any considerable period. These were the *Illinois Farmer*, of Champaign, and the *Northwestern Farmer*, of Dubuque, the latter becoming the *Iowa Homestead* in 1862. Meanwhile, other western agricultural papers like the *Valley Farmer*, of St. Louis, the Indianapolis *Western Cultivator*, Salem's *Ohio Farmer* and the *Western Rural*, of Detroit, and later of Chicago, found readers in Illinois and Iowa as well.[43]

"When I commenced making a farm on the prairie," wrote an Illinois pioneer, "I found myself engaged in a task by no means without its difficulties and perplexities. Whatever I had learned of farming at the East, had to be principally learned over again here. . . . It is in *opening* the farm, in cultivating the soil, and in the whole process of raising the crop, that Western experience is wanted." [44] With such sentiment the western editors professed to agree heartily and admonished their readers occasionally that eastern journals could be of little help to them. Acutely aware of the size of the western audience, some eastern editors solicited contributions from the Middle West or ran articles dealing with prairie agriculture. Appreciated as these offerings were by western readers, they appealed also to eastern readers with western relatives or plans of their own to move west.

Certainly the alert farmer could find considerable to interest him in the *Prairie Farmer*, the *Illinois Farmer*, or the *Iowa Homestead*. The editors of these papers frequently urged farmers to describe their experiences and methods for the benefit of their fellows. Those with questions were encouraged to lay them before the readers, who, not infrequently, wrote, in turn, to answer them. Sometimes the editors themselves had solutions, or additional comments that they appended to the letters they published. Descriptions of editorial journeys through parts of the Middle West or to particular agricultural showplaces often appeared, replete with descriptions of how the proprietors farmed the prairies. Frequent contributors, like "Old Settler",

[42] *Ibid.*, March 22, April 12, 26, 1871; April 8, 1873; April 1, 1874; March 28, 1883.

[43] Richard Bardolph's *Agricultural Literature and the Early Illinois Farmer* ("University of Illinois Studies in the Social Sciences," Vol. XXIX, [Urbana 1948]) is a very useful study of the agricultural press particularly.

[44] John D. Caton in *Union Agriculturist and Western Prairie Farmer* (May, 1841), pp. 34–35; (also quoted by Bardolph, *op. cit.*, p. 107).

of the *Iowa Homestead*, and "Wool Grower", of the *Prairie Farmer,* built up followings of friends and enemies who applauded or derided their ideas. The letters, editorial comment, special columns, and departments of these journals covered a broad range of problems and issues. Breaking, fencing, plowing, subsoiling, the advantages of good stock, feeding practices, live-stock diseases, dairying, grain culture, fruit culture, soil-building, rotation, drainage, grasses, agricultural machinery, farm accounts, market informa-tion, work routines — all merited discussion, as well as more erudite subjects like water witching and the influence of the moon on plants and animals. The editorial tone was, in general, hortatory; improved farming practices was the objective.

Yet there was much in the early midwestern agricultural journals that could hardly have been helpful to the prairie pioneer. Particularly in the early years of the *Prairie Farmer*, sections from agricultural texts or the speeches of dignitaries at agricultural exhibitions filled many columns. The relation of the texts — often European — to midwestern agriculture or even to farming itself was often hard to understand; and, if the exhibition addresses reaffirmed the farmers' pride in husbandary or their belief in prog-ress, they can have done little more. Despite their claim to serve a western constituency, the editors ran all too many items clipped from eastern ex-changes that had little value for western readers. They paid too much atten-tion to crop fads or novelties like sorghum, broom corn, or Chinese tree corn. Agricultural science was crude indeed; the advice of the editor some-times was only an illustration of the blind leading the blind. In their desire to be on the side of the righteous, they sometimes also lauded farming practices proved successful in other regions, like subsoiling, which had little value for the early generations of prairie farmers. It is not surprising that prejudice against "book farmers and book farming" was found among many "practical" farmers, particularly of the first couple of generations. Prejudice against book-farming, of course, did not originate in the Middle West; it was a reaction against the impractical nature of some of the agricultural reforms proposed in the older states and had in it also, no doubt, something of class prejudice, since many of the agricultural reformers of the early nine-teenth century in America were well-to-do squire or gentry types.

There is no doubt that the agricultural journals of the period could help a man to adapt to the peculiarities of prairie farming as well as to make himself a better farmer generally. But suspicion of book-farming or of the motivation of the editors, the scarcity of money, and the slow, even invisible, return on the investment — all kept the subscription lists of the farm journ-als within modest dimensions. Richard Bardolph has written, "It is clear that the circulation of agricultural papers in Illinois was not large at any time during the half-century before 1870. They certainly did not reach more than one farmer in ten, at best." [45] No doubt, this judgment would hold true

[45] Bardolph, *op. cit.*, p. 102.

in Iowa as well. But as we shall see in our discussion of the farm community, new ideas did not have to reach every farmer directly in order to influence his decisions. Undoubtedly the agricultural press was a very potent force in the early years of prairie agriculture. The biographer of a pioneer agricultural-machinery salesman wrote of his subject: "The agriculturists of this part of the state would read of a new machine in the *Prairie Farmer* and then came to Mr. Reichert to order one." [46] In 1854 one of Cyrus McCormick's agents sent him a dispatch from the field, describing the competition provided by John H. Manny: "He has advertised extensively in both newspapers and agricultural papers also in religious and when you find a religious bigot with his mind made up it is a *goner*. I believe more are reached in the agricultural papers than any other way. You may doubt it, but it is a fact nevertheless." [47]

In discussing the sources of ideas available to the prairie farm-maker, we must not overlook the county and state fairs. A number of county societies in both states sponsored exhibitions during the 1840's, and indeed, in Illinois there was precedent for such activity as early as the 1820's. In the early 1850's the state legislatures established state agricultural societies charged with the task of administering a state fair and overseeing the work of county societies. Although the systems of state and county aid that the legislators provided for the societies were far from lavish, they allowed energetic and sensible men to organize fairs without financial loss, except, perhaps, when bad weather struck on fair days. Now the number of county societies increased rapidly, and by the early 1860's most well-settled counties of the prairie triangle had their own organizations or at least participated in a union district. In proportion to its population, the Midwest had more agricultural societies than any other section of the country in both 1858 and and 1870.[48]

The impetus to organize county societies did not come solely, or in some cases even mainly, from the farm-operator group. The businessmen of the county seats were keenly aware of the trade that a fair would draw to town for a couple of days. An agricultural society contributed also to the image, which the businessmen of scantily populated counties liked to draw for the benefit of eastern capital, of a county with a go-ahead population and mature institutions. No doubt many of them sincerely believed that exhibitions would help their customers along the road to prosperity, and, as we have seen, others among them were directly involved in farming operations.[49] Yet the interest of the county seat businessmen in helping to organize county agricultural societies hardly revealed unalloyed altruism.

[46] C. Ray Aurner (ed.), *A Topical History of Cedar County, Iowa* (2 vols.; Chicago, 1910), II, 268.

[47] D. R. Burt, Elk Grove, Wisconsin, to Cyrus H. McCormick, May 20, 1854, ("McCormick Papers," Wisconsin State Historical Society, Madison, Wisconsin.)

[48] Wayne C. Neely, *The Agricultural Fair* (New York, 1935), pp. 84–87.

[49] See discussion of Hamilton County below.

One writer has called the period between 1850 and 1870 the "golden age" of the fair.[50] Another noted that "the whole burden of agricultural experimentation, instruction, extension, and recreation fell upon the agricultural societies whose work was carried on mainly through state and local fairs." [51] In these years the fair fathers strictly subordinated amusement to education. The central feature was the exhibition and judging of livestock. To attract a good display of agricultural machinery, the society officers frequently offered premiums, basing the awards sometimes on field trials. Plowing matches appeared on fair programs, and sometimes a best-local-farm or best-field-crop competition was held in conjunction with the exhibition. At evening sessions farmers heard addresses by experts and exchanged views on the problems of field and stable. At some key point in the events the farmer could hear some local or visiting dignitary affirm the virtues and future of husbandry. In these years the fair organizers frequently gave horse-racing a very minor place in the program or banned it altogether. Even the devotees of "female equestrianism" were forced to defend it as encouraging a skill that was essential to women who must brave the traffic on crowded city streets.[52]

If the agricultural exhibitions before 1870 "took the lead as agencies in improving livestock, in disseminating information regarding new varieties of plants and better methods of cultivation, in stimulating the invention and popularizing the use of new machinery, in advertising the products and the productive possibilities of the new regions," they came to share these functions with other agencies after that date.[53] The rise of farm organizations, the growth of the agricultural colleges, and increasing interest on the part of government in farm problems — all worked to this end. But the societies offered the newer agencies a showplace in which to attract the attention of farmers and continued their older functions as well. To some degree, indeed, the traditional services were improved — qualified specialists, for instance, replaced the premium committees of well-meaning amateurs whose decisions had so often caused ill feeling among exhibitors. The historian of Iowa agriculture believes that the county societies "reached the height of their interest and influence in the nineties." [54] By this time, however, commercialization and the urge to bring urban patrons through the wickets had changed the fairs. If not subordinated to it, education had to give amusement equal billing. The enemies of the horse race and the carnival retreated in despair.

Many farmers who never subscribed to the agricultural periodicals or paid much attention to the agricultural items in the local paper went to the

[50] Kenyon L. Butterfield, "Farmers' Social Organizations," in Liberty H. Bailey (ed.), *Cyclopedia of American Agriculture* (New York, 1909), IV, 292.

[51] Earle D. Ross, "The Evolution of the Agricultural Fair in the Northwest," *Iowa Journal of History and Politics*, XXIV (July 1926), 454.

[52] *Ibid.*, p. 457.

[53] *Ibid.*, p. 459.

[54] Earle D. Ross, *Iowa Agriculture: An Historical Survey* (Iowa City, 1951), p. 86.

fairs and benefited from them. Indeed, the greater emphasis upon amusement at the exhibitions after 1870 may have drawn more farmers than it
kept away. At the fair the farmer could have his questions about agricultural
machinery answered — by no less an expert than James Oliver himself,
perhaps — or see what a first rate steer looked like at two years old, or buy
a purebred sire. Many did these things and more.

The annual reports of the state agricultural societies contained much
material that interested progressive farmers. They included a summary of
the program at the state fair and also featured essays on varied aspects
of farming and reports from the county societies. The annual reports of
the State Agricultural Society today are one of the best sources of the history
of agriculture in Iowa and at the time must have been a gold mine for any
farmer interested enough to obtain a copy.

Presenting instruction in agriculture for the first time in the late 1860's,
the land-grant colleges of Illinois and Iowa also attempted to serve the
farm population. Until the late 1880's, at least, they were less important
as sources of new ideas than were the press and agricultural societies. Both
faculties and enrollments were small in the early years, and there was dis-
agreement over the curriculum and the tasks that the colleges should per-
form. Both institutions tried to organize county farmers' institutes during
their early years, but this activity flagged, and the widespread development
of institutes during the 1880's and 1890's grew out of the demands of a
variety of agricultural organizations and the direct response of the state
governments to these demands.[55] The colleges did, however, cooperate
by providing speakers for these agricultural gatherings. Although employees
of both the Illinois and the Iowa agricultural colleges conducted a variety
of agricultural experiments prior to the mid-1880's, major achievements
waited on the passage of the Federal Experiment Station or Hatch Act in
1887. The major contributions of the colleges prior to 1890 lay in the
introduction to improved farming methods, which they gave to small numbers of young men, and in providing speakers for farm meetings.

Most striking in these days of federal solicitude was the small part played
by the federal government in local agricultural affairs. Through the members
of the Iowa and Illinois congressional delegations, the Patent Office and
later the Department of Agriculture disseminated a considerable variety of
seeds to interested farmers. Acquired throughout the United States and
abroad, these seeds seldom proved successful in the hands of local farmers,
who sharply criticized the seed service as a result. From the 1840's onward
there issued each year from the same source a report on agriculture in the
United States, containing a wealth of material on agricultural topics. All too
few of these, no doubt, reached the dirt farmer.

[55] Liberty H. Bailey, *Farmers' Institutes: History and Status in the United States and
Canada,* John Hamilton, *History of Farmers' Institutes in the United States,* (U.S.
Department of Agriculture, Office of Experiment Stations, *Bulletin 79, 174,* [Wash-
ington, 1900, 1906]).

Active in the process of convincing farmers that they should accept innovations or change their farming practices in some way were a group of interested advocates. The processors of agricultural products like flax and sorghum contracted with farmers for the production of these crops. Importers and breeders of purebred stock, nurserymen, and seedsmen were also in this category as well as many farmers who tried to capitalize in a petty way on the seed from an exceptionally fine crop or the ownership of a few animals of an improved strain. Most impressive of the interested advocates during our period, certainly, were the farm-machinery men.

From the 1850's onward the agricultural-implement men campaigned relentlessly among midwestern farmers. Particularly able or fortunate captains in this infant industry guided their businesses from local, to regional, and finally, to national significance in the space of a generation, until as full-fledged generals they fought each other desperately for the lion's share of the market. Their struggles over patents and the control of patents were newsworthy and gave the agricultural-implement business much free advertising. Such publicity was only incidental to national advertising campaigns in the farm press, displays of machinery at the exhibitions, and participation in major field trials sponsored by the county and state agricultural societies and even by the international expositions of the time.

In the end, of course, the farmers decided which makers of agricultural machinery would prosper and which would fail. Nor did they always need to see the advertisements of the agricultural press or the displays at the fairs. Local agencies were eager to serve. Particularly down through the 1860's, local mechanics and blacksmiths made plows, horse rakes, or other simple implements, and might also purchase patent or agency rights for the manufacture or sale of machinery. Local merchants stocked agricultural machinery, and by the 1860's some stores specialized in it. The proprietors of such establishments competed with traveling salesmen based in the larger population centers. Farmers received the message of mechanization in local newspaper advertising, in farm-to-farm canvasses, in exhibits at the local hotels, and at field trials on the farms of co-operative farmers.

Particularly important were the field trials where farmers saw new machinery at work and, incidentally, implement salesmen under stress. Such tests sometimes produced an aftermath of gloating and infuriated rebuttal in the local newspaper, as the agents of successful machines tried to exploit their successes, and worsted rivals explained the reasons for failure. The agent for the Adams and French binder in Hamilton County, Iowa, explained, for instance, that the local Deering agents had flagrantly broken the rules in a local trial by using a machine that had already been thoroughly tested under a variety of cutting conditions, while he, on the other hand, had adhered to the rules and brought a factory-fresh binder to the trial with unfortunate results. Subsequent Deering advertisements caused him to explode, "It is said that the ordinary commercial traveler possesses the greatest amount of cheek of any known species of the animated creation. The government mule next, followed by the politician and 'machine agent,' but judging from a recent article . . . one would naturally conclude that the 'machine man' might yet be exalted to the rank preceding Uncle Sam's old standby." [56]

During the 1850's harvesting machinery was still very much an innovation on the farm. McCormick reaper-agents, writing to the home office during these years, discussed the factors that persuaded farmers to buy farm machinery. Economic conditions generally must be good, they believed, before many farmers would purchase. A good crop in the previous year was of some importance in affecting decision, but the crop prospects for the next harvest were crucial. When these were promising, farmers were most apt to order. Another series of factors involved the general manner of business and reputation of the company. It must faithfully observe the terms of any warranty or guarantee. Defective parts must be replaced promptly and, if possible, some form of recompense made voluntarily for losses suffered because of them. The machines must arrive at the time promised. Credit terms should be fair and moderately generous. The company was wise that avoided lawsuits with farmers, either as plaintiff or defendant.

Granted prosperous times and a good machine to sell, a great deal still depended on the local agent. He must be energetic, prompt, honest, and preferably not a lawyer if he was to win the confidence of the farmers. A series of letters written in 1854 by an astute agent D. R. Burt to Cyrus H. McCormick reveals a good deal about agent techniques and, incidentally too, about the farming community. In Iowa he reported reaper agents "as thick . . . as I ever saw the Yankee tin pedlers." At most hotels he encountered agents of John H. Manny, who were warning farmers to beware of machines infringing the Manny patent and promising that their machine could cut almost as much per day with two horses as the four-horse McCormick machine. As for the farmers, he found them somewhat indifferent, having become used to importunate reaper agents. He found himself "obliged to give my strategic history of machines of all kinds with much apparent knowledge of all and close by putting yours vastly ahead of all being the only real original reaper and improved to perfection." At Dubuque Burt scored a coup by inducing the president of the agricultural society to sell the Manny with which he was somewhat dissatisfied and take a McCormick machine. This gentleman was prepared to go further. Burt noted, "He is not known as an agent but recommends out of interest felt for the society and out of interest which I feel for his prosperity. I shall give him five dollars for each reaper he may assist me in selling." [57]

[56] *Hamilton Freeman*, August 2, 1882. The trial was described July 26, 1882.
[57] D. R. Burt, Waterloo, Iowa, to C. H. McCormick, April 30, 1854, ("McCormick Papers," Wisconsin State Historical Society).

When need be, Burt could dispense with undercover men and meet the enemy hand to hand. He wrote,

I found in the neighborhood . . . one of Manney's [sic] agents with a fancy-fully painted machine cutting the old prairie grass to the no small delight of the witnesses making sweeping and bold declaration about what his machine could do. . . . Well he had the start of me. . . . I began by breaking down on his fancy machine pointed out every objection. . . . And then stated to all my opinion of what would be the result should they purchase from Manney you pay one half money and give your note for the balance are prosecuted for the last note and the cheapest way out of the scrape is to pay the note keep the poor machine and in a short time purchase one from McCormick as Mr. Right has done. Now Gentlemen I am an old settler have shared all the hardships of this new country with you have taken it rough and smooth with [you] have often been imposed on in the way I allmost know you would be by purchasing the machine offered you today. I would say to all try your machine before your one half [payment] or any except the freight.[58]

He ended by offering McCormicks on this basis and sold twenty.

There was much effort on the part of agents to put machines in the hands of community leaders like — in Burt's case — the president of the Dubuque County Agricultural Society, whose example would lead others to follow suit. Key individuals in a community, however, sometimes popularized machines on their own initiative. In 1849 John Safley of Cedar County, Iowa, drove to Chicago and brought back the first reaper to enter the county. During that harvest he cut 200 acres of grain — considerably more than his own crop.[59] This illustrated the tendency of enterprising local farmers to capitalize on innovation by deriving profits from custom work. In an economy where custom milling had long been the practice, it was a logical develop-ment. Much of the agricultural machinery promised sufficient return on a reasonable investment so that most operators bought their own. Threshing machines or similarly expensive machinery that the farmer needed for only a few days generally remained the property of custom operators.

We can be sure that the problems of prairie adaptation and the new technology provoked a great deal of discussion among midwestern farmers. Much of this was informal, occurring at social gatherings or when neighbors met on the streets or in the stores of the little prairie trade centers and towns. The work-exchange groups or rings of neighbors, in which most farmers participated, must have been particularly significant forums for discussion and for the dissemination of new ideas. Here, corn-planting, harvesting, threshing, haying, or hog-killing was the work at hand; it was only natural that talk should turn to the technology of the task, or that

[58] *Ibid.*, June 26, 1854.
[59] Western Historical Company, *History of Cedar County, Iowa* . . . (Chicago, 1878), p. 672.

the farmers involved should discuss methods of increasing yields by different farm practices or by the introduction of new varieties of seeds.

Somewhat more formal organizations, dedicated to discussion, were the farmers' clubs, which were common if not numerous in many communities during the 1850's and 1860's. We know much too little about these clubs. The agricultural or local press referred to them on occasion, but they were local creations, often without constitution or set organization, meeting in the winter usually and designed to let farmers exchange views on farming problems. The clubs, no doubt, prepared the way for the Grange or Patrons of Husbandry, which spread like wildfire through Illinois and Iowa during the early 1870's.[60] In treating the history of the Grange, historians have often emphasized its political implications and the efforts of the members to regulate railroads and other middlemen or to establish co-operative enterprises. For the individual patron, however, the most significant aspect of membership may well have been the discussions that took place at most meetings of farm practices and the economic aspects of farming.

The characteristics of new communities undoubtedly affected the process of innovation. As we have seen, the persistence of new farmers did not change to any extent during the period of this study. But over time, a core of more permanent residents emerged in each community. In the earliest days of farm-making, the farm operators had only their experience in older settlements to guide them. The high turnover among the settlers meant that valuable experience in adapting to local conditions was lost to the new community. Newcomers must start from scratch, although increasingly, of course, they could draw upon the experience of old settlers among their neighbors.

The search for advice and leadership was more difficult, perhaps, than one might think.[61] When the farm-maker had moved to the West he typically ruptured a web of social relationships that had sustained him in his decision-making. Although pioneers frequently settled in areas where they had relatives or old friends, they must build up new systems of social relationships. Most important to the settler in this respect was the work ring of neighboring farmers. In this group he must find those whose advice was worth considering and reject the suggestions of others. There is some evidence to show that leaders in agricultural innovation were also leaders in other fields — politics for instance. Leadership in one sector reinforced leadership in another. But the period of community-making was typically a time of vigorous contest for political preferment; the power and influence structure

[60] Mildred Throne, "The Grange in Iowa, 1868–1875," *Iowa Journal of History* XLVII (October, 1949), 289–324; Solon J. Buck, *The Granger Movement: A Study of Agricultural Organization and its Political, Economic and Social Manifestations, 1870–1880* (Cambridge, 1913, 1933), pp. 40–79.

[61] I have explored frontier social processes tentatively in "Social Theory and the Pioneer," *Agricultural History*, XXXIV (January, 1960), 21–34.

of the community was not set as it would be twenty years or more later. The advice of some aspirants to leadership was better ignored.

Cultural factors, similarly, might slow the adoption of new ideas or techniques. The farmer of Kentucky or Tennessee antecedents undoubtedly followed the lead of another southerner more willingly than that of some Yankee newcomer to the community. One is on very dangerous ground, however, if he suggests that any particular cultural or national group was a great deal more progressive than others.[62]

In Hamilton and Bremer counties, Iowa, during 1880, the native-born and foreign-born farmers were not combining the factors of production much differently, although many members of the immigrant groups had been settled there for considerably less than a generation. In both counties the native-born did hire somewhat more labor than did the foreign-born.[63] In both counties, also, the native-born farmers did have a few more hogs and raised somewhat more corn and less wheat than did the foreign-born. In these respects the farming of the native-born more accurately forecast the patterns of the future than did those of the immigrants. Because the farm

[62] See chap. xi for a more detailed discussion of cultural differences.

[63] The Hamilton County figures appear in Allan G. Bogue, "Pioneer Farmers and Innovation," *Iowa Journal of History*, LVI (January, 1958), 34, where both a neighbor's and a 10 per cent random sample were presented. The random sample is reproduced below with the comparable Bremer County figures, also based on random 10 per cent samples of native- and foreign-born. Three hundred and ninety census returns were analyzed in the Hamilton County neighbor's sample; 150 in the random sample. Two hundred and seventeen census schedules are represented in the Bremer study.

FARMING PATTERNS OF THE NATIVE-BORN AND FOREIGN-BORN
FARMERS IN HAMILTON AND BREMER COUNTIES, 1880

	HAMILTON COUNTY		BREMER COUNTY	
	Native-Born	Foreign-Born	Native-Born	Foreign-Born
General:				
Farm size, acres	138.0	107.0	143.0	150.0
Value of machinery . .	$174.	$156.	$161.	$178.
Wages	50.	47.	64.	43.
Crops:				
Corn—				
Acres per farm	36.4	31.2	32.7	24.6
% of crop land	40.4	38.1	40.3	27.4
Wheat—				
Acres per farm	17.5	16.6	19.0	26.7
% of crop land	19.4	20.3	23.4	29.8
Oats—				
Acres per farm	9.5	5.5	11.2	14.3
% of crop land	10.5	6.8	13.8	16.0
Livestock:				
Milk cows per farm . .	5.7	5.5	6.1	7.6
Other cattle	12.0	6.6	9.0	10.9
Swine	29.5	19.0	37.1	33.0

units of the Europeans in Hamilton County were somewhat smaller than those of the native-born and since they owned fewer farm animals in general, I was at first inclined to attribute differences in their farming operations to lack of capital. This was perhaps true in Hamilton County, but in Bremer County the foreign-born farmers reported a few more cattle and slightly larger acreages to the census-taker than did the native farmers.

In every prairie community some men led in shifting their combination of enterprises in search of larger returns, in using purebred or high quality stock, and in introducing new crops and different varieties. They tried different cultivation practices, installed tile drainage, and used new types of fencing or methods of feeding stock. They improved the arrangement of their farm buildings and used improved machinery before their neighbors. From the county newspaper, biographical histories, and the agricultural society reports of Hamilton County, Iowa, I compiled a list of 110 individuals whose farming operations seemed progressive in one or more such ways or who held major offices in the agricultural society or Grange prior to 1891.

The annual reports of the Hamilton County Agricultural Society give the names of thirty-nine who filled one or more of the four major offices in that organization between its organization in late 1867 and the year 1890. Some of these men held such office for only a year, others for as many as five. Biographical information or the census returns of 1880 can tell us something of twenty-four of the men. Twelve were permanent residents of the county seat or else lived there for extended periods of time prior to retirement. This group included two mayors of Webster City, three of the leading bankers, several county officers, and two major stock-dealers who did not live on their farms.

The farm units of fifteen of the agricultural society officer group can be identified in the 1880 census returns. The average size was 234 acres in comparison to the county average in that year of 112 acres. Of fourteen who submitted returns for farming operations in the previous year, six had fed cattle on a considerable scale and three others had fattened cattle in previous years. The census of 1880 shows that approximately one out of every fifteen farmers in Hamilton County had either bought or sold as many as twenty cattle in the previous year or else reported "other cattle" in such numbers as to suggest that they were cattle-feeders. Evidently, the farming interest represented in the leadership of the agricultural society differed from the rank and file of Hamilton farmers in both scale of operations and in combination of enterprises.

Farmers organized eleven Grange chapters in Hamilton County during 1872 and 1873. The names of the first masters of nine chapters appeared in the *Iowa Homestead*. Biographical sketches of five of these men exist. The biography of W. W. Boak does not mention the amount of his education. Charles Whitaker, Ira Tremain, H. S. Orris, and J. W. Lee quite obviously had more education than the ordinary farmer.[64] Whitaker was a graduate of an eastern college, and Tremain finished his schooling at an eastern academy. Both Orris and Lee had themselves taught school. Four of the five also held elective office in the county or at the township level, and the fifth, Whitaker, had previously served in the war with the rank of lieutenant colonel. In addition to holding local office, Tremain ultimately represented the county in the state assembly.

The names of five of the nine Grange masters also appeared in the list of farmers who followed improved practices at an early date; in all cases they were advocates of improved stock. Two of the Grange masters, Boak and Tremain, also served the agricultural society in leading positions. It is difficult to discover the names of those who held minor office in the Grange, but the *Freeman* printed the complete slate of eleven male officers in the Saratoga chapter in early 1874.[65] Ten of these men returned agricultural schedules in the 1870 census. These showed that on the average they farmed units of 134 acres as compared to the township average of 129 acres. Only two of them were to be found among the twenty-four cattle-feeders in the township in 1880. Ten of the eleven, however, held township office during the 1870's or early 1880's.[66]

Livestock numbers increased considerably in Hamilton County during the 1880's. The manuscript census rolls of 1880 show that eighty-five Hamilton farmers either bought or sold as many as twenty cattle in the previous year. This method of selection excludes a few farmers who owned large herds of cattle and includes a few men who were primarily stock-dealers, but it certainly does give us a considerable number of the cattle-feeders who led in placing greater emphasis upon livestock in the county at the end of the pioneer period. The members of this group farmed 172 acres on the average, valued at $3,300, as compared to the county averages of 112 acres and $1,970. Although 20 per cent of the county farmers were tenants, only 16 per cent of the feeder group did not own their farms. Up to some point in middle age, farmers in general accumulate capital. Despite this rule and the fact that they operated larger units in a type of farming that demanded more capital than simple grain farming, the cattle-feeders were not appreciably older on the average than some 1,400 other county farmers.[67] Within the group of eighty-five the ratio of foreign-born to native-born farmers was roughly one to four and a half. Within the farmers of the county as a whole, this ratio was one to less than one and a half.[68]

[64] Lewis Biographical Publishing Company, *Biographical Record and Portrait Album of Hamilton and Wright Counties* . . . (Chicago, 1889), pp. 298–304, 318, 306, 385, 366.

[65] *Hamilton Freeman*, January 7, 1874.

[66] Through the kindness of Mrs. Percy Neese, of Stanhope, I was able to prepare a list of the early township officers of Hamilton Township from the township minute book, which she holds in her capacity as township clerk.

[67] The nearest whole number to both means was 42.

[68] This difference is statistically significant at the 1 per cent level.

Although the progressive farmer of one census year might well have
settled down to humdrum complacency ten years later, something may be
gained by a little closer analysis of the complete list of 110 agricultural
leaders that was mentioned earlier. Forty-five members of the group returned
agricultural schedules in 1880, showing the average farm size to be 203
acres and the average valuation $4,474. Only four tenants appeared among
the forty-five. Biographical data for all members of the group are not available, but at some point twenty-four of them held political office at the county
level or above. This method of establishing political leadership, of course,
works a hardship on the Democratic or independent candidates in the county
who seldom defeated the Republicans, but who still held the confidence
of many. Three members of the group of 100 ran strongly as candidates of
the minority parties on occasion. Twelve other members of the 110 held
offices of political trust on the township level, and this group might swell
considerably if lists of all township officers could be found. But at least
thirty-nine members of the group of 110 did demonstrate leadership in a
field of interest that was not directly related to agriculture.

Through our discussion of the leadership group in Hamilton County,
there runs consistently the suggestion that the innovators, those who first
introduced new or improved techniques, conducted farm operations that
were above the average in size. The big operator or the non-resident capitalist owner had the capital necessary to effect major alterations in his farm
business or to introduce new machinery as soon as it became available. If
his experiments were successful, he not only added to his store of capital
but educated the smaller farmers in the vicinity of his farm to the merits
of the innovations. This process could work two ways. The unsuccessful
experiments of large farmers also taught the neighbors a lesson. For some
of the innovators, the goal was more than a personal one. Of Judge Rose,
founder of Rose Grove Township in Hamilton County, a local historian
wrote:

As a farmer he was an enthusiast, and always expected to receive large financial
returns, while benefiting the community at the same time by introducing new
crops or new methods. Everybody . . . in the county at that time remembers
his attempt to revolutionize farming and hog-raising by the introduction of his
Jerusalem artichoke. Nearly everybody caught the fever . . . but the whole
scheme flattened out and left him a great loser.[69]

In Judge Rose and others like him the quest for personal gain merged with
the country-gentry ideal of public service.

Yet it was not the large operator alone who was interested in innovation
and improvement. A number of farmers of moderate means and business
in Hamilton County sought to introduce new varieties of seeds and called

[69] J. W. Lee, *History of Hamilton County, Iowa, Illustrated* (2 vols.; Chicago, 1912)
I, 152.

for a variety of improvements in farming methods. Neither the spirit of inquiry nor the desire for profit was restricted solely to the larger operators.

Once proven successful by the innovator, new practices spread through the prairie communities at a speed related directly to the savings or additional profits expected. In this process discussion and the decisions of respected members of the community were undoubtedly of great importance. Rural sociologists write today of innovators, community adoption leaders, and local adoption leaders. An agricultural economist has referred to varying types of entrepreneurship among farmers, suggesting the terms innovating, imitative, "Fabian," and drone entrepreneurship. The agricultural historian at this range, can hardly categorize with certainty. But we can safely conclude that illustrations of the practical use of new machinery, of the superior qualities of purebred sires, and of the merits of clover, and of tile drainage were found frequently at an early stage of community acceptance on the farms of the non-resident proprietors, the large stock-dealer, and the county-seat farmer as well as on a small proportion of the farms tilled by owner-operators. No matter the category into which such a proprietor fell, he usually had a larger than average holding and capital investment. Most frequently he was native-born, he was not appreciably above average in age, and he was more likely than most to be tapped for political office. His level of education was probably somewhat above average. On the farms of such men were first traced the unique patterns of Corn Belt agriculture.

CHAPTER XI

They Call It The Corn Belt

Did the middle-western pioneer follow a unique kind of agriculture? To some historians the pioneer has typically been a wheat-raiser; to others he was a subsistence farmer. Was the typical farm-maker a rugged individualist who planted the crops and raised the animals that pleased him regardless of the decisions of his neighbors? Or did the farming-type areas that the agricultural economists discovered in the middle-western states during the 1920's and 1930's have histories extending back to the nineteenth century? In answering such questions we can use the agricultural statistics of the federal censuses.

In the course of this study I have prepared maps that show the production of the various field crops per improved acre and the average number of the various kinds of livestock per farm in the counties of Illinois and Iowa in the federal-census years from 1850 to 1890.[1] On these maps I indicated

[1] Census Office: *Statistical View of the United States . . . Being a compendium of the Seventh Census . . .* (Washington, 1854), pp. 220–23, 232–35; *Agriculture of the United States in 1860 . . .* (Washington, 1864), pp. 30–37, 46–53, 197, 199; *The Statistics of the Wealth and Industry of the United States . . .* (Washington, 1872), pp. 130–37, 146–53, 349–50, 351; *Report on the Production of Agriculture as Returned at the Tenth Census* (Washington, 1883), pp. 111–12, 114–15, 149–50, 151–52, 185–86, 187–88, 220–21, 223–24, 266–70, 272–75; *Report on the Statistics of Agriculture in the United States at the Eleventh Census: 1890* (Washington, 1895), 134–37, 138–41, 204–06, 207–08, 243–44, 246–47, 283–84, 285–86.

Agricultural historians have long plotted the data of the agricultural censuses on maps as an aid to understanding the varied patterns of American agriculture. Often they have used the dot map, which, by the texture of its stippling, shows the relative amounts of livestock held by the farmers of a particular state or region. The dot map or other maps that simply present the crude statistics of the agricultural census in pictorial form can give a misleading picture of the types of farming in a region or state if the density of the population varied considerably from area to area or if the land in some counties was more generally improved than that in others. This, of course, was the case in the era of settlement. Longer settled counties had many more farmers and a higher percentage of improved land than did those more recently occupied. Much preferable to dot maps, therefore, are ones which show agricultural production in relation to the number of farmers and the degree of improvement in a particular county. On the other hand, it seemed unnecessary for my purposes to use the sophisticated isoplethic mapping techniques that agricultural geographers are using today. Two earlier efforts to map nineteenth-century farming patterns in Illinois and Iowa are: Peter Nelson, "A History of Agriculture in Illinois with Special Reference to Types of Farming" (unpub-

whether the crop production or the number of livestock placed a county in the first, second, third, fourth, or fifth and lowest quintile of counties in the state — using quartiles in the case of Iowa in 1850 when a relatively small number of counties was involved. The production maps did reveal concentrations of high-, intermediate-, and low-producing counties, which suggested that the farmers of various districts in Illinois and Iowa combined the enterprises in their farm businesses differently than did the farmers of other sections of these states.

Maps showing the relative acreages that were devoted to the various crops would have been most revealing, but unfortunately, the federal censuses did not contain this information until 1880. Prior to that year a number of Iowa state censuses did list the acreages of land occupied by the different field crops.[2] Maps based on some of these data, and on the acreage figures of the 1880 federal census, conformed, in general, with the appropriate production maps. Obviously, bad crop years and, to a lesser extent, differences in soil fertility might cause variations between maps based on acreage and those based on production.

In 1849, the crop year of the 1850 census, the farmers of northern Illinois placed greater emphasis upon the wheat crop than did those of central and southern Illinois. All but one of the counties in the two northern tiers fell within the first or top quintile. By 1869, however, the farms on which wheat was most important in Illinois extended from the lower Military Tract south through the watersheds of the lower Illinois and Kaskaskia rivers to the southern tip of the state. In none of the five census years did the farmers of east-central Illinois emerge as leading wheat-producers. Only once did McLean County, for instance, rise as high as the third quintile among wheat-producing counties.

In part, the range between the high- and low-producing counties indicates the degree to which the farmers of various districts specialized in a particular crop. In 1849 Boone County headed the first-quintile counties; the farmers here harvested 4.9 bushels of wheat per improved acre. In contrast, the farmers of Hardin County produced only 0.05 bushels per improved acre. The range varied little from this in 1859 and 1869, but in 1879 and 1888 the farmers of the leading Illinois county, Monroe, raised approximately ten and nine bushels of wheat for each acre of improved land in the county while those in Ford did not raise enough to show in the first two digits past the decimal point. Wheat was apparently more important in the farming patterns of the farmers of 1879 and 1889 in southwestern Illinois than it had been on the pioneer farms of northern Illinois some thirty years earlier.

lished Ph.D. dissertation, University of Illinois, 1930) and Duane C. Hawk, "Iowa Farming Types: 1850–1880" (unpublished M.A. thesis, State University of Iowa, 1957).

[2] The Iowa state census data are most conveniently collected in *Census of Iowa for 1880 . . . with Other Historical and Statistical Data . . .* (Des Moines, 1883).

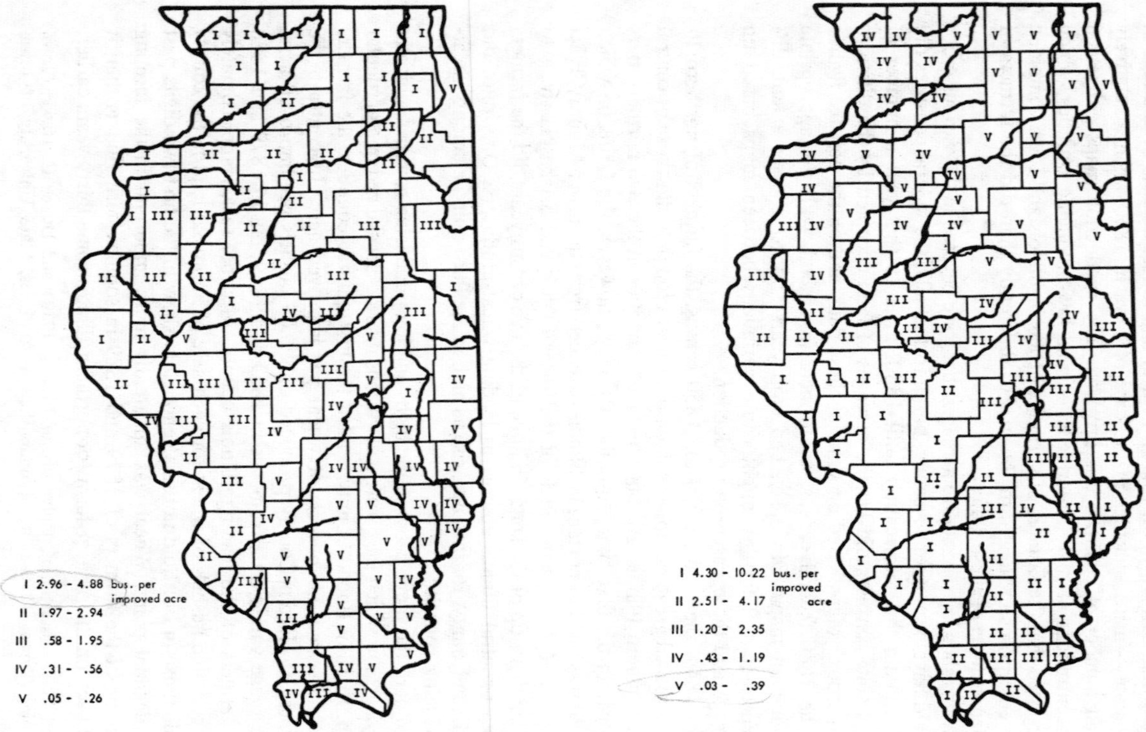

Fig. 5. — Wheat production in Illinois in 1849 (*left*) and in 1879 (*right*)

by 1880 produced less wheat

I	4.30 - 10.22 bus. per improved acre
II	2.51 - 4.17
III	1.20 - 2.35
IV	.43 - 1.19
V	.03 - .39

I	2.96 - 4.88 bus. per improved acre
II	1.97 - 2.94
III	.58 - 1.95
IV	.31 - .56
V	.05 - .26

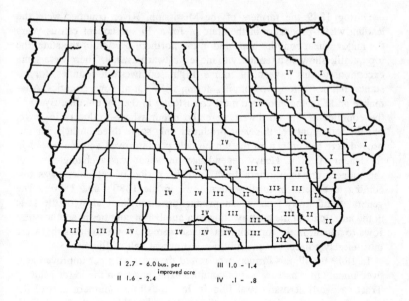

I 2.7 – 6.0 bus. per
   improved acre
II 1.6 – 2.4

III 1.0 – 1.4

IV .1 – .8

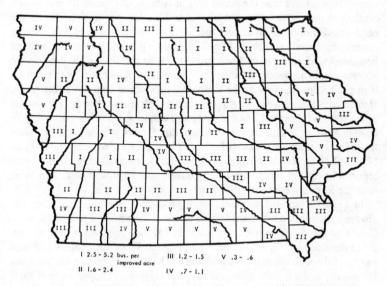

I 2.5 – 5.2 bus. per
   improved acre
II 1.6 – 2.4

III 1.2 – 1.5

IV .7 – 1.1

V .3 – .6

Fig. 6. — Wheat production in Iowa in 1849 (*top*) and in 1879 (*bottom*)

During 1849 the farmers of the Mississippi River counties were the leading wheat-producers in the state of Iowa. In subsequent census years the major wheat counties appeared in the northern portion of the state, the top quintile showing a tendency to move westward as well. There were some exceptions to this pattern, of course. Eight southwestern counties, for instance, fell in the top two quintiles during 1859. Of all Iowa counties, Allamakee and Clayton appeared most consistently in the top quintile. By 1889 the counties of the northwest were the major wheat-producers in Iowa, but the top county of this year produced only some three bushels per improved acre in contrast to the ten bushels per improved acre harvested in the leader of 1869. Heavy dependence on wheat was a characteristic of the pioneer era in northern Iowa, and the period of settlement was just coming to an end in northwestern Iowa in the 1880's and 1890's. The general trend away from wheat production throughout most of the state in the latter part of the century allowed a number of counties in southeastern Iowa to appear in the top quintiles. These were the Iowa counties that were most closely adjacent to the southwestern wheat belt of Illinois.

In 1849 the Illinois farmers who raised the most corn per improved acre lived mainly in a narrow belt of counties extending from the lower Military Tract eastward across central Illinois. In the extreme southern part of the state a few counties of the top quintile bordered the Ohio and the Mississippi. Most of the lower- or fifth-quintile counties lay in northern Illinois, above the Illinois River. Over time the major area of corn production in Illinois moved northward somewhat in central Illinois and the low-production area of the north steadily diminished in size. Increasingly, too, numbers of fifth-quintile counties appeared in southern Illinois. A distinct break in production patterns had developed as early as 1849, running along the line of the Shelbyville Moraine and the divide between the Illinois and Kaskaskia watersheds — high-production counties to the north, low-production counties to the south. If the census figures were accurate, a questionable assumption perhaps, some of the Illinois farmers of 1849 placed more emphasis upon corn than did the leading farmers of later census enumeration. Six counties reported production of more than twenty bushels of corn to the improved acre in that year. Not until 1879 did the farmers of the leading corn-producing county again report a harvest of more than twenty bushels per improved acre. Ten years later the leaders were below this figure.

In Iowa the area of maximum corn production per improved acre was always concentrated to a considerable extent in the southern half of the state. Over time this district moved westward. By 1889 the area of heaviest production extended north from Fremont and Page to Woodbury and Ida, thence eastward through central Iowa and Story. The counties of east-central Iowa fell usually in the middle quintiles, but good crop years carried some of them into the highest rankings. By 1889 a section of low production had developed in the southeast. Emphasis on corn in the northeastern counties was always

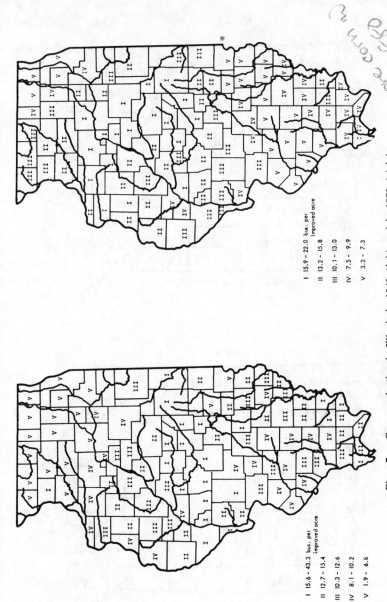

More corn (1880)

I 15.6 – 43.3 bus. per
improved acre
II 12.7 – 15.4
III 10.3 – 12.6
IV 8.1 – 10.2
V 1.9 – 6.6

I 15.9 – 22.0 bus. per
improved acre
II 13.2 – 15.8
III 10.1 – 13.0
IV 7.5 – 9.9
V 3.2 – 7.3

Fig. 7.—Corn production in Illinois in 1849 (*left*) and in 1879 (*right*)

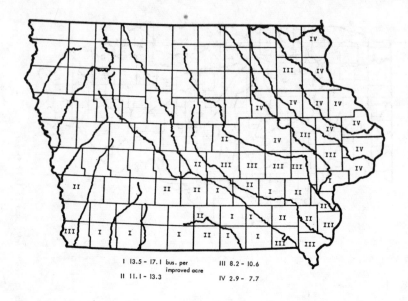

I 13.5 - 17.1 bus. per   III 8.2 - 10.6
improved acre

II 11.1 - 13.3   IV 2.9 - 7.7

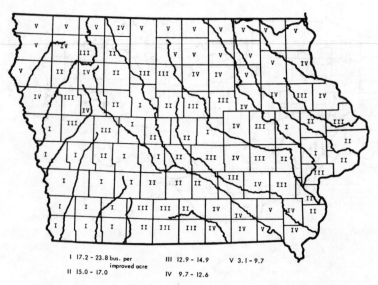

I 17.2 - 23.8 bus. per   III 12.9 - 14.9   V 3.1 - 9.7
improved acre

II 15.0 - 17.0   IV 9.7 - 12.6

Fig. 8. — Corn production in Iowa in 1849 (*top*) and in 1879 (*bottom*)

relatively light, and in 1889 the counties of the two northern tiers in Iowa appeared generally in the two lower quintiles of corn-producers. Farmers in the leading counties in 1889 were not producing strikingly larger amounts of corn per improved acre than had the leaders in 1849, although there had been a distinct trend toward greater corn production per improved acre in the state as a whole.

In the years between 1849 and 1889 the farmers of northern Illinois consistently relied more heavily upon the oat crop than did those of southern Illinois. Down to the 1870's the farmers of the Kaskaskia Valley were an exception to this rule. By 1879 only one county in that region remained in the top two quintiles of oat-producing counties and ten years later there were none. Although a few counties of the Sangamon watershed were in the upper 20 per cent in 1849, most central Illinois counties appeared in the middle quintiles or even the bottom fifth. By 1889 almost all of the central counties from the Sangamon watershed northward were in the upper 40 per cent of oat-producing counties.

By 1869 the oat crop was a rather good indicator of farming differences between the northern and southern districts of the Illinois Military Tract. Some of the northern counties of the tract fell within the second quintile while the cropping programs of farmers in the lower counties placed them among the low 20 per cent of Illinois counties. The range from lowest to highest producer among Illinois counties showed little change until the decade of the 1880's, although the top county always showed some gain over the leader of the previous census. In 1889, however, the farmers of Will County harvested 10.8 bushels of oats for every improved acre in the county, while the leaders of 1879 in Boone County had raised only 5.8 bushels for every improved acre in the county. During this decade the range from lowest to highest county rose from 5.6 to 10.3 bushels.

The Iowa farmers who depended most heavily upon the oat crop in 1849 farmed in the northeastern river counties and in a block in the southeastern corner of the state, athwart the lower Des Moines and Skunk rivers. In later years the counties of the top quintile usually appeared in northern Iowa, with the district moving westward somewhat, census by census. In 1889 the upper 20 per cent of oat-raising counties lay in a solid block in north-central Iowa, extending as far south as Boone and Story counties and ringed by the counties of the second quintile. The southern counties of Iowa and the western slope were districts of particularly low production. The history of the production range from lowest to highest producer was very similar to that of Illinois, although prior to 1879 the top Iowa counties reported a slightly higher average production per improved acre than was true in Illinois. As in that state the leading counties showed a very marked gain in the decade of the 1880's, reflecting considerably greater emphasis on this crop in the areas of highest production.

Barley, rye, and flax were all minor field crops, but they did offer the prairie farmers alternatives to the culture of the three major grains. Among Illinois farmers, barley apparently attained its largest popularity around 1869 when the census marshals of twenty-four counties in the northern part of the state reported more than 0.1 of a bushel per improved acre. In that year the farmers of Ogle County, the leading producer, harvested a bushel of barley for each of their improved acres.

Iowa farmers depended on the barley crop to a greater extent than did Illinois farm-operators. In the leading county in 1859, Iowans produced almost 1.5 bushels of barley per improved acre, and in the next three federal-census years this maximum figure rose to 2.7, 3.3, and in 1899, 4.4. Between 1849 and 1869 the major barley counties lay along the Mississippi River where farmers supplied the breweries of the central river towns. Barley was usually a commoner crop in northern Iowa than in the southern part of the state. By 1879 the farmers of northwestern Iowa were showing considerable interest in this cereal, and in 1889 a group of nineteen counties in that region raised more than 1 bushel per improved acre. The farmers of both Ida and O'Brien counties harvested more than 3.5 bushels for each improved acre. The increasing importance of barley as a grain crop in northwestern Iowa coincided with the declining importance of wheat in that region. None of the northwestern counties, however, had displaced Scott County as the leading barley county in Iowa. The farmers of this Mississippi River county produced the largest barley crop per improved acre in every census year from 1849 to 1889.

The farmers of Illinois and Iowa placed less reliance upon rye than upon barley. In neither state did the farmers of any county ever produce as much as 1 bushel of rye per improved acre in a census year. In Stephenson County, Illinois, they harvested 0.95 bushels per improved acre in 1889. In 1849 rye was primarily a crop of the lower Wabash watershed in Illinois; thereafter, we find it grown more generally in northern Illinois and in the counties of the central Illinois Valley. Through 1869 the Iowa farmers of the lower Des Moines, Skunk, and Iowa-Cedar river systems were most likely of all Iowa farmers to grow rye, although the operators of Allamakee, in the northeastern corner of the state, led those of all other counties in production of the crop in 1849. In 1879 and 1889 rye remained primarily a crop of southeastern Iowa, but the farmers of the northern Mississippi River counties generally were showing a somewhat greater interest in it. In the latter years, Allamakee farmers again led the list of Iowa rye-producers, harvesting about one-third of a bushel per improved acre.

Particularly in southeastern Illinois and southeastern Iowa, farmers reported minor production of flax, mainly for fiber, in 1849 and 1859. During the 1870's the farmers of east-central and northern Illinois and central and northwestern Iowa began to grow the crop for seed in larger quantities. The crop of 1879 in Ford County, Illinois, yielded nine-tenths of a bushel for every acre of improved land in the county. The farmers of Osceola County, the Iowa leaders, produced one-third of a bushel for every acre of improved land in the county. Production of flax in Illinois had fallen off sharply by 1889. Iowa farm-operators produced almost 2,300,000 bushels, with a marked concentration of production in the northern interior and, particularly, in the northwestern corner counties. Farmers in O'Brien County harvested slightly more than a bushel of flax seed per improved acre of farmland in 1889.

Since pioneer farmers made a great deal of hay from the prairie grasses of the public domain and the unimproved lands of non-residents, figures showing the number of tons of hay cured per farm unit in each county are more indicative of farming practices for the early census years than are statistics that relate the hay crop to improved acreage. The patterns that the index, tons of hay cured per farm, revealed on county maps of Illinois and Iowa remained remarkably consistent through the last half of the nineteenth century. In Illinois the farmers to the north of the upper bend of the Illinois River consistently cured enough hay to place their counties within the upper 40 per cent of Illinois counties. Counties below the mouth of the Illinois fell almost invariably within the lower 60 per cent, and those below the mouth of the Kaskaskia were almost inevitably in the lowest 20 per cent.

In Iowa the area of greatest hay production lay consistently in the northern section of the state, but in 1870 a district of high output on the Missouri slope extended into southern Iowa. In eastern Iowa farmers usually cured large amounts of hay in an area extending from north-central Iowa diagonally in a southeasterly direction down the Iowa-Cedar, the Wapsipinicon and the Maquoketa river systems. In Illinois the farmers of the leading county in 1849 cured 26.7 tons of hay on the average, as compared to 69.3 tons in 1889. In Iowa the comparable figures were 30 and 84.3 tons.

Although a few counties of the Military Tract appeared in the top 40 per cent of Illinois swine-producing counties in 1850, most of the counties of the two top quintiles lay to the east of the Illinois River and below the Sangamon. Morgan County and its immediate neighbors formed a cluster of high swine producers and another group of top-quintile counties lay in the lower water-shed of the Wabash in southeastern Illinois. The counties of the lowest 20 per cent made an almost solid block, lying north of the big bend of the Illinois. Over time the counties of the upper quintile appeared increasingly above the mouth of the Illinois River. In 1860 this tendency showed itself by a projection of the Morgan-Sangamon cluster of top-quintile counties farther to the eastward. Ten years later nine counties of the upper 20 per cent lay in the Military Tract.

By 1880, six counties of the lower Rock River region lay in the top quintile of Illinois hog production, and of the northern counties in Illinois only Lake and Cook were still ranked in the lowest quintile. From 1870 onward the district of lowest hog production per farm settled south of the Shelbyville Moraine. Of the counties lying below the mouth of the Illinois River, only

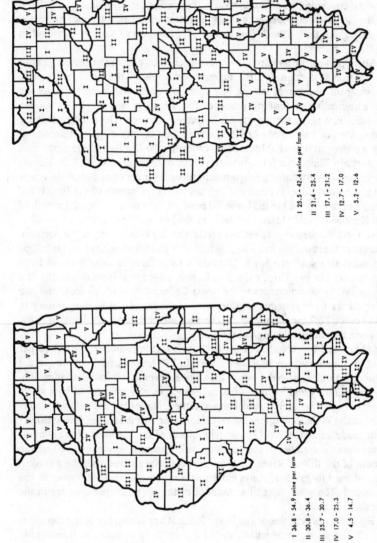

Fig. 9. — Swine production in Illinois in 1849 (*left*) and in 1879 (*right*)

I 25.5 - 42.4 swine per farm
II 21.4 - 25.4
III 17.1 - 21.2
IV 12.7 - 17.0
V 5.2 - 12.6

I 36.8 - 54.9 swine per farm
II 30.8 - 36.4
III 25.7 - 30.7
IV 17.0 - 25.3
V 4.5 - 14.7

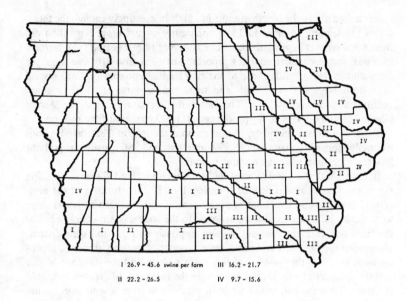

I 26.9 - 45.6 swine per farm   III 16.2 - 21.7

II 22.2 - 26.5   IV 9.7 - 15.6

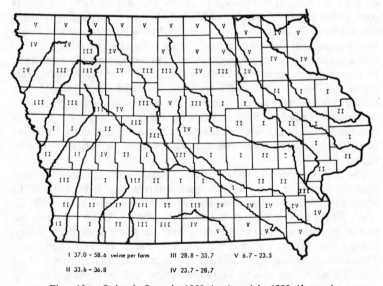

I 37.0 - 58.6 swine per farm   III 28.8 - 33.7   V 6.7 - 23.5

II 33.6 - 36.8   IV 23.7 - 28.7

Fig. 10. — Swine in Iowa in 1850 (*top*) and in 1880 (*bottom*)

three ranked above the fourth quintile in 1880. Interestingly enough the farmers of the leading counties in 1850 apparently owned more hogs than did their counterparts in any subsequent census year of our period. The farmers in Knox and Alexander counties reported sixty-five and fifty-five hogs per farm unit in 1850, while those of the two leading counties of 1860 owned thirty-four hogs per farm unit, and their counterparts of 1870 reported twenty-six and twenty-three. Thereafter the trend was upward. Mercer County farmers, the leading producers of 1890, counted fifty pigs on the average. We must remember, of course, that the hog of 1850 lived a considerably longer life than that of 1890, and that the 1850 census was perhaps less accurate than were later enumerations.

In both 1850 and 1860 most of the Iowa counties that led in swine-raising lay in the four southern tiers of counties. By 1880 the farmers of the east-central counties and the counties of the central and southern Missouri slope were the major swine-producers in Iowa. In the southeastern counties below the third tier, farmers were putting less emphasis on pigs, and their district, along with the northern and northwestern counties, was an area of low production. By 1890 the counties of the western slope and the Raccoon Valley and the counties of east-central Iowa were the two areas of greatest output in the state. To some extent the range of production from low to high county reveals a pattern similar to the Illinois picture. Here, too, the farmers of the leading county of 1850 had more hogs than their counterparts of 1870, forty-six hogs per farm in comparison to twenty-five. But by 1890 the leading counties had eclipsed those of 1850, since the highest county average of 1890 was sixty pigs for farm. The lowest county of 1890 in Iowa averaged seventeen hogs per farm unit, as compared to an average of seven in Illinois.

Sheep-raising was an important enterprise in the business of many Illinois farmers during this period. In 1850 the farmers of the central Military Tract and central Illinois, east of the Illinois River, reported flocks that placed many of their counties in the top two quintiles. The counties of eastern Illinois from Will south to Crawford all fell in these same categories. Sangamon and Knox counties led all others with averages of thirty-seven and thirty sheep per farm. Sheep were few in northwestern, southwestern, and extreme southern Illinois.

The censuses of 1860 and 1870 showed that the greatest number of sheep per farm were to be found in the Wabash watershed and in the valley of the upper Kaskaskia. A cluster of counties in the northeast also appeared in the upper 20 per cent of counties in both of these years. Sheep were least important in a belt of counties stretching from the lower Rock River Valley, through the northern valley of the Illinois to the eastern side of the state. Thereafter, a few counties of northeastern Illinois, some of the counties of the lower Illinois Valley and the Sangamon region, and the Wabash watershed were the major centers of sheep-raising in the state. These changing patterns occurred, of course, while the number of sheep in Illinois was declining, but the decline was more clearly apparent in some areas than in others. By 1890, Lake County with its average of 28.6 sheep per farm was the only Illinois county whose farmers counted more than ten sheep per farm on the average.

Analysis of the federal-census figures reveals a more consistent pattern of sheep production in Iowa than in Illinois. Most of the upper 20 per cent of sheep-producing counties in Iowa always lay in southern Iowa where a block of counties in the lower Des Moines and Skunk River valleys formed the nucleus of the largest block of top-quintile counties. Of this group Van Buren County led all sheep-producing counties in Iowa in four of the five census years from 1850 to 1890. The top Iowa counties never reported as large a number of sheep per farm as did those in Illinois, but in 1890 three of the counties in Iowa reported an average of more than ten sheep per farm, while farmers in only one Illinois county averaged above ten sheep per farm. In 1880 a block of counties on the north-central slope and in the upper watershed of the Des Moines River appeared in the top 40 per cent of Iowa's sheepraising counties. Although interest had subsided in those counties ten years later, six counties in the northwestern corner of the state did fall in the top two quintiles.

Areas of high and low concentration of milk cows appeared on the censusdata map of Illinois in 1850, but the patterns were much more broken than would later be true. Milk cows were most common in the northern Military Tract, along the upper Illinois River and in the section between the Sangamon and Kaskaskia valleys. One district of low concentration occurred in the counties of the southern tip and stretched north along the Wabash. The counties of the lower Military Tract and northern tier provided others. By 1860 there had clearly emerged a major regional pattern in which the northern counties reported the greatest number of milk cows, southern Illinois provided most of the lower 40 per cent of Illinois counties, and the central counties fell into the intermediate quintiles. A few counties of the lower Illinois Valley appeared consistently in the lower quintiles and provided an exception to this rule.

By 1890 milk cows appeared in heaviest concentration in Illinois above the northern bend of the Illinois River. The boundary of the low-concentration area of fourth- and fifth-quintile counties in southern Illinois was less neatly outlined. From southern Illinois these counties extended north through eastern Illinois to include Champaign County, while counties of the second and third quintiles ran from the lower Illinois Valley southward to Randolph and Perry counties between the Kaskaskia and Big Muddy rivers. The increase in the number of cows reported by the farmers of the leading counties, census by census, reflected the growth of a specialized dairying region in northern Illinois. Standing at 8.3 in 1870, this figure had risen to 17.5 in 1890.

Throughout the counties of central, eastern, and southeastern Iowa, milk cows played their most important role relatively in 1850. Ten years later the numbers of cows in these counties still placed them among the leaders in the state, but a number of counties on the western slope and in the northwest also appeared in the top 40 per cent. The picture was similar in 1870, although the region of major concentration in eastern Iowa had moved north and now ran northwesterly to some degree along the river valleys of northeastern Iowa. This was the region that is today the dairying area of Iowa. By 1890 the western areas of high concentration had moved east to meet the northeastern district in north-central Iowa. Only one county in the top quintile lay south of the four northern tiers of Iowa counties.

The federal census enumerations of "other cattle" would probably have been more revealing of farming practices if the marshals had done their work in December rather than in the summer as was usual. By the first of June the cattlemen of Illinois and Iowa had often cleared the winter's steers from their lots and planned to replace them in the late summer or early fall. This distortive factor was probably much less important in 1850 and 1860 than later, because cattlemen in those years still finished many of their steers on grass during the late spring and early summer or carried cattle, bought as stockers, through two winters and a summer. Feeder cattle probably played a more important role in the agriculture of east-central Illinois in 1880 and 1890 than maps of the "other cattle" population reveal.

As in the case of other types of livestock, the maps showing the average numbers of other cattle per farm unit in the various Illinois counties do indicate districts of high and low production as early as 1850. In that year a number of counties in the top two quintiles lay in the lower Rock Valley and the upper Military Tract. The greatest number of counties in the upper 20 per cent appeared in a belt to the east of the Illinois River, lying below the Sangamon and extending eastward from its watershed. Smaller numbers of other cattle appeared in the northeast, along the northern border of the state, and in a district that ran from Clark County south along the Wabash to include thirteen counties of the Illinois tip. By 1870 almost all of the fourth- and fifth-quintile counties lay in southern Illinois. Through 1850 and 1860 the counties of the middle Kaskaskia Valley had ranked in the two upper quintiles. In 1870 these counties, like their neighbors, appeared in the lower 40 per cent. In this year Morgan and Sangamon counties and a few of their neighbors in the Illinois-Sangamon region still reported large numbers of other cattle per farm as did a few counties directly to the east, but now the northern Military Tract and counties still farther to the north ranked in the top quintile. Ten years later only Morgan, Sangamon and Edgar below the Illinois remained in the upper 20 percent, and most of the counties of that group lay in a solid block formed by the northern Military Tract and counties to the north and northeast. In 1890 some counties immediately east of the lower Illinois had improved their positions, but the general pattern was similar to that of 1880. As in the case of swine, the farmers of the leading county of 1850 had a larger average number of other cattle than did those of the leading counties in succeeding censuses. This remained true actually until 1890, when the average of eighteen head of other cattle per farm reported by the farmers of Warren County was finally greater than the seventeen reported from McLean in 1850.

There was somewhat less tendency for the Iowa counties where other cattle were found in considerable numbers to form contiguous blocks than was the case in Illinois. However, we can generalize to some extent from our census-data maps. A number of the central counties of eastern Iowa were always numbered among the top 40 per cent of Iowa counties. Consistently also, a number of counties of the western slope fell into the top two quintiles, although they were not always the same counties. From 1860 onward more than half of the top-quintile counties were located in the western half of the state. After 1870 the southeastern counties of the lower Des Moines and Skunk valleys formed a low-concentration area, and the same was true of the northeastern counties. Plymouth, Cherokee, and the four counties to the north of them formed a district where the farmers consistently kept small numbers of other cattle. As in Illinois, the farmers of the top county of 1850 listed more other cattle than did those of 1860, but thereafter the average number in the leading county rose steadily to an average of twenty-two per farm unit in 1890 in Union County. This was a higher figure than any recorded in Illinois.

Much of the writing on the frontier of the Middle West suggests that there was a kind of agriculture typical to pioneer regions. To some writers this pioneer agriculture was evidently synonymous with subsistence agriculture. Others have stressed the importance of wheat as a pioneer crop, which farmers largely abandoned after the settlement period by shifting to heavier production of other grains and livestock. Maps that show the farming patterns of Iowa and Illinois at ten-year intervals only, can neither prove nor disprove such theories, but they do allow us to test them to some degree. One gains the general impression from the census maps that the various regions of Illinois and Iowa did not pass through exactly the same progresson of cropping patterns. The pioneer of northwestern Iowa during the 1870's and 1880's, indeed, placed considerable dependence on a crop that was little grown on the older frontiers of the state — flax. The wheat crop was apparently much more important to the early farmers of northern Illinois than to those of central Illinois, and we can draw the same contrast between northern and southern Iowa.

If the pioneers had followed a subsistence type of agriculture, the frontier counties in any particular census should not have ranked among the leading counties of their state in the production of any particular crop or kind of livestock. They should instead have appeared in the central sections of the rating lists, because the frontier farmers were maintaining a considerable variety of farm enterprises while concentrating on none. Of the forty-four Iowa counties listed in the federal agricultural census of 1850, nineteen had population densities of less than six to the square mile — the Turnerian definition of the agricultural frontier. These counties extended from Alla-makee in the northeastern corner of Iowa, southwesterly to Pottawattamie and Fremont in the southwestern corner of the state. Isolating these counties, I compared them to discover where they appeared in the lists that ranked the Iowa counties in terms of corn, wheat, and oats production per improved acre, the average number of tons of hay cured per farm, and the numbers of hogs, sheep, other cattle, and milk cows per farm. Apparently the production patterns of the frontier counties in Iowa in 1850 did not uniformly reflect a system of subsistence agriculture. Nine of the counties appeared in the top two quartiles among the wheat-producers, and eight stood among the top two quartiles of corn producers. In the case of every crop or type of livestock the frontier counties placed between nine and fifteen of their number in the top or bottom quartiles, indicating specialization, rather than a generalized sub-sistence-farming type.

Using Allamakee County as anchor, I ranked the other eighteen counties according to the number of quartiles by which they differed from that coun-ty's quartile ranking over the eight variables (see Table 21). Most similar to the production patterns of Allamakee were those of Clinton County. Where Allamakee farmers harvested enough oats to place that county in the top quartile of oat-producers, Clinton fell in the second quartile. Where Alla-makee as a hog-producer ranked in the third quartile, Clinton fell in the fourth or bottom 25 per cent. The other quartile scores of these two counties were the same and the quartile variance of Clinton from Allamakee was two. Next came Delaware with a variance of five, and at the bottom of the list stood Madison County with a variance of nineteen.

In general, the scaling pattern ranked the Iowa frontier counties from north to south. The first six counties all lay in the northern half of the state. Of the top ten only Fremont was located in the southern three tiers of Iowa counties. Of the bottom nine counties, seven lay in the southwestern part of the state and two in the central region. Quite clearly the frontier agriculture of the top six counties revealed a different proportioning of farm enterprises than was the case in the southwestern counties lower in the scale. There was no uniform frontier type of agriculture in Iowa in 1850.

It would call for a book in itself to explain the regional variations that the production maps revealed in the agriculture of Illinois and Iowa between 1849 and 1890. Agricultural economists have suggested that regional agricul-tural patterns develop because of similar adjustments on the part of neigh-boring farmers to the natural factors — soil, temperature, rainfall, and topography — and to economic determinants like the prices of agricultural products, the distance to market, and the transportation facilities that are available at any particular time. The individual farmer's adjustment to such factors, of course, might vary, depending on the knowledge of them that he possessed, his personal background and farming prejudices, as well as the amount of capital at his disposal.

As early as 1849 the line of the Shelbyville Moraine seems to have marked a break in corn-production patterns in east-central Illinois. Differing from their northern neighbors in topography, vegetation cover, and soils, the counties of the southern Military Tract were supporting an agriculture that was substantially different from that in its northern district by the late 1860's. More broken and eroded than the drift-mantled regions of northern Iowa, the loess area of southern Iowa was always the region of heaviest sheep produc-

TABLE 21

QUARTILE RANKING OF PRODUCTION IN 19 FRONTIER COUNTIES
IN IOWA, 1850

	Variance	Corn	Wheat	Oats	Hay	Hogs	Sheep	Other Cattle	Milk Cows
Allamakee	—	4	1	1	1	3	4	1	1
Clinton	2	4	1	2	1	4	4	1	1
Delaware	5	4	1	2	1	4	2	1	2
Clayton	6	4	1	1	1	4	4	3	4
Jones	7	4	1	2	1	3	2	3	3
Buchanan	9	4	2	1	1	4	3	4	4
Fremont	9	3	2	3	2	1	2	1	1
Benton	10	4	1	4	2	4	4	4	3
Iowa	12	3	2	4	2	3	4	4	4
Fayette	13	3	4	3	1	4	3	3	4
Wayne	13	2	4	1	4	3	4	3	4
Warren	14	2	4	4	2	1	4	3	2
Decatur	15	1	4	2	4	1	1	1	1
Lucas	16	2	4	4	3	3	3	3	4
Page	16	1	3	3	3	1	1	1	3
Taylor	16	1	4	3	3	2	1	1	3
Jasper	17	3	4	4	3	2	3	4	4
Marshall	17	2	4	4	3	1	3	4	2
Madison	19	2	4	4	3	1	2	4	3

tion throughout the history of the state. The greater dependence of farmers in both northern Illinois and Iowa upon hay and commensurately less stress on grain corn stemmed, in part surely, from the fact that the nineteenth-century farmer did not have corn varieties that he could rely upon to ripen invariably in the shorter growing seasons of northern Illinois and Iowa. The summer temperatures of the southern sections of these states were somewhat too warm for the liking of the oat plant. Winter wheat undoubtedly lost favor among the farmers of northern Illinois, in part, because of the tendency of this crop to winter-kill in that region. The loessial soils and relatively low humidity of northwestern Iowa proved particularly congenial to the barley plant.[3]

We can discern economic factors at work also. In 1849 the Iowa counties that produced the largest crops of wheat per improved acre lay mainly along the Mississippi River. The difficulty of transporting wheat for long distances overland had much to do with this pattern. If climatic factors helped to prejudice the farmers of northern Illinois against winter wheat during the early

[3] John C. Weaver, *American Barley Production* (Minneapolis, 1950), p. 31.

1850's, low wheat prices at the same time undoubtedly helped convince many that they should place less emphasis on the crop. Perhaps the most spectacular relation between prices and farming decisions appeared among those farmers who acquired or enlarged flocks of sheep during the Civil War. In the war years the numbers of sheep rose sharply outside the districts where these animals were most popular during the 1850's. When prices declined abruptly after the war, most farmers lost interest in the woolly tribe as rapidly as they had developed it. The tendency of observers to emphasize the role of disease or pests sometimes obscured the relation between changing prices and farming patterns. Writers stressed the depredations of dogs and the ravages of scab and foot rot, when the ovine legions thinned, and gave undue credit to blight, rust, and winter-killing when farmers decreased their acreages of wheat.

The production patterns of corn, hogs, cattle, and the other livestock and grains, of course, had their relationships to each other. Reasonably enough, the maps showing milk cows and other cattle in the various census years were very similar to each other. From 1850 through 1880 most of the same counties appeared in the top quintile on both maps in each of the two states. Between 1880 and 1890, however, a considerable change occurred as the farmers of northeastern Iowa, and northern Illinois increasingly emphasized dairying, and cattle-feeders obtained more feeder stock from the plains. Of the ten Iowa counties reporting the largest numbers of other cattle in 1880, eight also appeared in the ten counties whose farmers kept the greatest number of milk cows. A similar comparison in 1890 showed only two counties common to the top ten among the owners of milk cattle and other cattle. Since the censuses did not distinguish between cows used in dairying enterprises and beef matrons, the cattle maps are less revealing than one would like.

Crop and livestock enterprises were related to each other in a variety of ways. Not surprisingly, corn and hogs were strikingly complementary. Frequency tables based on the production returns of ninety-nine Illinois counties in the agricultural census of 1850 show, for instance, that forty-nine counties appeared in the same quintile as corn-producers that they occupied as hog-producers. Tables illustrating the relationship between corn production and other cattle, and corn production and milk cows show much weaker relationships. Only twenty-eight counties ranked in the same quintile as producers of both corn and other cattle; in the case of corn and milk cows the number was only sixteen. The census returns of 1890 showed the same rank order of correlation, but the relationship between corn production and hog-raising had weakened, while that between other cattle and corn-raising had strengthened somewhat; with 102 counties reporting, the quintile correlation of corn to hogs was forty and that of corn to other cattle was thirty-four. Some farm enterprises in the prairie triangle were notably antipathetic to each other. High wheat-producing counties were seldom high corn-producing counties, for instance.

In the study that they published in 1934 of farming types in Illinois, two agricultural economists suggested:

The characteristics of the people settling in different sections of Illinois and their customs have influenced, to some degree, the types of farming in areas where there is considerable choice as to the products that may be grown. A good example of this fact is found in Stephenson and Jo Daviess counties, which were early settled by many people from New York state, the Scandinavian countries and Switzerland. The dairy industry, particularly cheese production, was de-

TABLE 22

QUINTILE FREQUENCIES
CORN · HOGS · WHEAT

1850

hogs	corn I	II	III	IV	V
I	10	4	2	4	0
II	7	8	4	1	0
III	2	3	8	5	2
IV	2	4	5	8	1
V	1	0	1	2	15

1890

hogs	corn I	II	III	IV	V
I	12	5	1	1	1
II	5	8	5	0	2
III	4	3	5	1	7
IV	0	3	5	8	4
V	0	1	4	10	7

1850

wheat	corn I	II	III	IV	V
I	2	1	2	3	12
II	1	5	4	6	4
III	9	4	6	2	0
IV	4	8	4	2	0
V	5	2	4	7	2

1890

wheat	corn I	II	III	IV	V
I	0	6	4	5	4
II	4	5	7	4	1
III	5	1	2	5	7
IV	7	0	4	5	4
V	5	8	3	1	5

veloped in those counties not only because the industry was better adapted than grain farming to that area but also because of the training and knowledge of these early settlers.[4]

Many other writers have similarly stressed the importance of cultural factors in promoting a particular adaptation to the agricultural resources of a region or district.

Such emphasis on cultural adaptation has grown rather naturally out of distinctions current in the settlement period. Among the native-born, if we are to believe contemporaries, a cultural gulf yawned between the Yankee stock and the settlers from below the Ohio. A rather complimentary evaluation of the southerners saw in them "a heartiness of character in lieu of the reserve of Plymouth Rock, minds of natural strength and shrewdness, rather than cultivated cuteness and traditional talent for trading. . . . The dollars [did] not haunt them as they [did] most men." [5] To another writer Yankees were "a shrewd, selfish, enterprising, cow-milking set of men." [6] A reporter from Hardin County, Iowa, noted in 1859 that the settlers "of Yankee origin" were planting orchards rather generally.[7] If these suggestions carry the implication that the Yankees provided the "go-ahead" element in the western communities, they should be balanced by the comment of a traveler in Macoupin County, Illinois, who introduced his readers to a section of the county "where you see farming done on a big scale — Kentucky style, lots of fine stock, cattle and hogs." [8] Writing in 1868, an Iowan maintained:

The Eastern farmer who has migrated from New England relies more upon his early teachings and customs than Western ideas of farming. We notice generally that this class are the first for experiments for fruit and for raising stock. Our farmers who migrate from the South bring with them the lesson of pork and grain which they have learned in the South. The native born [western born] farmers generally have adopted ideas derived from the Eastern and Southern farmers and their own experience as farmers.[9]

Richard L. Power has described the contrast between Yankee and southerner in great detail.[10] Contemporaries stressed the industry and neatness of

[4] H. C. M. Case and K. H. Myers, *Types of Farming in Illinois, an Analysis of Differences by Areas* (University of Illinois, Agricultural Experiment Station, *Bulletin* No. 403, [Urbana, 1934]), p. 123.

[5] *Emery's Journal of Agriculture*, I (1858), 182 (quoted by Russell H. Anderson, "Agriculture in Illinois During the Civil War Period, 1850–1870" [unpublished Ph.D. dissertation, University of Illinois, 1929]), p. 20.

[6] Chicago *Weekly American*, February 4, 1837 (quoted by William V. Pooley, *The Settlement of Illinois from 1830–1850* [University of Wisconsin Bulletin, "History Series," Vol. I, (Madison, 1908)]), [99] 385.

[7] Iowa State Agricultural Society, *Report, 1859* (Des Moines, 1860), p. 246. Hereafter this series will be cited as I.S.A.S.R.

[8] *Prairie Farmer*, July, 1849, p. 205.

[9] I.S.A.S.R., *1868*, p. 480.

[10] Richard L. Power, *Planting Corn Belt Culture: The Impress of the Upland Southerner and Yankee in the Old Northwest* (Indianapolis, 1953).

the foreign-born settlers from Germany and Scandinavia and their willing-
ness to allow their womenfolk to work beside them in the fields. Iowa observers believed that German farmers were more apt to raise barley than were
the native-born and to use mules in preference to horses.[11] Some believe that
the emphasis upon wheat-growing in some of the southwestern counties of
Illinois was linked in part to the heritage which German settlers in the region
brought with them from the wheat-raising regions of Germany.[12] In their study
of the history of the pig, Wentworth and Towne wrote:

> But what pulled most of the debt-ridden out of the red was the combination
> of pluck, perspicacity, and pigs. This was particularly so in the case of the
> German and Swedish immigrants. Less skilled in the management of horses,
> sheep, and beef cattle than the English and native Americans, they concentrated
> with dogged tenacity on their hogs. . . . The chief economy practiced by the
> German farmer that made him competitively efficient was fattening his hogs
> behind beef steers, utilizing the latter's droppings.[13]

There are actually two propositions involved in the discussion of cultural
factors that appear in the accounts of midwestern agriculture. First, it is
argued that the different cultural and ethnic groups brought a varied assort-
ment of skills and predilections with them. There can be little criticism of
such statements. No doubt English immigrants did introduce drainage techniques in the English Prairie region as George Flower suggested, and prairie
farmers may have owed the technique of hedge-plashing to the English as
well.[14] Quite possibly Hungarian refugees to Iowa did bring the seed of
"Hungarian grass" or millet with them.[15] Much more suspect is a second
proposition which holds that over a considerable period of time the members
of ethnocultural groups farmed in ways that were significantly different from
the practices followed by others with different backgrounds in the same
neighborhoods.

Most generalizations about the cultural factors and farming patterns have
been subjective and too little based on careful research. Few, if any, scholars
have carefully checked to learn whether the Scandinavians, Swiss, and Germans who turned to dairying in northern Illinois and Iowa were indeed from
European districts where major stress was placed on dairying. Nor did Wentworth and Towne have strong evidence for their comments about Germans,

[11] Herbert Quick, *One Man's Life* (Indianapolis, 1925), p. 194; U.S. Commissioner
of Patents, *Agricultural Report, 1850* (Washington, 1851), p. 242; I.S.A.S.R., *1863*,
p. 378, *1865*, p. 400, *1870*, pp. 483, 490, 527.

[12] John C. Weaver, "Changing Patterns of Cropland Use in the Middle West," *Economic Geography*, XXX (January, 1954), 19.

[13] Charles W. Towne and Edward N. Wentworth, *Pigs: From Cave to Corn Belt*
(Norman, 1950), pp. 208–9, 210–11.

[14] George Flower, *History of the English Settlement in Edwards County, Illinois,
Founded in 1817 and 1818 by Morris Birkbeck and George Flower* (Chicago, 1882),
pp. 165–66; *Prairie Farmer*, August 12, 1865, p. 111.

[15] *Northwestern Farmer*, December 1857, p. 457, June 1858, p. 191.

Swedes, and pigs. In a statistical analysis of farming patterns in Hamilton and Bremer counties, Iowa, I found that one of the few common patterns in both counties was that the foreign-born farmers owned fewer pigs than did the native-born farmers. On the other hand the European-born farmers in both counties grew proportionately more wheat and less corn than did the natives, as well as using less hired labor.[16]

Perhaps cultural differences among western farmers were more apparent than real — most obvious in food ways, dress, and lingual traits, and less important when the farmer decided on his combination of major enterprises. We can agree, of course, that the farmer who came from New York or Tennessee would have preferred to farm in the way that he had learned as a boy or young man. But, as one New York emigrant to Illinois in 1837 admitted later in the *Prairie Farmer*, he learned "that the mode of culture pursued in Western New York" would "not do." [17] Some New Yorkers were fortunate enough to discover that the dairying patterns that they had known were indeed profitable in the West; no doubt many others changed their practices as they learned the lessons taught by physical environment and the local price structure.

The farmers of all of the older regions of the United States knew both the pig and the corn plant well. Adaptation to western conditions was ordinarily for the native-born farmer a process of changing emphasis rather than one in which inexperienced men learned to grow new crops or work with different species of farm animals. For the foreign-born the situation was somewhat different. It is true that the German or Scandinavian or Irish farmer had an agricultural background, but they found the differences more extreme than did the native-born. "I can truthfully say," wrote one Norwegian immigrant from Iowa, "that the only things that seem to be the same are the fleas, for their bite is as sharp and penetrating here as elsewhere." [18] But the foreign-born farmer typically underwent a period of acculturation in which he either worked for native Americans or earlier immigrants of the same nationality, or else he settled close by a fellow countryman who could give him advice on local agricultural practices. For most the adjustment seems to have been a rapid one. John Sandahl wrote to his relatives in Sweden, "The women never work in the fields — not even milking cows. We men must do that. When I first began to milk, some of it went into my coat sleeves, but that didn't bother me: I emptied them when they became full."[19] The jest was obvious, but his words carried a deeper meaning as well.

By the end of the Civil War, at least, there was an awareness in the Middle

[16] See chapter x.

[17] A. N. Harris in *Prairie Farmer*, July, 1852, p. 312.

[18] Pauline Farseth and Theodore C. Blegen (trans. and ed.), *Frontier Mother: The Letters of Gro Svendsen* (Northfield, 1950), p. 28.

[19] John Z. Sandahl, Rome, Henry County, Iowa, to Jonas P. Zackrison, January 7, 1860 in Swedish Historical Society of America, *Year-Book*, VII, 1921–1922 (Chicago, 1922), 60.

West of both increasing specialization among farmers and regionalization of agricultural production. In 1866 the editor of the *Prairie Farmer* commented:

Now [as compared to 40 years ago] we have stock growers, stock feeders, pork raisers, hay growers, orchardists, etc. Each having a leading staple around which others play a secondary part. The stock grower has great pastures and wide spreading meadows. The stock feeder may not own a foot of land, he may be a renter, pasturing the outlaying prairie, purchasing corn by the thousand acres, and feeding it from the shock in the field. The pork raiser has great corn fields and a timber lot. The hay grower bales and ships his hay to distant cities — to the pineries of the north or to the cotton fields of the south. The orchardist covers his broad acres with fruit trees and ships their rich products.[20]

Late in 1867 the editor pointed out that there were regional variations to be found in the agriculture of the state.

If we were asked to name the great staples of the state we should say for Northern Illinois that spring wheat, dairy products, pork and wool predominated; passing southward to Central Illinois we meet large fields of spring wheat, but corn is the great ever present staple, for shipment, for distilling and for the fattening of beef and pork. We go down into the 'Basin of Upper Egypt' and find extensive orchards; some winter wheat, a fine show of corn and the outlying prairie sprinkled with herds of cattle, not for fattening, but young stock that will in time find its way to the great corn plateau, to be put in order for the market. We enter the timber belt and along its northern edge we find cotton and tobacco and fruit growing the dominant objects of attention.[21]

This is not to suggest, of course, that the farmers in every district followed patterns that were identical with those of their neighbors. If specialization was noteworthy by the end of the Civil War, there was still much of what was referred to as "general farming." The character of a district was given not only by the relative number of specialists there but also by the additional emphasis that the "general farmers" placed on certain crops and types of farm stock.

William Warntz suggested recently that "by 1879 there existed a well defined, although unnamed, corn belt . . . " occupying the same general region that we still call the Corn Belt today. The first printed use of the term "corn belt" that he could discover occurred in *The Nation* during 1882.[22] In late 1870, however, the *National Livestock Journal* quoted a story from the *Journal*, of Jacksonville, Illinois: " 'Travelers state that cattle are now coming in from Missouri and Kansas in large numbers, most of which are purchased for this part of the State.' The same anxiety to obtain feeding stock is observ-

[20] *Prairie Farmer*, August 18, 1866, p. 102.
[21] *Ibid.*, December 7, 1867, p. 353.
[22] William Warntz, "An Historical Consideration of the Terms 'Corn' and 'Corn Belt' in the United States," *Agricultural History*, XXXI (January, 1957), 40.

able throughout the western 'corn belt.' " [23] Nine years later, a resident of Allamakee County, Iowa, remarked, "Situated as we are on the northern border of the corn and the southern border of the spring wheat belt, we seldom have a good crop of both the same season." [24] It would be years after 1870 when the phrase "Corn Belt" became a part of national or official parlance. But out in Illinois and Iowa the farmers had long known that productive soils and the recurring miracle of broad-leafed fields of green, growing in rain and summer heat, had set their land apart.

[23] *National Live Stock Journal*, November, 1870, p. 78.
[24] I.S.A.S.R., *1879*, p. 335.

CHAPTER XII

Farmers In The New Settlements

I

During the last half of the nineteenth century, as we have seen, the production plans of farmers throughout Illinois and Iowa were different enough so that we can detect areas of high and low production of the various farm crops and farm animals. But what of neighboring farmers? How great was the change when John Smith clambered over his line fence? Let us follow the census marshal as he travels from farm to farm in Center and Rochester townships of Cedar County, Iowa, in the late spring days of 1850. What did his enumeration show when he emerged from the roughly-hewn door of the one hundred and first farmhouse and mounted his horse to move on through the openings?

Table 23 summarizes the findings of our census-taker. The most striking contrast from neighbor to neighbor was one of scale. Acres per farm, improved acres, farm value, and value of livestock are all indexes of the size of farming operations. The median farmer of our 101 listed a holding of 120 acres, but one of his neighbors owned 640 acres. The median farmer had improved 50 acres, but one man in the community had broken 320 acres to the plow. The median farmer valued his holding at $700, but the most affluent of the group believed that his farm was worth $6,000. The livestock of the median farmer was worth $220, that of the most committed stockman, $1,960.

Obviously, neighboring farmers differed somewhat in their combination of farm enterprises and methods of farming. Almost all the 101 farmers owned horses, milk cows, and swine but only 59 owned sheep. Twenty-five owned oxen, and 23 listed no "other cattle." Almost all the farmers raised wheat and corn and cured hay, but only 69 reported that they had harvested oats in the previous crop year. A scattering of farmers grew minor field crops of which the most important was buckwheat — raised by 14 of 101 farmers in 1849. Only two had harvested clover seed. Eighty-nine households made butter, but only 13 reported the manufacture of cheese. The individual census figures may of themselves, of course, have masked fundamental differences in farming patterns. Twenty-three farmers for instance reported

TABLE 23
PRODUCTION STATISTICS
101 CEDAR COUNTY FARMERS
CENSUS YEARS 1850–80 *

Iowa

	Farmers Reporting		Medians		Maximums	
	1850	1880	1850	1880	1850	1880
Acres per farm	101	101	120 acres	160 acres	640 acres	1,120 acres
Improved acres	101	101	50 acres	150 acres	320 acres	1,100 acres
Farm values	101	101	$700	$5,200	$6,000	$31,200
Value of livestock . .	101	101	$220	$900	$1,960	$15,250
Horses and mules . . .	97	100	2	6	12	26
Work oxen	25	0	0	0	26	0
Milk cows	99	98	3	4	15	42
Other cattle	78	75	3	5	50	330
Sheep	59	7	7	0	50	185
Swine	98	97	16	72	100	350
Wheat †	98	71	180 bus.	30 bus.	1,000 bus.	500 bus.
Indian corn	98	96	400 bus.	2,800 bus.	3,000 bus.	9000 bus.
Rye	1	8	0	0	30 bus.	0
Flax	4	0	0	360 bus.	100 lbs.	580 bus.
Oats	69	83	50 bus.	0	500 bus.	1500 bus.
Barley	6	15	0	0	80 bus.	450 bus.
Buckwheat	14	8	0	0	200 bus.	122 bus.
Clover seed	2	5	0	0	3 bus.	22 bus.
Grass seed	4	14	0	0	5 bus.	185 bus.
Hay	99	90	8 tons	2 tons	60 tons	160 tons
Butter	89	98	100 lbs.	350 lbs.	1,200 lbs.	1550 lbs.
Cheese	13	0	0	0	300 lbs.	0

* Taken from the manuscript United States Census of Agriculture, 1850.
† In 1880 twenty-one farmers reported wheat "not cut" — an obvious misunderstanding of his duties on the part of the census marshal.

that they owned no "other cattle." Some members of this group were small farmers, owning but a cow or two and selling or butchering the calves at an early age. But even at this early date a few of them may well have been feeding stock and received the census marshal after they had disposed of their steers and before they had purchased their next lot of feeders.

In the categories of Table 23 the median farmer was always much closer to the smallest operator than to the largest in the scale of his operations. Looking behind the measures of tendency in Table 23 to the actual figures in the various categories of production, one discovers usually that a handful of farmers — from three or four to as many as ten in some instances — listed production or livestock numbers that were three times or more greater than those of the median farmer. This was probably the case throughout Iowa and Illinois and is important to our understanding of the local economy, because the large business and the small were interrelated. The smaller farmer frequently looked to the larger as a market both for some of his production and for some of his labor. The larger looked to the smaller for labor in times of extra need, for stock cattle and pigs, and for an extra crib of corn or stack of hay that he might buy when his own suppplies ran short.

As Table 23 also shows, the picture had changed somewhat in Center Township by 1880. The first 101 farms that the census-enumerator visited in 1880 were larger, more highly improved, more valuable, and, understandably, more productive than in 1850. The farmers of the region generally were putting greater dependence on a smaller number of farm enterprises. But the individual differences from farm to farm were still there. And indeed, to the surprise of the newcomer to the Corn Belt today, they still are to some extent today, when one may see a herd of Holsteins grazing in lush pasturage around a sign reading "Dairy Farming Pays" located in the very heart of the cash-grain region of north-central Iowa.

The reasons underlying contrasts from farm to farm include many of the factors that account for regional or subregional farming patterns. Soils, topography, even climate changed from farm to farm. In the nineteenth century differences due to cultural factors were doubtless more apparent in the neighborhood than in the statistics that blended the production programs of a county of farmers. Probably, however, differences from neighbor to neighbor most often reflected the capital resources available to the individual farmer, and these, of course, were linked in part to the age of the operator.

If we would understand the way in which the pioneer farmer combined his varied farm enterprises to make a farm business, we must, of course, go beyond the census materials and consider actual farm records. These, alas, are few, scattered, and incomplete, particularly so for the years before 1870. Yet some survive, and in the following pages we will consider the farm operations of a number of middle-western farmers in Illinois and Iowa between 1830 and the 1880's. They did not all, of course, face the same problems. We have already seen that technology and market structure changed drastically in the 60 years after 1830. Farm-management problems too, were linked directly to the progress of the settling-in process in any particular area. We will first visit a few farms, located in communities where the settling-in process had not long been under way.

II

A Maine-raised Yankee William Sewall moved from Prunty Town, Harrison County, Virginia, in 1829 and established himself at Jacksonville, Illinois, in March, 1830.[1] The move was not an unpremeditated stab into the darkness of central Illinois. A relative in the Jacksonville area had written of the country and urged Sewall to come. In later years Sewall himself was the lodestone that drew his sister and her family from the East to settle in the same region. Sewall was thirty-three years of age when he decided to go to Illinois. He had worked mainly as a school teacher or clerk, but he had some acquaintance with farming. We cannot know exactly how much he was

[1] This account of William Sewall's farming operations is based upon John Goodell (ed.), *Diary of William Sewal, 1797–1846, Formerly of Augusta, Maine, Maryland Virginia and Pioneer in Illinois* (Beardstown, 1930).

worth when he moved to the West. Sums mentioned in his diary and the fact that he started west with several slaves suggest that his assets totaled between $600 and $1,500 but were possibly greater. To his chagrin he discovered that it was a mistake to bring human chattels above the Ohio. After "troublemakers" in Indiana encouraged them to flee, he returned his slaves to the South for sale — with the exception of one girl whom he retained as a house servant.

William Sewall bought a house and lot in Jacksonville for $271.37½ and established a school. Soon, however, he turned to farming. In August of 1830 he entered 240 acres of land at the federal land office in Springfield for which he paid the government minimum price of $1.25 per acre. This land lay in the Sangamon Valley within the trading orbit of Beardstown in Cass County, Illinois. Maintaining his residence in Jacksonville at first, he hired a man to work on the farm and spent much of his own time there as well. In 1832 or 1833, however, he rented his Jacksonville property and moved his wife Eliza and the children to the farm. It would be his home until he died in the spring of 1846. None can argue that William Sewall was the typical pioneer of Cass County, Illinois — his holdings were too broad, his designs too ambitious for that. But he faced the same problems as did his less-affluent neighbors.

Two hundred and forty acres of land was not to be the limit of William Sewall's purchases of land. Infected perhaps by the speculative optimism of the 1830's, he acquired more federal land in 1835, borrowing funds to do so. Three separate purchases in this year totaled approximately 210 acres. In 1836 he entered another fractional quarter of government land. He did not eventually receive patents for all of his purchases of 1835 and 1836. It seems clear from Sewall's diary that much of the acreage that he purchased in 1830 was prairie land. Some of the land in the later acquisitions was timbered, selected to meet his needs for rails, building timber, and firewood. In 1838 Sewall rounded out his holdings by purchasing a neighboring farm, the "Northern place," probably an eighty-acre tract. He borrowed $300 to make the purchase. In his own farming operations, of course, Sewall was never able to utilize all of his land. In 1836 he rented two strips in his improved fields to others, one of whom paid $2.00 per acre. The "Northern place" he also rented. On the other hand he himself rented 4½ acres of improved land for oats in 1835, giving one-third of the grain in sheaf as rent.

Able to hire labor in considerable amounts, Sewall apparently pushed the improvement of his farm quite rapidly. On April 30, 1831, he "set off with a team and a prairie plow" that had come in "late last night with instructions" and began to break prairie. In 1832 he sowed some thirty acres to wheat. He carried on his breaking less rapidly thereafter, evidently, but by the spring of 1837 he had perhaps broken 120 acres on the farm. In September of 1831 he contracted to have a ditch dug on his boundaries at a cost of 31¼ ¢ per rod. The bank of earth so raised, Sewall crowned with rails, hopeful that this prairie fencing would serve his needs. He hired more ditching of the same sort done in 1832, noting that he was building a cap-and-stake fence on top of the balk. Thereafter he put increasing dependence on the more orthodox varieties of rail fence because the ditch fence failed to protect growing crops from his hogs. Finally in 1840 he recorded that he was plowing down the ditch fence and "placing thereon a good and substantial worm fence." [2] Cutting stakes and rails was a standard winter task on the Sewall farm through the 1830's and 1840's. Sewall sometimes hired men to work for a month or two, solely to cut rails. In 1838 he contracted with a neighbor for "a parcel" of 10,000 rails to be cut in his timber lots, agreeing to pay $125 for the work. Improvements at the farmstead continued year by year. The first residence was a small cabin, hardly weatherproof. But at the end of the decade he enlarged it, adding brick chimneys, a porch, and other improvements. Meanwhile he had built stables, sheephouse, and meat house. In 1833 he dug a well, striking abundant water at twenty-six feet. A mason walled it for him with rock.

In the published diary, at least, Sewall's entries do not clearly reveal the relative emphasis that he placed upon the various field crops. In the first several years of farming. Sewall sowed much of his improved acreage to fall wheat. He may well have planted some of this wheat on spring breaking that had already carried a crop of sod corn or oats. The wheat crop of 1833-34, however, was so poor that he decided, after a day of cutting, to let his hogs pasture it. That fall he sowed little if any wheat and planted twenty-six acres of corn in the next spring. In the fall of 1836 he sowed almost thirty acres of rye and more than twenty-five acres of oats during the next spring as well as forty acres of corn. In succeeding years, however, he again planted considerable acreages of wheat and in 1838 harvested good crops of both fall and spring wheat. The latter, he noted, was a "new article" with him. Consistently, Sewall planted some oats, although seldom on the scale of 1836. Occasionally, he grew a little buckwheat. Wheat and corn, however, were his major field crops, and the acreage planted to either seems to have risen or fallen in inverse proportion to the area planted in the other. Sewall cured some hay each year, although he apparently never put up large quantities. Often it was prairie hay, but in 1836 he obtained six bushels of clover seed from Ohio on a debt owing to him and planted a considerable acreage of clover. Some years later he mentioned sowing a mixture of timothy and clover.

The years between 1830 and 1845 revealed only the first hints of the revolutionary technology that would sweep middle-western farms in the thirty-five years between 1845 and 1880. In the early years in Illinois Sewall sowed his small grain by hand, covered it with a triangular wooden harrow of his own construction, harvested it with a cradle scythe, stacked the bundles in his stackyard, "got out" the grain under the feet of his workstock in the "tramping yard," and winnowed it in the wind. Only one piece of equipment that Sewall used in these routines could have cost as much as $100 when new.

[2] *Ibid.*, August 17, 1840.

That was his wagon; Sewall paid $100 for a new one in 1837. The first introduction of more complex machinery to Sewall's culture of the small grains occurred in 1835 when he borrowed a fan to clean his grain. Two years later he contracted with a Dr. Lancaster to thresh his oats and rye with a machine that "was the best article to get out grain" he had ever seen.[3] This was a fateful event for Sewall. After having his grain threshed by machine again in 1840, he himself purchased a separator from the firm of Benjamin and Davis, Winthrop, Maine, while home on a visit in 1841. How this machine differed from the Pitts machine, which was operating in the Beardstown area three years later, we do not know. Sewall recorded one other innovation in small-grain technology in 1842 when he mentioned that one of his hired men was seeding wheat with a machine and horses. This implement must have been an early horse-drawn broadcast seeder.

As is usual in midwestern farm diaries, there is little direct discussion of the problems of corn culture in Sewall's farm record. After plowing the corn ground, Sewall and his hands "furrowed" it and "cross-furrowed" it, dropped corn kernels where the furrows crossed, and covered them with a hoe. As soon as the green cylinders of leaves were above ground, they replanted the hills where seed had failed to germinate, or squirrel and cutworm had been busy. With this task completed, they could soon "break up the box" with a harrow or plow and begin the month, or month and a half, of corn-plowing that would continue until they laid the crop by in early July.[4] Sewall never described the corn plows that he used in these crucial weeks.

William Sewall evidently cut and shocked little of his corn crop. On one occasion he did mention that he was feeding corn fodder, but usually he preferred to pull the ears from the standing corn, crib or pen them in the shuck, and pasture the stalks. Sometimes, however, he was still gathering corn in the late winter months, so his stock could have had little time to glean the cornfield. In the fall of 1838 he recorded that it was a good day's work to gather and crib five wagonloads of corn. The wagon box, he noted, held nineteen bushels of corn in the shuck. The labor force at this time consisted of a hired man, Sewall himself, and son Henry, then in his early teens. In November, 1843, Sewall recorded a basic change in his corn-gathering technique when he wrote that he had shucked ten rows of corn for the hogs in the field and planned to harvest all of his corn "in that manner" unless the weather became too cold. In 1839 Sewall brought home a mechanical cornsheller, but he did not describe its workings in detail. Consistently during his farming years in Illinois, Sewall cleared the old corn ground of stalks with a horse-drawn wooden stalk rake that he had constructed himself.

Sewall stocked his farm with hogs and cattle immediately and ran some sheep as well. In January, 1837, he noted that he was feeding thirty-five cattle and twenty-four sheep. This seems to have been a somewhat larger

<hr/>

[3] *Ibid.*, November 6, 1837.
[4] Use of the quoted expression appears in *ibid.*, May 15, 1837.

number of cattle than he usually kept. Ordinarily he prepared from fifteen to thirty fat hogs for slaughter in the winter of each year, although in some years the number was less and, on a couple of occasions, slightly more. Oxen provided much of the farm power in the first years, but he placed increasing dependence on horses after he purchased a threshing machine in 1841. Until then he had maintained one team of horses and probably at least two yoke of oxen. Although he mentioned fencing a pasture, Sewall ran his stock at large a good deal of the time. His hogs ranged the Sangamon bottoms until it was time to pen them for fattening on corn. In one year when he evidently had fewer hogs than usual and a small corn crop, he allowed them to fatten on mast alone. The meat, he noted, was excellent — an evaluation of mast-fed pork that many did not share. The ranges along the Sangamon had their peculiar dangers for livestock. In spring or fall freshet the water rose with dangerous swiftness, and in one year Sewall lost several hogs by drowning when he failed to drive them out in time. As we have seen, Sewall gave his cattle the run of the stalk fields after corn-picking, but he might also feed them hay or corn fodder at the farmstead in the more inclement winter months. Despite the rude regime that his stock enjoyed, Sewall evidently was interested in improving the quality of his animals. In 1840 he purchased a "Shorthorn Durham" bull calf and five years later bought a "Burkshire male hog." [5]

William Sewall placed considerable dependence upon hired labor. For at least several months of every year he employed a hired man and, at times, kept one the year round. In seeding time, harvest, or on other special occasions he might employ additional help. At times he hired men specifically to work in the woods — cutting out rails, building timber, cordwod, and less often, shingles. After he began a custom threshing business in the early 1840's, he hired at least one man to help with the machine. From 1835 onward he could count, to some extent, on family labor; in that year he first mentioned that his son Henry was driving the team for him. Henry, however, could hardly have rendered a man's services until the 1840's and was, on occasion, away at school. By the 1840's another son, at least, was helping with the farm work.

It is possible to prepare a table showing monthly wage rates on the Sewall farm in most of the years from 1831 to 1845. In considering this table, however, we must remember that the age, skill, and experience of the workers involved may have varied considerably as well as the boarding arrangements provided. Amos Smith who received $20.00 per month in 1841 was evidently a skilled joiner and perhaps boarded himself. Two workers who received $6.00 per month in 1842 were probably mere boys. The length of the labor contract and the time of year undoubtedly influenced wages to some extent also.

The laborer, of course, expected to receive more when he worked by the

[5] *Ibid.*, December 5, 1840, March 4, 1845.

TABLE 24
Monthly Wage Rates

1831	$10.00	1839	$15.00
1833	11.00		12.00
	10.00	1840	12.50
	12.00	1841	13.00
1834	7.00		20.00
	8.00	1842	11.00
	4.00		11.00
1835	10.00		6.00
	10.00	1844	10.00
	12.00		10.00
1837	15.00		8.00
	12.00		7.00
1838	15.00	1845	9.00

day. Harvest help — cradlers and binders — often obtained $1.25 per day in Cass County during the 1830's. But one dollar per day was a common wage for day labor, and sometimes Sewall paid only 75¢. One labor agreement that he made in October, 1838, provided payment of 75¢ per day at ordinary farm tasks and $1.25 per day when he asked the man to work in the timber. The standard pay for helpers at hog-slaughtering seems to have been 75¢ per day, and in 1844, Sewall paid only 62½¢ per day for hauling and stacking wheat. In 1834, however, his hands quit when he proposed to pay only 75¢ per acre for mowing grass. To the brick-maker whom he hired in 1839 to mold 100,000 bricks for him, Sewall paid $2.00 per day.

Sewall's experience with hired labor was not always happy. He dismissed a number of laborers for conduct that he failed to describe in his diary. Perhaps this supports the contention of some that good agricultural laborers were hard to find in new western communities. Perhaps, however, it reveals Sewall to have been less than a completely satisfactory master. Undoubtedly Sewall's most happy choice was Lewis Clanniham Spice who agreed in December of 1831 to work for $10.00 per month, washing included. Spice died in Sewall's employ in January of 1834 when the dirt-roofed camp that he had built to live in while cutting rails in the Sangamon bottoms collapsed on him while he was asleep. The obituary in Sewall's diary doubtless could have applied to many others of the Sangamon region at the time. "He was an excellent work hand and a good hunter, but a man who could not read nor had an[y] desire to learn. He never made any profession or pretention of religion." [6] As he became financially embarrassed during the 1840's Sewall did not always settle his debts promptly, and several of his hired men obtained small judgments against him. Although of New England stock and much concerned with religion, Sewall solved the problem of domestic help by retaining one of the slave women whom he had brought from Virginia with him. Because he chastised this "girl" in 1837, he had to defend himself before

[6] *Ibid.*, January 19, 1834.

the church congregation, and he gave up his post in the Sunday School where he believed that the incident had compromised his usefulness. We do not know when Susan obtained her freedom.

There is surprisingly little mention in Sewall's diary of labor exchange between neighbors. He assisted at raisings, and his neighbors helped him raise the frame of his enlarged house in 1839. At his request a number of his neighbors gathered in 1845 to assist him in moving a line of rail fence to take in a piece of new breaking. He does not seem to have traded labor in harvest or haying, however. His laborers in these seasons worked for dollars and cents rather than in the expectation of receiving similar help.

Sewall marketed his farm products in Beardstown, where the merchants maintained connections by water with St. Louis and the Mississippi system generally. Here he sold his wheat to merchants mainly, although sometimes the brewery or one of the gristmills purchased some of his crop. In the summer of 1844 he shipped wheat directly to the St. Louis market and, to his chagrin, received only 40¢ per bushel for it — the commission merchant reporting that it had arrived in bad shape, infested with crickets. A few days later Sewall sold wheat in Beardstown from the same bins for 48¢ and concluded that there was "something mysterious" about the St. Louis market.[7] Typically, Sewall teamed his wheat to Beardstown shortly after he had "got it out" — a process that might take place any time between October and March. In some years Sewall had surplus oats that he also disposed of in Beardstown or sold at a nearby stage station. At times, also, he sold some of his corn, but, for the most part, this crop went to market as pork.

Usually Sewall penned his hogs for a period of fattening in October and slaughtered them in December or January. In some years he cured the hams and shoulders, and pickled the remainder of the carcasses before sale. On other occasions he evidently teamed the fresh pork to Beardstown for delivery to one of the merchant firms there. In one year he drove his hogs to Beardstown and had them slaughtered by a packing firm there. Sewall's diary entries contain much less about his other farm stock than about hogs and the hog market. He evidently sold several cattle each year, but the largest single transaction was in 1840 when he sold four three-year-old steers for $64.00. In 1844 cattle-buyers purchased in the area a herd that they planned to drive to Brighton Market at Boston, Massachusetts. Sewall boarded the drovers overnight but did not mention selling any animals to them. Although he maintained a small flock of sheep during this period, he did not record any sales of wool. He did, however, mention a trip to the carding mill at Princeton where he picked up rolls of carded wool. Eliza Sewall undoubtedly spun a portion of the clip into yarn and used it to weave cloth; Sewall paid off at least one farm hand in fabric. There were a few minor sources of farm income Sewall occasionally mentioned the sale of butter in Beardstown, and sometimes there was a surplus of watermelons or turnips.

[7] *Ibid.*, August 30, 1844.

Sewall's diary entries are not complete enough to allow any precise estimates of farm income. Yet we can set some limits. Sewall probably never
raised more than 250 bushels of wheat for sale from his own acres. The price
ranged from 75¢ to 40¢ per bushel. When growing oats or rye in the mid-
1830's, he may have had larger crops, but the prices were lower. He mentions
prices for oats ranging from 18¢ to 36¢ per bushel. He did not usually butcher
more than twenty-five hogs. The price of pork during the 1830's evidently
stayed close to $3.50 per cwt. Sewall's hogs seldom weighed in excess of 200
lbs. when slaughtered. Since pork and cash grain were to some extent competitive enterprises, it is doubtful if the two together ever returned income in
excess of $300, and probably the figure was considerably below this. To this
we may add an additional $125–$150 derived from the sale of cattle and an
extra $25 from the sale of incidentals — butter, roots, and the like. Gross
farm income was probably between $400 and $500 during the late 1830's —
surely little more and, perhaps, considerably less. The farm labor bill was at
least $60 per year and in some years was more than twice that much. In
modern terms this was a small scale business indeed. But it was probably
larger than that of 80 per cent of its neighbors. On the other hand, the range
of articles purchased was much less than that of the modern farm family —
but little food or clothing, and very little in the way of educational or medical
services.

Sewall and his neighbors were apparently quite willing to buy or sell on
credit. At the end of each year, Sewall ordinarily settled his accounts with
the various merchants of Beardstown. He both bought and sold livestock on
credit. This was normal enough when one considers the irregular nature of
farm income. Sewall sought credit for larger designs as well. In 1835 he
borrowed $216 on short term at 12 per cent in order to enter government
land. In 1838 he borrowed $300 from the branch of the Bank of Illinois in
Jacksonville and used it, evidently, to purchase the "Northern place." By
December of 1840 he had paid off this note, but almost immediately he
obtained a new bank loan of $400. He was successful in retiring this loan but
in 1845 found it necessary to borrow $320 from one Thomas Williams at
12 per cent and $107 at 8 per cent from the commissioner of the school fund.

Meanwhile, evidence of financial embarrassment was accumulating in his
diary. In January of 1840 Sewall recorded a summons on a debt of $32.68 —
wages owing to a former hired hand. Thereafter Sewall sprinkled his diary
entries with references to summons, judgments, delinquent taxes, and, ultimately, levies on grain in shock and tracts of his real estate. Some of the debts
he evidently owed to merchants, some to hired men for unpaid wages, and
others to neighboring farmers. Most of the debts were small, but a few were
substantial.

Sewall's entries are not complete enough to reveal the process by which
debts accumulated. Some of the major elements, however, are clear. There
was consistently an outlay for labor that was large by the standards of the

time. In 1839 he bought materials for enlarging and improving his house. When he visited his relatives in Maine during 1841, he purchased a grain separator for $100 and a horsepower for $113. Both of these he obtained on one year's credit at 6 per cent interest. Freight charges raised the cost of the machinery by an additional $45.00. To his chagrin he found that the horsepower, although purchased from "the inventor of horse power," was unsatisfactory. After a frustrating season of threshing, he purchased a new horsepower from a local mechanic for $100. If he was to do custom threshing, of course, he needed additional horses for the horsepower. In 1841 he bought four horses from neighbors at prices ranging from $80 to $95, paying these men in part by contracting to thresh grain for them, in part by giving his note. Still enthralled by the possibilities of threshing machines, he purchased the patent rights to the "Pitts" separator in his county in 1842, agreeing to pay $500 in wheat over the next three years.

It is clear Sewall took on unusual financial responsibilities after 1838. His forecast of the future proved to be much too optimistic. His threshing operations were a frustrating story of broken castings and failure to maintain the steady flow of threshing engagements necessary to pay for an outfit that was purchased on credit. At the same time the price of farm products fell sharply during the early 1840's. The depression of 1837 seemed to have little impact on western business conditions as revealed in Sewall's diary. The years from 1841 through 1845 were different. Where Sewall had sold fat pork for $3.50 per cwt. in the thirties, he was now offered prices ranging from $2.00 to $1.50, depending on the size of the carcass. "I shall not get pay for my corn!!," he complained in December of 1841.[8] The wheat that had been worth 75¢ per bushel in the mid-1830's now sold for as little as 40¢ per bushel. Plain bad luck frustrated him as well. In March of 1845 a vagrant stubble fire leaped to a corn pen and destroyed some 300 bushels of grain.

Despite his difficulties, Sewall managed to keep his lands unencumbered during the early 1840's. In 1845 he saw some of them sold for debt and placed a land mortgage on some of the remainder. Whether Sewall could have extricated himself in the more prosperous years of the late 1840's, we cannot know. He died in the spring of 1846. Eliza, his widow, was successful, with the help of her sons, in clearing off the debts and establishing a prosperous farm business. Perhaps here was the better head, but the business tides were flowing in her favor also.

III

Some have suggested that large farming operations simply did not pay on the Illinois and Iowa frontiers. Can we explain William Sewall's problems during the 1840's in this way? I believe not. Sewall suffered, not because his farm unit was larger than average, but because he made rash commitments in the face of falling prices. While Sewall was slipping into debt in Cass County,

[8] *Ibid.*, December 18, 1841.

Illinois, George F. Green, of Jackson County, Iowa, was demonstrating that there were profits to be derived from farming operations that were larger than the average.[9]

Born in Rhode Island, George F. Green came to Jackson County, Iowa, in 1839. He was twenty-nine years of age. He paid thirty-five dollars for a claim in the southeastern part of the county between five and ten miles from Sabula. From 1839 to 1849 he maintained a sketchy diary and business ledger from which we can reconstruct the major outlines of his farming operations. We do not know how much capital he brought with him; it was probably less than that of William Sewall when he came to Illinois. But he did bring with him a reservoir of labor in the shape of his two brothers-in-law, Nelson and Nathaniel Kimball. These young men developed their own farms while boarding with the Greens, but they worked out their board at times and seem to have raised some crops in partnership with Green. Green bought his land at the federal land sales at Dubuque in 1845 and reported 200 acres, of which 100 acres was improved, in the census of 1850.

Work routines on the Green farm were typical of the period and the region — much the same as those on Sewall's farm near Beardstown, Illinois. Interspersed through the normal seasonal tasks connected with raising wheat, oats, corn, pigs, and cattle were those dictated by the constant need to improve what was almost completely raw land in 1839. Year by year, breaking, cutting rails, and fencing went on, and improvement after improvement was added to the farmstead. In these years wheat was Green's major crop. In 1842 he sowed forty acres; by 1845 he had raised this acreage to 120. Since he listed only one hundred acres of his farm as improved in 1850, he was evidently counting wheat raised in partnership with the Kimball brothers or on land that he had rented. In these years Green grew both spring and winter wheat, on occasion planting fall wheat on spring breaking and between the rows in his cornfield. He never mentioned the exact dimensions of his cornfields, but he grew enough of this crop so that he could fatten at least twenty-two hogs in 1845. He also grew oats for sale in some years. From the milk provided by a small herd of milk cows — he reported seven in 1850 — he made both butter and cheese. For his wheat, oats, butter, cheese, and pork Green found markets within the immediate community and in Sabula, Dubuque, and Galena. These, of course, are Mississippi River towns; Green did not face the transportation problems of farmers in the interior. Wheat, pork, and cattle on the hoof were the major money-makers. His accounts in the mid-forties contain two references to steer-feeding partnerships with neighbors.

During the 1840's George Green evidently maintained a storeroom in his

[9] "George F. Green, Ledger and Diary, 1839–1849." This diary was made available to the writer through the kindness of Mr. Green's great-granddaughter, Mrs. Curtis Frymoyer, Wilton Junction, Iowa, who also allowed it to be microfilmed by the Special Collections Department of the State University of Iowa Library.

home stocked with pioneer staples brought from Chicago. Neighbors who purchased such items from Green often worked out their accounts on Green's farm. Here, too, was another source of labor. On occasion, also, Green hired men to work by the month. His accounts of the 1840's show that wages in Jackson County were much the same as those in the Beardstown area during the same years. Green's diary reveals a man of energy and common sense — one who was alert to business opportunities but with much less of Sewall's speculative bent.

The milestones of the census show Green's growing prosperity. In 1850 he valued his 200 acres at $1,500. He owned three horses, seven cows, 20 other cattle, and 30 swine — all worth $466. In the previous year he had gathered 550 bushels of wheat, 500 bushels of corn, 100 bushels of oats, 25 bushels of pulse, and put up 15 tons of hay. From the cream produced by the cows, the Greens had made 200 lbs. of butter. During the 1840's George Green had laid the foundation for a very prosperous future by maintaining a farm business considerably larger than most of his neighbors. By 1870 he had enlarged his holdings of land to 340 acres, valued at $17,000, supporting livestock to the value of $5,000. The wheat farmer of the 1840's had become a stockman and feeder. Although he harvested 300 bushels of wheat in 1869, his farm produced 1900 bushels of the feed grains, oats and barley. In 1849 he had gathered a smaller quantity of corn than of wheat. In 1869 his corn crop yielded 4,000 bushels.

IV

Now we can visit the farm of Ole and Gro Svendsen in northwestern Iowa. In this case, too, we would like to know more about the farm than we ever can, but Gro Svendsen's letters to her family in Norway picture it with some clarity.[10] Arriving in America in 1862, this young Norwegian couple lived for a short time among their countrymen at St. Ansgar, Iowa. During the next spring Ole journeyed west and staked a claim to a fractional quarter section of land near Estherville in Emmet County. Close by lay the claims of other Norwegians. Leaving Gro with his father and mother for the summer, Ole worked for an American in Emmet County. The wages were good — $15.00 per month was a common wage, perhaps he earned more — and he could guard the claim that he hoped to homestead. During the fall of 1863 he brought Gro to the claim, and they began the tasks of farm-making. The Svendsen's land was prairie with few trees. So few trees were there, indeed, that Ole purchased 12½ acres of wooded land that lay six miles away. Here was the raw stuff of house, stable, and fences for an outlay of $100 that Ole borrowed from his father at 7 per cent interest, with five years in which to repay.

The Svendsens lived on their claim for ten years before they obtained a

[10] Pauline Farseth and Theodore C. Blegen (trans. and ed.), *Frontier Mother: The Letters of Gro Svendsen* (Northfield, 1950).

title to it. Lest failure to become a citizen should compromise his homestead entry, Ole began naturalization proceedings as rapidly as possible. As a result, or so the Svendsens believed, he was drafted in 1864 and enjoyed the dubious pleasure of serving under General Sherman in the closing days of the war. And in the end they failed to secure their claim under the homestead law. They discovered instead that they must buy it because it was adjudged to lie in a railroad land grant. During 1873 they borrowed $500 from a loan office in Estherville and bought the farm for $480, mortgaging it immediately as security for the loan. Ole Svendsen acquired no additional land in Iowa. Gro died in childbirth during 1878, and in the following year Ole quitclaimed his farm for $1.00. Following his brother's trail to the Goose River region of Dakota Territory, he once more began to cut a farm from the virgin prairie.

Ole Svendsen purchased a yoke of oxen for $30 in 1862 and never thereafter lacked the animal power necessary to work a farm. Yet improvement of the holding went slowly. He had broken only a few acres of land when he went to war, and his younger brother broke just three acres during the season of 1865. With the soldier safely home, farm-making moved more rapidly; Gro reported 21½ acres under the plow in 1867. Although Svendsen did not apparently break large acreages at any time thereafter, the arable grew slowly over time.

The dwelling that Ole built in the fall of 1863 was "very small and humble," but Gro reported in 1867 that they were now well housed "both man and beast." Near the house were two wooden stables, large enough to shelter more than 24 head of cattle, with a shed between "for the bulls." [11] By 1867, also, they had dug a well to provide a supply of water close at hand. Svendsen cut the wood for his improvements from his timber lot during the winter and had it sawed to dimensions, when necessary, at a nearby mill. From the woodlot also he hauled the rails to protect his crops from the livestock that ranged the unimproved land of the neighborhood.

While the arable on the Svendsen claim still numbered only a few acres of land in 1865, Gro Svendsen described crops of corn, sorghum, potatoes, and watermelons. After the veteran had enlarged the breaking, he placed his major dependence on wheat. In 1866 and 1867 he had some ten acres of this crop; by 1869 the land devoted to it was eighteen acres. In the latter year he sowed three acres of oats also and had a few acres of corn and sorghum in addition to the inevitable potato patch. A year later he sowed a little barley as well. Gro would speak gratefully of the sorghum molasses, extracted and refined on the equipment of a neighbor for half the product. Since Ole Svendsen ordinarily grew little corn and kept a fair number of livestock, he must have cut considerable prairie hay each August and September.

Year after year the young Norwegian couple planted their crops and hoped for the best. Svendsen harvested 320 and 340 bushels of wheat in 1868

[11] *Ibid.*, pp. 72, 138. On the basis of internal evidence I have set the date of the letter given on pp. 137–138 as 1867.

and 1869 — years of bountiful crops and good prices. The years of the 1870's were apparently hard in Emmet County. Grasshoppers had appeared in 1868 without damaging the Svendsen crops to any extent, but in 1873 Gro reported, "In many places there will be no harvest. We did get a little, enough for our own living, but none to sell." [12] A year later she wrote, "The pests . . . consumed everything except a little of the corn and the potatoes." [13] In July of 1876 the pests returned again, "causing a great deal of damage." [14] Although the Svendsens and their neighbors agreed to burn their prairie grass at the same time during the spring of 1877 in order to destroy the eggs of the grasshoppers, the insects worked considerable damage in that year as well. Anticipating their ravages, the Svendsens planted only corn in 1877 and harvested an indifferent crop. Still there was an abundant crop of grass for the livestock, and the Svendsens made twenty-nine gallons of syrup from sorghum that they saved from the locusts. They had not yet suffered, Gro informed her family in Norway, and the grasshoppers had left no eggs. Surely they were delivered from this plague.

If others did as the Svendsens, the pioneers of northwestern Iowa adjusted to the hopper invasion by putting more stress on the corn crop. But evidently corn was not highly successful in this region during the 1870's. The farmers of northwestern Iowa did not renounce their commitment to wheat for some time yet, although those in older settlements to the south and east were doing so during this decade. The corn planted in northwestern Iowa by the new settlers evidently was not adapted to the shorter seasons of that area; greater emphasis on the crop had to wait until the farmers found strains that would ripen more rapidly.

In a letter to her family in 1863, Gro Svendsen included a little sermon in practical economics. Discussing the yoke of young oxen that her husband had purchased in the previous year for $30.00 she wrote:

You ask me why we use oxen. . . . In the first place, it is better to have cattle than cash. Currency fluctuates constantly. . . . We actually have nothing but paper money. There is no sign of gold or silver money. So you see it's far better to have cattle than the practically worthless paper money. . . . The price of cattle . . . does not fluctuate so much, and the young oxen will rise in value each year. If we were to sell them in the fall, we would surely get 45 or 50 dollars a yoke, good returns for the winter fodder. They continue to rise in value till they are eight years old, when they will bring anywhere from 80 to 100 dollars. When they are fully grown, they can do all the work. Therefore, anyone who intends to buy land should buy and raise young oxen. They are easy to care for, hay is plentiful, and in a very short time they are old enough to work. Then, too one can hire them out by the day. Even if one doesn't plan to buy land, it is wise to raise oxen and sell them, because of the profit.[15]

[12] *Ibid.*, p. 122.
[13] *Ibid.*, p. 124.
[14] *Ibid.*, p. 130.
[15] *Ibid.*, p. 34.

In part for these reasons no doubt, and probably in part, also, because the distance to the nearest railroad limited the amount of grain that could be sold from the farm, the Svendsens consistently kept more livestock than one might have expected. In December, 1865, they were feeding twenty-three head of cattle, although a few of these were boarders belonging to other members of the family. During that fall Gro sold $35.00 worth of butter. Ordinarily thereafter the Svendsens kept between twelve and twenty head of cattle on their farm. During the 1870's Gro consistently reported six cows and a variety of younger stock. From a herd of this size the Svendsens were probably able to sell three or four animals each year and slaughter the occasional beef or old cow for family use. Six cows, doubtless, also provided Gro with sufficient cream so that she could make butter in amounts beyond the needs of her growing family.

Despite Gro Svendsen's endorsement of oxen in 1863, her husband was not permanently committed to them. By 1871 he owned a team of bay horses, "fine looking — the finest in the countryside," and had sold his work oxen.[16] By 1877 the number of horses on the farm had grown to five although Ole owned a yoke of five-year-old oxen in addition. But the fine bays were now gone. The horses instead were "ponies" that the members of the family used mainly for driving and riding. When Gro enumerated the farm census for the last time in November of 1877, she listed five horses and sixteen head of cattle, including two "driving oxen", six cows, three heifers soon due to calve, two that would not, and three calves. There were in addition, twenty sheep, two pigs, twenty-five chickens, one dog, and one cat. The flock of sheep was a development mainly of the 1870's, although the Svendsens had owned a few during the 1860's. The Svendsens had apparently little liking for hogs. Gro never reported more than four pigs in any of her letters, and generally the number was less. This was no corn-hog farm. Evidently, Ole Svendsen fattened a litter each year for family use, and there his interest in porkers stopped.

When writing to her relatives in Norway, Gro Svendsen told little that was specific about farm income. But from the crops and stock and the few comments that she did make, it is easy to reconstruct the general outlines of the Svendsen farm business. Each year they sold a few head of cattle — often young oxen already broken to the yoke. During the late spring and summer, the milk cows produced sufficient milk so that Gro could churn a surplus of butter for sale in Estherville. The price per pound was low — between five and ten cents in all probability — but she reported proudly that she had sold $35.00 worth in 1865. Since the Svendsens increased the number of their cows shortly from four to six, Gro doubtless produced larger quantities of butter in subsequent years. This increase in output was balanced, to some extent, by the growth in size of her family and by lower prices. When the small-grain harvest was good, it added considerably to farm income. If we

16 *Ibid.*, p. 114.

use the state average price for these years, the 320 bushels of wheat produced in 1868 and the 340 of 1869 were roughly worth $440 and $310, although the Svendsens may have received much less. Some of the wheat was retained for family use and seed; much of it was sold. In 1868 Ole drew wheat to the railroad at Waseca, Minnesota, and undoubtedly the local community in Emmet County absorbed considerable grain as a stream of new farm-makers flowed in during the late 1860's.

Even in 1868 and 1869 the cash income of the Svendsen farm could hardly have been much more than $400, if that, and in earlier and later years it was undoubtedly much less. In several locust years the grain crop was a flat failure, and the Svendsens could look only to the livestock for cash income. At all times they avoided the purchase of store goods with an ingenuity that would amaze a modern farm family. In one of the early years in Emmet County, Gro sheared their lone sheep twice. We find in her letters the purchases that the Svendsens must have considered to be major milestones in the history of their farm. During 1864 they purchased a wagon for $35 and a stove for $25. This money they borrowed at interest from Ole's father. During 1867 they acquired a new harrow — price unknown but considered costly — and in 1868 Ole paid $26 for a new plow. The next year he purchased a new wagon for $90. In 1871 a new harness cost $40. Two years later one of the horses developed a sore leg during the summer working season and Ole must buy "Jack" at a cost of $150.

The year 1873 was a particularly discouraging one for the Svendsens. The grasshoppers preyed upon the fields in the spring so that the crop was meager, they found that they must buy the land that they had hoped to homestead, and there was the expense of the new horse. This last outlay was all the more frustrating because the sick animal had recovered by autumn. "Times," wrote Gro, "have been hard this fall — much harder than any since we came to this land. The future is uncertain. . . . We have been thinking not a little of selling this land." [17]

The Svendsens were appalled, at times, by the prices that they must pay for labor. The picture was by no means one in which cooperative pioneers traded their labor freely. Some labor exchange there undoubtedly was, but the Svendsen's kept a hired man intermittently — no less hired because sometimes a relative — and they paid cash for labor at harvest and threshing times. In 1868 a neighbor cut their eighteen acres of wheat with a reaper while five men bound the sheaves and one shocked. Ole and "our handy man, old man Hagen," were sufficient force to stack the grain.[18] In the next year the "cost of reaping, binding, shocking, and stacking came to exactly fifty dollars. (Fifteen dollars for reaping alone.)" Threshing amounted to a further $42.00, which included the "wages of three men and the use of three teams of horses that accompanied the threshing machine," as well as the wages of eight extra

[17] *Ibid.*, p. 123.
[18] *Ibid.*, p. 88.

men and the cost of two additional teams of horses needed to run the five-team horsepower.[19] To Gro this was a considerable sum to set against a crop of 340 bushels on which the price ultimately fell to 50¢ a bushel. In August, 1872, she estimated that their debt at the end of the summer would be over one hundred dollars of which the greater part was owing "to brother Sevat for wages." [20]

"When one begins to farm, it takes a great deal to get started — especially when one must begin with nothing and must go into debt besides.[21] So wrote Gro Svendsen in 1864. The Svendsens occupied their claim on railroad land in Emmet County for ten years before they finally purchased it. Although the land had stood tax free in all probability, they still lacked savings that they could apply on the cost of the land. When Ole Svendsen decided to move to Dakota in 1879, the land was still encumbered.[22] The sixteen years in Emmet County were not completely wasted years for the Svendsens, however. They wrested a living from the land and fed a constantly growing family. Nine children were living when Gro died in 1879. Despite these facts, the Svendsen story was one of painfully slow progress toward unencumbered ownership and security. The grasshopper years and the low prices of the 1870's undoubtedly explain the pattern to a considerable extent. These were the years also that constituted the first period of labor scarcity in the labor cycle of this farm family. Only in the mid-1870's did Ole's oldest sons become large enough to help him materially on the farm. Ole Svendsen was not a poor manager as William Sewall perhaps was. Ultimately he became a prosperous farmer in North Dakota. Unquestionably, however, he must have looked back upon the 1870's in Iowa as hard years, and so would many other farm-makers of northwestern Iowa.

[19] *Ibid.*, p. 104.
[20] *Ibid.*, p. 118.
[21] *Ibid.*, p. 49.
[22] When Ole Svendsen left Emmet County he quitclaimed his land in return for $1.00, indicating that the land was still encumbered, presumably by a trust deed. Emmet County, Quit Claim Book 1, p. 537. Estherville, Iowa.

CHAPTER XIII

The Farmer In The "Old" Community

Only a relatively few farmers knew pioneering at its rudest in the prairie communities. Croft Pilgrim and John Savage were among the army of men who began their farming careers on the prairies of Illinois and Iowa after the settlements had taken shape.

I

Croft Pilgrim was born in England during 1834 and emigrated with his father and family to Peoria County, Illinois, in 1852. Three years after arriving in America, young Pilgrim married Susan Swank. The young couple evidently sought their fortunes in troubled Kansas during the late 1850's or early 1860's because Croft Pilgrim's first diary and account book lists the receipt of $414 on September 8, 1863, "from Kansas of Isac Hiner for land." How the young man had obtained money to buy land in Kansas we do not know, and we can only guess why he and his young wife left that embattled state. When Pilgrim started his journal in 1862, he had recently purchased an 85-acre farm in Stark County, Illinois. Six days after receiving the money from Kansas, he paid $184.95 to the attorney of the Egbert estate in partial payment for this Illinois farm. Pilgrim's deed listed a consideration of $376.[1] Although Croft Pilgrim's diaries and accounts provide only a fragmentary record of his farming operations during the 1860's and have regretable gaps in the next two decades also, they do present an informative picture of Corn Belt agriculture in evolution.[2]

Croft Pilgrim's farm business was undoubtedly a small one during the early 1860's. His crops of grain in 1862 yielded 343 bushels of wheat and 252 bushels of oats, harvested, probably, from no more than thirty acres of cropland. His livestock consisted of a few pigs and cattle and probably a

[1] "Stark County, Deed Register, Q, 290." A commissioner's deed, filed some years later in settling the estate of Henry Swank, Pilgrim's father-in-law, suggests that the young couple may have received aid in this purchase from Mrs. Pilgrim's parents (see Deed Register, 32, 331). If this was the case, this family debt was probably liquidated in the settlement of the Henry Swank estate, since the Pilgrims were entitled to one-fifth of it after the widow's dowry was set aside. The deed registers are in the office of the county recorder, Toulon, Illinois.

[2] "The Croft Pilgrim Diary," Iowa Department of History and Archives, Des Moines, Iowa.

team of horses. The agricultural census-taker in 1880 would discover Croft
Pilgrim established on a large farm of 310 acres in Poweshiek County, Iowa.
The valuation of this farm was $11,100, ranking it as the seventh most
valuable of the 176 farms in Grinnell Township.[3] At the same time Pilgrim's
two eldest sons were buying other farms from their father. Croft Pilgrim had
won this comparative affluence in a period that agricultural historians portray as one of agricultural depression.

The major steps in the emergence of Croft Pilgrim as a successful farmer
seem clear. During the 1860's he apparently paid off the debts on his original
farm in Illinois, improved it by breaking and fencing, and began to accumulate additional capital. Wheat, at war prices, was evidently his largest
source of income, although the share that he and his wife received of her
father's estate may have smoothed the path materially. By the late 1860's
he wanted more land. During 1869 he rented an additional forty acres of
land, concluding, after keeping a meticulous record of labor and seed expended on it, that he had lost $82.00 by the transaction. In 1870 he tried to
borrow on trust deed from a widow in Peoria in order to buy the farm of his
brother John. At this point Susan Pilgrim, ordinarily referred to in the diaries
cryptically as "the wife," takes on character and personality for the reader.
She refused to sign the trust deed, although her husband had already paid
down several hundred dollars on the purchase. By 1873, however, Susan's
reluctance to buy land had apparently diminished, and Croft Pilgrim purchased an 80-acre farm from a neighbor for $3500.[4] During 1876 he made
his last payment and received the deed for this land, which lay in Bureau
County.

In February, 1877, Croft Pilgrim spent two weeks in Iowa where he
examined farms in Fayette, Buchanan, and Poweshiek counties. Later in,
1877 he purchased 320 acres from J. K. James in Grinnell Township,
Poweshiek County. At this point he sold the Illinois farm to the tax-collector
in Stark County for $10,500. This young man, however, had second thoughts
about the transaction, and Pilgrim agreed to cancel the contract in return for
some $400 of damages. Despite the loss of anticipated income from the
Illinois sale, Pilgrim could still tender the initial payment of $3500 for his
new farm in Iowa. When the rest of the family moved to Poweshiek County
during the spring of 1878, he left the farm in Illinois under the management
of his eldest son, Charles Morey, who soon contracted to purchase the portion lying in Bureau County. In 1881 Croft Pilgrim sold the old home place
to his brother William for $4500.[5]

Why would a successful Illinois farmer sell his farm, break his community
ties, and transfer his family and business to Iowa? More important still, what

[3] "Manuscript Federal Agricultural Census, 1880," Iowa State Historical Society,
Iowa City, Iowa.
[4] "Bureau County, Deed Register, 73, 383." The deed registers are in the office of
the county recorder, Princeton, Illinois.
[5] "Stark County, Deed Register, 48, 343."

was there about Croft Pilgrim's farm business that allowed him to accumulate land and capital through the depression-torn 1870's? The implications of these questions spread far beyond the story of Croft Pilgrim, because he was not unique in the emergent Corn Belt. A detailed analysis of Pilgrim's accounts and diaries provide some tentative answers.

Through the twenty years of this study, Croft Pilgrim depended mainly on the sale of grain and hogs for his income. One might call his farm a cash-grain-and-hogs operation. During the Civil War he evidently grew and sold considerable amounts of wheat; by the early 1870's his wheat crop was intended primarily as a source of flour for the kitchen and of chicken feed. Consistently he raised comparatively large quantities of oats — mainly for sale rather than for feed on the farm. Consistently, also, he kept a few cows. From the milk the family churned butter that was mostly consumed at home, although Pilgrim traded some at the local store. He might raise and sell a few animals for veal or beef, but he was short of pasture despite the purchase of additional acreage. In 1876 he rented pasture for ten head of young stock. Ordinarily his major income from stock came from hogs. Of these he was selling several carloads a year by the late 1870's. To feed the hogs and also, to some degree, for cash sale, he grew corn. In 1879 he reported 150 acres of corn — an acreage equal to that in all other crops and hay. At first Pilgrim sold all his products locally. He continued to dispose of his grain in this way by dealing with local grain merchants. His cattle, too, he sold to local drovers or farmers. By 1873 he was accompanying his hogs to the stockyards in Chicago.

In even the small farm operation of the early 1860's there were periods when the farm-operator needed assistance if he was to work efficiently. When his diaries begin, Pilgrim was a member of a small group of seven neighbors who helped each other in haying, grain harvest, stacking, and threshing. Within the group minor patterns of exchange occurred at corn-planting time or when Pilgrim or a neighbor butchered a beef or one or two hogs. The first record that Croft Pilgrim kept was a harvest account in which he tabulated the amount of labor given and received within the work ring. Here, labor was a commodity that was used to pay the rent for machinery or additional horsepower. Pilgrim owned no reaper in the earliest years of record and tried to give additional labor to the neighbor who cut his grain. Consistently, members of the work ring brought their teams to help run the horsepower of the threshing machine. During the late 1860's and early 1870's neighbors were using Pilgrim's mower and reaper. In late fall or winter the neighbors balanced out the labor accounts with small cash payments to the members who had given more labor than they had received. Aside from the work ring, Croft Pilgrim hired no farm labor during the span of his diaries with the exception of skilled workmen whom he retained for various projects of farm improvement — masons, carpenters, and tile layers. At intervals, a hired girl did assist Mrs. Pilgrim in her task of caring for six sons and a daughter.

As his family of six sons matured, Pilgrim's dependence on the neighbors diminished somewhat, and the work ring of the early 1880's had a membership of only five in comparison to the seven of the early sixties. We cannot overemphasize the importance of this growing family in Croft Pilgrim's business success. As they reached their teens, his sons entered increasingly into the work of the farm and provided a reliable supply of labor. The eldest boys, Charles Morey and John Henry, began to work for other farmers for several months at a time when they were in their mid-teens, and their employers paid the wages to Croft Pilgrim. Some 15 per cent of Pilgrim's receipts in 1873 came from the sale of labor in some form, and the largest item by far in this total was the money received in payment for the labor of Charles Morey and John Henry, then 17 and 16 years of age.

Croft Pilgrim was able to exchange labor directly for cash in another way as well. In an age when gross cash receipts were small by twentieth century standards, a few dollars derived from political office or jury duty was of considerable importance. Croft Pilgrim frequently served on the county juries, and as local roadmaster in 1873 he bargained with some of his neighbors to work out their road tax, thus deriving an additional income of some $30.

Pilgrim's terse diary entries reflected the changes in agricultural technology that were revolutionizing midwestern agriculture during the last half of the nineteenth century. He owned no reaper in 1862, but at least one member of the work ring did. Thereafter Croft Pilgrim acquired a succession of mowers, reapers, hay rakes, sulky plows, and John Deere iron-beam plows. By 1873 his sons no longer dropped corn before the flashing hoes of their father and a member of the work ring; Croft Pilgrim was using a borrowed horse-planter. During the next year he purchased both corn-planter and cultivator. In 1878 a Grinnell merchant brought a check-rower attachment to the farm for trial; it did not work satisfactorily, Pilgrim recorded. Through the 1860's and 1870's he watched his teams and those of his neighbors monotonously circling the central gearing of the horsepower during threshing. In 1882 he noted that his thresher was using a steam engine.

Pilgrim's farm improvements also revealed the changing technology of the times. Board and hedge were his earliest fencing materials, and trimming hedge was a task that occupied several days of his time between the seeding of the small grains and corn-planting during the early 1870's. After he moved to Iowa, he noted large expenditures for fence posts and wire, and one entry recorded a payment for labor expended in placing barbs on old wire. During the mid-1870's he engaged a ditching-and-tiling outfit to lay 202 rods of tile on his property. Technically speaking, the results were evidently excellent. He bought several carloads of tile shortly after establishing himself near Grinnell.

Pilgrim's earliest venture in tiling disrupted the harmony of the neighborhood. No sooner was the drain completed than his neighbor Tom Mellor dammed the outlet, claiming that the tiling system was flooding his fields. Thus in 1876 began a long-drawn-out litigation, which started in the court of the local justice of the peace and moved ultimately into the district court. After a series of decisions and appeals, the case still stood on the docket at Toulon, the county seat, in 1882, and by this time had cost Croft Pilgrim several hundred dollars. Despite the location of his land, Mellor was not, incidentally, a member of Pilgrim's work or visiting circle — an indication that the nineteenth century rural neighborhood was not the pool of togetherness that some rural sociologists have imagined. To compound the unpleasantness of the warfare, a former member of Pilgrim's labor ring and ally in local politics joined Mellor's camp and instituted a companion action.

The young Pilgrims did not grow up in an age of homespun. During the 1860's and 1870's Susan Pilgrim did make many of the work clothes for her family from hickory shirting, denim, and the like, but the members of the family purchased suits and shoes and occasional overalls in the nearby trade centers. Although Pilgrim slaughtered hogs and cattle for home use, he frequently bought beef from a local butcher during the summer. The family did most of its trading at the nearby station and post office of Bradford; they also patronized the stores of Buda in Bureau County, and specific needs or errands took them to Neponset, Lombardville, and to the county seat, Toulon.

During their residence in Illinois, the Pilgrims did business consistently with four merchants — a harness maker, a blacksmith, an agricultural-implement salesman, a cobbler, and the proprietor of a coal bank. To Brewer, Davis, and Company at Bradford, Croft Pilgrim sold his grain, and from them he purchased his lumber and some general merchandise. Household supplies for the Pilgrim family came, for the most part, from the store of Pilgrim's brother William, a general merchant of Bradford. All of the general merchants were willing, on occasion, to take butter and eggs on account, and with all of them, Pilgrim kept small running accounts that he settled every few months. After moving to Iowa, he developed a similar trading pattern among the merchants of Grinnell.

In some years' Croft Pilgrim kept a day-by-day record of expenditures and receipts. Table 25 shows statements of his farm business during the years 1873, 1877, and 1882 based on the memoranda in his diary. Unfortunately, he was not entirely consistent in recording his business transactions. On occasion, he evidently entered the same expenditure twice. Other entries were so terse that they are difficult to categorize. The family used a few items, notably salt, in both house and barn; these were counted among the household expenses. The costs of travel posed a similar problem. On occasion, Pilgrim or members of his family traveled on business, sometimes on pleasure, and, probably most often, they mixed both motives, merging farm and household expenses. Pilgrim did not record his tax bill in 1873; that of 1877 was probably incomplete. Nor was it possible to learn the value

TABLE 25

CROFT PILGRIM'S FARM BUSINESS *

	Receipts		
	1873	1877	1882
Butter & eggs ....$	93.00	$ 5.55	$ 4.20
Grain	244.04	525.20	1,936.81
Potatoes	......	6.00	......
Stock	780.06	1,508.35	1,202.45
Labor	214.85	76.74	......
Miscellaneous	88.58	17.25	30.60
	$1,420.53	$2,139.09	$3,174.06

FARM EXPENDITURES			
Equipment, Improvements and supplies	$114.59	$125.75	$618.19
Seed and crop expense	15.50	2.50	55.35
Stock	154.00	73.70	331.88
Labor	21.15	23.35	36.70
Threshing and shelling	21.44	30.78	37.94
Legal services	30.16	38.56	17.23
Taxes	......	16.35	98.97
	$356.84	$310.99	$1,196.26

HOUSEHOLD EXPENSES			
Provisions and supplies	$334.96	$205.45	$520.22
Apparel	82.13	109.92	217.44
Labor	7.00	14.00	128.01
Education	2.55	60.55	8.00
Gifts	6.00	......	60.00
Miscellaneous	5.27	......	2.35
	437.91	389.92	936.02
Travel	20.45	84.07	23.65
	$458.36	$473.99	$959.67

* Data drawn from the Croft Pilgrim Diary.

of improvements made in the various years, nor changes in the inventory of stock, grain, and feed. Granted such limitations, however, Table 25 does shed considerable light on Pilgrim's farm business during the 1870's and early 1880's.

Croft Pilgrim's receipts in 1873 show a diversified farm business in which he had at his disposal more labor than he could use effectively in his own operations. Subsequently, as he increased the size of his farm, he was able to utilize the labor of his growing family of sons at home. As he enlarged his grain and hog enterprises, the income from barnyard poultry and milk cows became of little importance. Hogs, corn, and oats were the dominant enterprises by the mid-1870's at least.

The statements of expenses in Table 25 speak largely for themselves. The rather large outlays on farm account in 1882 reflect extensive improvements that he was making on the new farm in Iowa, including, evidently, some remodeling of the house. After deducting farm expenditures from gross receipts, the net sum left assignable to depreciation account, to labor, and to capital was 75, 81, and 61 per cent. (Since some of Pilgrim's expenditures for improvements might properly be considered additions to capital rather than farm-business expenses, the calculations are crude.) After the deduction of household expenses, Croft Pilgrim still had 42, 63 and 32 per cent of the total receipts left at his disposal. Assuming that missing expenditures like the taxes of 1873 might reduce the figures by 5 or 10 per cent, the showing was still a handsome one. The Pilgrim family obviously had no pressing need for the several hundred dollars that Mrs. Pilgrim inherited from her mother's estate in 1873.

The accumulation of money brings pleasantly vexatious decisions about its management. Croft Pilgrim could no doubt have channeled much of his money into farm improvements. Unquestionably, he did improve his holdings. Diary entries show him buying lumber, bricks, fencing materials, and drainage tile. We cannot know, of course, the degree to which these expenditures simply represented repairs in contrast to new improvements. Pilgrim's major long-run decision in the management of his profits has already become obvious. He bought more land. In the interims between purchases and payments, he loaned a good deal of money — usually in sums of several hundred dollars. Some of these loans the Stark County farmer made to Brewer and Davis, a local mercantile firm; others were to William Pilgrim, his merchant brother; still others went to surrounding farmers. Most of these loans were for periods of only a few months, and in many cases the interest rate was not clearly revealed in the diary entries. Some of Pilgrim's farmer-borrowers, however, paid 10 per cent. Pilgrim did make smaller loans in amounts of $5.00 to $50.00. Usually the borrowers in such cases were members of Pilgrim's work ring, and the transactions were short-term accommodation loans. Occasionally, Pilgrim himself might borrow a few dollars from one of the group if momentarily pressed for funds.

His diaries show Croft Pilgrim to have been a hard-working, punctilious man, slightly litigious, perhaps, who regarded farming as a business and not simply as a way of life. Whether by luck or sound planning, few disasters happened on his farm. Occasionally, he found it necessary to replant corn, or the team ran away. Major crop failures or losses of stock did not occur. He was relatively well informed. He attended the agricultural fairs of his region regularly and in 1876 visited the Centennial Exhibition in Philadelphia. Apparently, however, he did not subscribe to an agricultural periodical. He was a man who was careful of his expenditures, although, judging from the nature of the occasional purchase not penurious. The uses of credit he well understood, and, Granger though he was, he was not afraid to put his knowledge to the test.

Croft Pilgrim did not allow himself to become intoxicated by the new technology of agriculture. He experimented with machines owned by his neighbors before he himself purchased implements of the same type, and he frequently obtained them on trial. He was no pioneer in laying tile, but he did so as soon as the advantages of doing so became established.

The combination of enterprises on the Pilgrim farm — cash grain and hogs — was not the only one that Croft Pilgrim could have made. He could instead have fed cattle or concentrated still more on the production of cash grain, for instance. But his combination of swine and grain balanced his business without demanding the capital investment that feeder cattle involved. Even when he was raising considerable amounts of wheat in 1862, he was growing more oats than was usual in central Illinois at the time, and his cropping decisions foreshadowed the growing importance of this crop in the 1870's.

In part, Croft Pilgrim benefited from the general increase in land values underway in Illinois after 1860; he had paid far less than the $10,500 for which his Illinois holdings were tentatively sold in 1877. If the deed register tells the whole story, the 85 acres in Stark County increased in value from $376 in 1861 to $4,500 in 1881.[6] Some of his success was attributable to the happy combination of genes that made him the father of six healthy boys. He held to the patriarchal tradition that the labor of the sons belonged to the father until they had reached their majority. On the other hand, he recognized an obligation to help them acquire their own farms when they reached an appropriate age.

His diary entries make Croft Pilgrim's success appear absurdly easy — even inevitable. But we know that many Illinois and Iowa farmers found that success was neither easy nor inevitable during these same years. Perhaps the road to affluence did not seem easy to Pilgrim either. While he was making the decisions that spelled success, he was supporting the creed of the Granger and the Greenbacker. Anomalous though this may appear, it was by no means unusual. Commercially-oriented farmers with larger businesses than average provided much of the Grange and Greenback leadership in Iowa and Illinois.[7] The fertile but relatively low-priced lands of Iowa might draw such a man irresistably.

II

During the mid-1850's William Savage moved to Iowa from New York, bringing with him his wife Mary and four children, Rose, Mary, John, and Thomas. An Englishman by birth and a tailor by craft, Savage purchased a small farm in Salem Township, Henry County, Iowa. Here he tailored and farmed until his death in early 1877. The younger son, Thomas, died while serving in the Union Army during the Civil War. Much of the work and direction of the farm fell to John Savage, who remained at home con-

[6] *Ibid.*

[7] For instance Mr. Harry D. Jackson, State University of Iowa, has shown in an unpublished paper based on manuscript census returns, that Iowa Grange chapter presidents and secretaries evidently operated farms that were substantially larger than the county averages.

tinuously and inherited his father's interest in the farm on the death of William Savage. In 1862, then aged 24, John married Tacy Crew — a union that was to be blessed by a large family.

In some respects the Savage farm differed from the traditional picture of a holding occupied by an operator who devoted all of his time to its management. The tailoring craft occupied William Savage to a considerable extent, and John typically taught the winter term of four months at one of the nearby schools. Actually we can regard the Savages as illustrative of a rather large number of mechanics, artisans, craftsmen, or professionals who maintained farms. From late in 1860, at least, John Savage kept a rather detailed diary. As he noted on the day of his marriage, "Who ever looks for sentiment in this book will find it a scarce article," but it does allow us to reconstruct many aspects of the Savage farm business during the 1860's and 1870's.[8]

The farm that William Savage purchased in 1856 was seventy-five acres in size. In 1867 John Savage bought forty acres of brushland, the "Wilson forty," adjacent to the original holding, for $360, and three years later he acquired a five-acre timber lot for $25. This he held for a short time only. Late in 1879 he purchased the "Hockett farm," approximately 150 acres, of which about 100 were in cultivation. Almost every year during the 1860's and 1870's, John Savage rented additional cropland, varying from four to forty acres, in the neighborhood, usually on the "Allen farm." Sometimes he paid the rent in cash — $60 for forty acres in 1862; sometimes one-third of the crop was the consideration. In several years of the mid-1860's, the Savages also rented pasturage for their flock of sheep during part of the season. The Savages put together their operating unit, therefore, partly by renting and partly by purchase. When John Savage acquired the Hocket farm, he had for the first time more land than he could himself farm, so he rented part of it to a tenant Samuel Smith.

The farmstead, particularly, changed greatly in appearance in the twenty years between 1860 and 1880. In 1860 we can visualize a farmstead where the original log cabin still stood, but where the family now occupied a small frame house. A picket fence surrounded a nearby garden. A rail fence enclosed the farmyard. A straw-covered pole stable provided winter shelter for the horse and two cows. Probably an open-fronted straw shed protected the sheep and other livestock in the wintertime. In the late summer each year the Savages built a small rail pen for the fattening hogs near a crude corncrib, although on occasion the hogs occupied the old log cabin. If a steer was to be fattened for slaughter, it also occupied a pen in the barnyard, beginning in the late summer or early fall. In the appropriate seasons small stacks of wheat, oats, and hay stood in, or adjacent to, the barnyard, protected from the farm stock by temporary rail fences. Similarly the

[8] "John Savage Diary," October 23, 1862, Iowa State Department of History and Archives, Des Moines, Iowa.

Savages protected the corn fodder that they hauled to the farmstead during the fall and winter.

John Savage's diary reflected steady improvement at headquarters. A few years after his marriage to Tacy Crew, he employed a joiner to build a new house that was attached to the old one, providing more adequate living quarters for his own growing family and his mother and father. When he purchased a second horse in 1861, he built a more elaborate stable. As the number of cows grew on the farm, they, too, acquired their own stable, made from lumber cut at a nearby sawmill. The roofing on these stables, however, was still straw. Year by year, a new pump, a smokehouse, a granary, drive shed, or corncrib appeared at the farmstead. Finally in 1871, the Savages hired a local builder to erect a barn twenty-six by thirty-six feet in dimensions. For this they paid him $450 — the builder "finding" all the materials but the foundation stone.

The appearance of the farm itself changed over time also as father and son brought more of the brushland under cultivation and removed the grubs from the older fields. In the 1860's the fencing was solely of worm rail fence, laid seven or eight rails high, with the conventional stakes and riders. Such fence enclosed the improved portion of the farm, and father and son shifted the interior fencing as the need arose to protect the winter wheat after they had turned stock into the meadow in late summer or into the stalk field in the late fall or winter. About 1870 John Savage may have planted some hedge fencing. In 1870 he was beginning to fence brushland for enclosed pasture. Until this time much of the unimproved land had lain open to all of the neighborhood stock. John Savage had his first experience with wire fence in the late 1870's when one of the cows returned in the evening slashed "as if cut with an axe," and he discovered that a neighbor had run a barbed wire fence along his property line through the timber.

We cannot work out a detailed summary of the labor utilized in the various farm enterprises from the information in the diary of John Savage. But the general routine of farm life is clear. The year 1861 can serve as an illustration. In January the Savages butchered their hogs for home use, cut rails and fire wood in the timber, and hauled "shock corn" from the field to the barnyard, where they husked it before feeding. In February the woodlot tasks and the drawing of fodder continued. During March the Savages continued to split rails and began to grub in ten acres of brushland that they proposed to break that spring. Lambing began in this month. In April they washed their apple trees with a solution of lye and lime, sowed oats, and altered the lambs. In this month, too, the task of tending stock at the yard lightened when father and son turned out the cattle and most of the pigs. In May they planted potatoes, sorghum, and corn. Work on the ground to be broken continued as they cut hazel brush with scythe and axe, used the grub hoe, and burned brush. At the same time they hauled rails from the timber and relaid the outer fence around their improved acreage to include the newly-grubbed land. Just at the end of the month, they washed the sheep. In June they sheared the sheep, worked out their road tax, and broke the new patch of ground. But particularly in this month they plowed corn.

Early in July the Savages laid the corn by, and turned to haying and the wheat and oat harvest. In August the harvest ended, with oats and wheat safely stacked. Now they could haul manure to the winter-wheat ground, plow for wheat, and, unusually early, pick some seed corn. In September they planted their fall wheat, brought in the fattening hogs, and penned them in the barnyard, built a new stable, repaired the barnyard fence, stripped and cut the sorghum for grinding, and began to thresh in the neighborhood. Between these tasks they started to cut and shock corn. Local threshing continued during October, but now cutting and picking corn were their major tasks. In this month, too, they picked the apples and dug the potatoes. By November they had husked and fed out the standing corn and begun to husk the corn that they had shocked earlier. In this month they drove the fat hogs to Salem for delivery to a buyer and hauled rails from the timber. December was open enough so that they could do a certain amount of grubbing. They split additional rails, too, to protect the fodder when brought to the farmyard, because the cattle were now spending most of their time there. Some tasks, of course, like going to the mill at Oakland Mills or to market at Salem and Mount Pleasant were repeated at frequent intervals throughout the year.

Over the next twenty years the basic tasks would remain much the same, although emphasis changed somewhat. Although John Savage bought forty acres of brush in 1867, he seems to have used it mainly for wood and pasture. He broke some of it for cropland, however, and there was still a certain amount of grubbing to be done in the older fields. In the intervals between tending crops and livestock, fencing occupied much of his time. Bit by bit father and son enclosed the open lands of the farm. Rails decayed in the older fences and found their way to the woodpile after the Savages had replaced them with new ones. Constantly, it seemed, father and son were rearranging the interior division lines to conform to the new crop boundaries. Different or new crops sometimes shifted the emphasis of the work load, as when the Savages grew buckwheat, rye, or timothy for seed. In general, farm technology changed far more in the twenty years between 1860 and 1880 than did the farm tasks themselves.

From their fields in 1859, the Savage family gathered 85 bushels of wheat, 600 bushels of corn, 20 bushels of beans, 30 bushels of potatoes, and they cured three tons of hay. They sold $10 worth of market truck, probably beans and potatoes, and $25 worth of apples. To this list of crops John Savage would add oats in the early 1860's as a customary crop, and occasionally he and his father grew buckwheat or rye. Early in the 1860's they were seeding their meadows with timothy, and during the late 1870's,

John Savage threshed relatively large amounts of timothy seed. In 1859 they probably grew between five and ten acres of wheat and between fifteen and twenty acres of corn. In 1880 John Savage listed an acreage of twenty-four acres of wheat, sixty acres of corn, and sixteen acres of oats. In the mid-1860's the Savages increased the size of their orchard and by 1880 listed eight acres of bearing trees — a rather large farm orchard.[9]

Since the Middle West evolved its own unique method of corn harvest, it is of some interest to examine the methods used on the Savage farm. Often father and son fed green ears to their hogs when they first penned the animals for fattening in August or September. As the crop ripened and the corn harvest proper began, the Savages cut a portion of the crop with corn knives and shocked it in the field. From this part of the crop they husked the grain either in the shock or after they had hauled it to the barnyard. The cut stalks provided corn fodder, the basic item in the winter diet of the cattle and sheep on the farm. Husking corn from the fodder was a common early-morning task for John Savage before he set out to teach school in the winter months. From the remainder of their corn crop the Savages gathered the grain in the field, leaving the stalks standing. Their practice here varied during the twenty years between 1860 and 1880. Sometimes they husked the corn directly into the wagon, but on other occasions they merely snapped the corn off in the husk and cribbed it. If such corn was to be ground, they undoubtedly husked it later; when it was destined for the hogs, it may well have reached the trough in jacket.

In 1860 William Savage reported one horse, two oxen, two milk cows, three other cattle, nine sheep, and thirty swine. In 1861 John Savage purchased a mare, giving the farm a team of horses for the first time. The team, young Savage noted, could plow two acres a day, the yoke of oxen only one and a half. By purchase and natural increase the number of horses on the farm increased through the years, despite the occasional sale. John Savage reported six horses in the 1880 census. Similarly the numbers of the other kinds of livestock rose so that the 1880 census listed eight milk cows, fourteen other cattle, 139 sheep and eighty-six swine.[10] During the Civil War years, the Savages increased the size of their flock of sheep rapidly in response to the high wool prices of those years. When wool prices declined, John Savage decreased the size of his flock by slaughtering sheep for meat and selling a number alive. During the mid-1870's, however, he once more increased the size of the flock.

On occasion, the management of the livestock on the Savage farm would have seemed highly casual to the Iowa farmer of today. The workstock, of course, the Savages held close to the farmstead, as they did the nursing ewes and lambs or sows with very young litters. They might turn their other

---

[9] This paragraph is based on the manuscript "Federal Agricultural Census returns of 1860, 1870, and 1880" at the Iowa State Historical Society, Iowa City, Iowa.

[10] *Ibid.*

stock "into the road" to forage in the brushland of the neighborhood that lay open to all the local domestic animals. Their complaining offspring at the farmstead ordinarily brought the cows home for milking in the evening. When maternal affection waned during the summer, the cows might not appear, and then John Savage or his father spent half a day or more, looking for them. Like their woodland companions, the Savage cattle bore distinguishing notches in their ears to aid in identifying them if they roamed far. The sheep and swine carried the same marks although, on occasion, the Savages painted them on the smaller animals. During late August or early September father or son rounded up the hogs in the woods and confined those to be fattened in a pen at the farmstead. Now, also, they brought in any sows, expected to farrow in the fall. During the fall the sheep and cattle might run in the enclosed meadow, but with the definite onset of winter they spent their time in the stalk field or in the farmyard where they lived on straw, hay, and, particularly, corn fodder. These rations the Savages often enriched with a few cobs of corn each day. It is clear that the farmers of Salem Township were fencing pastures during the 1860's and early 1870's, although the process was still incomplete at the end of the latter decade. The commons long persisted in Henry County.

John Savage was apparently rather successful in his management of livestock. More than half of the hogs on the farm died from hog cholera in 1863, but aside from this catastrophe, he made few references to animals lost by accident or disease. Some of the sheep contracted foot rot, and Savage treated them with blue vitriol. Lambs, on occasion, received a dousing with tobacco water to control scab. The horses once suffered in an epidemic of vaguely-described "horse disease" but recovered. Savage was not a blooded-stock man, although he did pay $32.50 for a good buck in 1864 and purchased a Poland China boar during the late 1870's. Purebreds in general, apparently did not interest him, in this period at least. Despite the fact that the number of milk cows on the farm had risen to eight in 1880, he had still not purchased a herd sire, relying instead on his neighbor's beasts. Savage seems usually to have kept the maximum number of animals that the farm would support, gauging this so closely that he frequently had to buy small amounts of corn or other grain during the late winter or spring months.

These were years of striking changes in farm technology. The equipment on the farm in 1860 evidently included a buggy, a wagon, a plow, and a harrow. William Savage valued the lot at $75 for census purposes. In 1862, John Savage made a large sled for hauling in winter. The plow, of course, was a basic implement, and the Savages bought two new walking field plows and one second-hand field plow in the twenty years between 1860 and 1880. They evidently never owned a breaking plow. When John and his brother broke one of their plows "to pieces" in the hazel roots of a patch of new breaking in 1861, they borrowed a breaking plow from a neighbor to complete the task. In August of 1878 John Savage watched a trial of sulky plows on a nearby farm and was not impressed enough to purchase one. Although he borrowed a roller on occasion from neighbors, John Savage never purchased one in this period. Indeed, he noted in his diary in 1879 that dragging a log across cloddy ground did more to pulverize it than a roller could. Not until 1878 did he add a riding cultivator to the plows and harrows with which he worked his land.

Like most of their neighbors, the Savages were planting their corn with hoes during the early 1860's, first marking the field with a shovel plow and a wooden marker. In the spring of 1865, they borrowed a corn-planter from one of their neighbors, but it was not until eight years later that they paid $40 for a horse-drawn planter of their own. In 1864 John Savage paid $30 for a two-horse, walking, corn plow that plowed on both sides of the row at the same time. This implement, he believed, would allow closer and more careful cultivation than the variety of one-horse corn plows then in use. Three years later he sold the two-horse implement for $25 and bought a double-shovel corn plow and a bar-plow corn plow for a total of $16. Not until 1874 would he buy another two-horse corn plow.

The Savages approached the machinery of the small grains and the hayfield with some circumspection. Although they grew a respectable acreage of wheat, the Savages never did purchase a grain drill during this period. By 1870, at least, they had begun to rent a drill from a neighbor who charged 75¢ when the drill left his shed and 25¢ for each acre sown. As the 1860's opened, they were cutting their rather small hay crop with scythes and using the cradle for their small-grain harvest. Not until 1865 did they hire a neighbor to cut their grass with his machine. Thereafter, they usually engaged a local farmer to cut their hay for 75¢ per acre, but they did not retire the cradles so quickly. In 1872 a neighbor cut most of their small-grain acreage as well as the meadow at the same rate per acre. In the following year, John Savage became ill while cradling wheat, and a custom reaper finished the job. Before the next grain harvest began, John Savage purchased a Manny combined reaper and mower in partnership with one of his close neighbors, splitting the $185 purchase price equally with him.

Intermittently during this period the Savages borrowed a horse rake in haying time. Not until the late 1870's, however, did John Savage buy a hay rake. Judging by the price paid, $6.00, it was evidently a simple revolver rather than a wire- or iron-toothed dump rake. Father and son stacked their hay near the farmyard or even within it. After they had built a barn, they filled the loft with hay before stacking the remainder outside. The Savages, of course, bound the small grains by hand and shocked them in the field. Harvest was complete when they had safely stacked the sheaves at the farmstead and raised a rail fence around them to protect them from the farm livestock. Threshing was a custom operation and might take place at any time from the late summer through the early winter. The first machine mentioned in John Savage's diary was a two-horsepower one that did the job rather poorly. At the end of the 1870's, he noted that he had drawn up a supply of wood to fuel the thresher's "steamer."

Apparently, John Savage recorded most major items of farm income in his diary. Occasionally, his description of a sale of butter or eggs was incomplete, and he may well have omitted some minor transactions altogether. He seems to have been less careful in noting farm expenditures.

The income from hogs was usually the largest single item of income. Generally, the Savages sold their fat hogs in one or two lots in December or early January. Local hog-buyers from Salem and Mount Pleasant called at the farm during these weeks and made tentative offers. Occasionally, when prices were depressed, William or John Savage had to seek out buyers. On delivery date the Savages, accompanied by a neighbor boy or two, drove the hogs to Salem or Mount Pleasant. On such trips they took the wagon along to carry any porkers that became mutinous along the way. Although they usually killed several hogs at the end of the feeding period for family use, the Savages never dressed any considerable number of hogs for sale. They did sell small amounts of fresh or cured meat.

Typically, the Savages sold a few cattle each year, and on occassion, the income from this source rivaled that from hogs. Ordinarily, they saved a couple of male calves from each year's calving to rear as steers and sold them at the age of two or three years. At times they might sell a cow or cow and calf also. Most of the buyers were local people, evidently but occasionally Illinois buyers purchased the steers. Typically, too, the Savages fitted one beef each year for slaughter during the winter months. From the early 1860's onward, the income from wool was an important item in the farm revenues. Returning only $5.60 in 1860, it added $131.33 to farm income in 1880. Proportionately, wool was most important during the late-war and immediate post-war years. At 55¢ per pound, the wool brought $114.95 in 1865. Local buyers ordinarily took the clip. In the post-war years and early seventies, the Savages sold numbers of wethers for mutton. Occasionally, John Savage sold a horse, but the horses did not provide the steady source of income that the other kinds of farm livestock did.

The orchard was an important source of income during the early 1860's. From the crop of 1862, the Savages sold apples to the value of $161.13. They found their market at Mt. Pleasant and Salem mainly, but on at least one occasion a local buyer shipped some of the Savage fruit to Nebraska for sale. During the 1870's particularly, the sales of grain and grass seed to the grain-buyers of Salem and Mt. Pleasant became of more importance. Timothy seed, especially, was a money-maker in 1880. Occasionally, the Savages made small sales of corn or seed to neighboring farmers. The diary of John Savage was probably least complete in detailing receipts obtained from butter and eggs. Such sales, ordinarily made at Salem stores, the Savages customarily traded out for store goods, and John may well have ignored

TABLE 26
RECEIPTS AND EXPENDITURES ON THE SAVAGE FARM *

Farm Receipts		Farm Expenditures	
1861			
Hogs	$214.92	Principal & interest	$179.00
Apples	52.23	Mare	65.00
Pork & lard	15.32	Rails (1300)	10.40
Beef	6.26	Steer	10.00
Wool	5.60	Corn & grain	8.70
Chickens & eggs	1.85	Harness & halter	8.55
Hides	1.59	Farm tools	3.50
Butter	.32	Machinery repairs	2.00
		Taxes	??
	$298.09		$287.15
1862			
Cattle	$103.00	Principal & interest	$137.00
Hogs	101.72	Rent	60.00
Apples	98.17	New plow	10.00
Wool	22.40	Threshing	6.50
Ox rent	.75	Machinery repairs	3.50
Wood	.25	Timothy & rye seed	3.12
		Taxes	??
	$326.29		$220.12
1870			
Hogs	$154.25	Two cows	$ 65.00
Cattle	97.00	Corn	52.60
Wool	70.08	Taxes	38.64
Wheat	37.70	Principal & interest	12.50
Butter & eggs	33.41	Machine rent	10.12
Meat	18.92	Seed wheat	8.00
Wood	6.60	Labor, harvest,	
Miscellaneous garden		shearing	7.60
& orchard	5.95	Bridle	3.50
Potatoes	5.46	Lumber	3.45
Floor	4.50		
Road-tax refund	3.00		
Tallow	1.10		
	$437.97		$201.41
1880			
Hogs	$ 767.12	Principal & interest	$185.03
Timothy seed	175.08	Corn	56.16
Wool	131.33	Taxes	28.48
Wheat	97.99	Boar	7.80
Cattle	60.00	Wages	5.60
Apples	17.54	Road tax	2.39
Hay	15.00	Machinery repairs	2.90
Potatoes	14.85		
Meat	11.43		
Oats	9.80		
Butter	9.40		
Haulage	1.73		
Calf's hide	.60		
	$1,311.87		$288.36

* Data in this and the following tables all appear in the John Savage Diary.

transactions made by his father and mother. By the late 1860's, at least, butter and eggs were providing a significant addition to farm income.

Undoubtedly during the same years many other farmers in Illinois and Iowa operated farm businesses that were similar to that of the Savages. No doubt also, the Savage business contrasted with that of many farmers in these states in the degree to which wool, and particularly fruit, added to farm revenue. We must remember, also, that the Savages derived additional returns from the younger man's "school money" and his father's skill as a tailor. During the early 1860's John Savage was obtaining $90 for his services in the four-month school term. For most of the period his salary was $140. Occasionally, he received additional compensation for repairing the schoolhouse or supplying wood for the fire. In the 1870's for a time he received a small salary as treasurer of the township's school board. We cannot know how much William Savage obtained from his tailoring work, but his son frequently noted that his father was sewing. Both father and son, on occasion, obtained small sums from contributing roadwork beyond their quota and from jury service. In 1864 William Savage regretted the circumstances that brought a payment of $126.92 to him, representing the back pay and enlistment bounty of his son Thomas. Tacy Crew did not come with completely empty hands to her marriage, although we cannot know exactly the amount of money that she derived from her father's estate. Certainly she brought a heifer with her when she was married, and there are a couple of references in her husband's diary to payments made by the executor of her father's will.

There are undoubtedly many gaps in the farm expenditures that John Savage noted in his diary. He makes no mention of paying service fees, for instance, although the Savages owned neither bull nor stallion. Taxes and threshing costs are missing from some of the yearly expenditures summarized in Table 26. This table does, however, give us some idea of the kinds and amounts of expenditures that the Savages made on farm account. In many years, expenditures for farm machinery, however, were considerably more than was the case in any of the four years summarized. Table 27 lists the major purchases of machinery on the Savage farm between 1860 and 1880.

Taxes on the Savage farm and personal property rose sharply during the early 1870's. Wages did not constitute a major item in any of the years summarized in Table 26, but occasionally the Savages hired skilled laborers to make improvements in the house, to build a barn, or to dig and wall a cistern. John Savage often hired neighbors, skilled as shearsmen to assist at sheepshearing, paying them at the rate of 7¢ per fleece. In a variety of ways, they obtained help with normal fieldwork. They traded labor in haying, harvest, and threshing with their closer neighbors, and occasionally one of the neighbors worked out the price of a coat or other apparel that William Savage made for him.

An orphan lad of the neighborhood worked briefly for John Savage in the early 1870's, but was sent packing when he was discovered prowling the family sleeping quarters, in search, John Savage believed, for money. By 1878 John's eldest boy Thomas was large enough to begin helping his

TABLE 27
FARM MACHINERY PURCHASES

Year	Machine Purchased	Cost	Year	Machine Purchased	Cost
1861	—plow (second hand)	$ .50	1869	—plow	$ 16.00
1862	—plow	10.00	1873	—corn-planter	40.00
	—shovel plow	3.50	1874	—corn plow—double shovel	5.50
1864	—2-horse corn plow	30.00		—Manny reaper (½ int.)	92.50
1865	—wagon	136.00		—Wier corn plow	25.00
1868	—corn plow—double shovel	6.50		—buggy	127.50
	—corn plow—bar plow	9.50	1876	—harrow	
			1878	—cultivator	20.00
			1879	—horse rake	6.00

TABLE 28
SAVAGE PROPERTY TAXES

Year	Tax	Year	Tax
1863	$10.56	1872	$54.90
1864	14.95	1873	40.37
1865		1874	41.90
1866	12.68	1875	36.70
1867	15.44	1876	36.80
1868	18.25	1877	35.20
1869	19.57	1878	
1870	38.64	1879	29.86
1871	16.31	1880	28.48

father on the farm. Although the Savages cut their own firewood, John was normally teaching school in the period when most of their neighbors split rails. As a result they hired neighbor youths to cut rails on a number of occasions. The price was 80¢ per hundred during the early 1860's; John Savage did not record the price of later agreements. Neighbor boys might be hired also to help in driving hogs or cattle to Salem or Mt. Pleasant for delivery to buyers. When John Savage purchased a second farm in 1879, he placed a tenant, Samuel Smith, upon it, who worked for him, on occasion, as well as paying share rent on the acreage directly under his control.

There are few references to store credit in John Savage's diary, although the family probably used it. Credit relationships within and without the community appear in many entries, however. The county records do not make clear the exact details of the purchase of the original seventy-five acres in

1856. Evidently the note and mortgage that William Savage signed in lieu of part of the purchase price was not recorded. In 1859, however, Thomas LeFevre of Salem recorded a mortgage in which William Savage and wife Mary acknowledged indebtedness of $300 on the farm. If I interpret a cryptic diary note of John Savage correctly, William Savage very possibly paid $400 down on a purchase price of $1,000. Interest on the LeFevre note was at the rate of 10 per cent per annum, and during the war years the Savages had to pay varying, and sometimes quite substantial, exchange rates in the process of sending money to Mrs. LeFevre who was living in New York at the time. By the spring of 1863, the Savages had cleared their seventy-five-acre farm of debt. When John Savage purchased the "Wilson forty" for $360 in 1867, he agreed to pay $120 on January 1, 1869, and similar amounts at the beginning of the next two years, the rate of interest on unpaid principal to stand at 8 per cent — a very generous level for the time. To complete the payments on this land, he borrowed $160 from a friend and neighbor in 1871. When he purchased the Hockett farm in 1879 for $3250, John Savage again found it necessary to borrow money. From Throop & Cise, mortgage-brokers of Mount Pleasant, he obtained $1200 at 8 per cent interest, payable annually, mortgaging 138 acres as security for this loan. This loan was payable in not less than two nor more than five years. He also borrowed $500 from a neighbor for one year at 8 per cent per annum but gave no land mortgage in this transaction. To make up the remainder of the purchase price, he assumed Hockett's obligation of $818.30 to an estate of which Hockett was executor, Savage taking over administration of the estate. Finally, John Savage gave Hockett a personal note for $431.70. With the initial down payment of $300 that he made from savings or current income, these obligations totaled the purchase price of $3250.[11] It is obvious that the Savages considered debt to be a completely normal accompaniment of acquiring land.

On occasion John Savage borrowed money for other purposes than land purchases. In 1865 he borrowed $150 from his brother-in-law to buy a mare and wagon. In 1872 and 1876 he mentions other short-term loans of $50 and $60. A few smaller obligations represented credit extended to Savage by neighbors or businessmen in sale transactions, as when he bought a ram in 1864, paying $17.50 down and giving a note of $15.00 for the remainder. John Savage and his father also loaned money out to neighbors and business acquaintances or extended credit to them when they purchased farm products or livestock from them. Between 1864 and 1876 John Savage noted at least eight transactions that fell into these categories, usually involving sums that ranged from $5 to $70. A certain amount of

[11] See "Henry County, Deed Register, M, 599; S, 549; T, 395; X, 258; 33, 104;" and "Mortgage Register, B, 506" — all in the office of the county recorder, Mount Pleasant, Iowa. The will of William Savage is in the Will Record, 1, 448 in the office of the county clerk of the court, Mount Pleasant.

petty lending and borrowing also went on in farm products — they might lend or borrow a wagonload or more of corn, subject to repayment with a few bushels extra when the next crop was harvested, or a few bushels of oats or wheat on similar terms.

For the period the Savages were no doubt considered progressive farmers. In 1861 they spread forty-one loads of manure on their fields and always used this product of the barnyard as wisely as possible. They traded seed wheat and corn with neighbors, evidently, so that their strains would not "run out." They believed in bringing in new blood to their flock and did this by purchasing new bucks or exchanging rams with their neighbors. They attempted to fight borers in their orchard by washing the tree trunks with soap or a lye-and-lime solution, and on occasion, at least, by wrapping wool around the trunks "to keep the worms down which lay the eggs to produce the canker worms." [12] They were growing clover by 1871 at least. In the early sixties the family was subscribing to five papers or journals, including the *Rural New Yorker*, but John Savage's diary was matter of fact in the extreme about new developments. The entries give little clue as to the source of his ideas about them. When the Savages wished advice on the varieties of trees to plant in their new orchard, John Savage went to a local orchardist for counsel. John Savage helped to organize a farmers' club in 1866, and subsequently he joined the Grange, although not until 1873. When his chapter decided to establish a farmers' store, however, he became a member of the supervisory committee, where his school-teaching skill in arithmetic was of considerable service to his neighbors. Father and son, however, were no doubt more conservative than many in acquiring new machinery.

Despite the great contrast between the cash income of the Savage farm in the 1860's and 1870's and that from an "average sized" Iowa farm of today, it is clear that the Savage farm was no subsistence operation. In the early years the Savages labored to retire the mortgage on the farm as rapidly as possible, and thereafter they worked to enlarge and improve the farm at a rate that only commercial farmers could have achieved. Yet there were many aspects of life on the Savage farm that are missing on the Iowa farm of today. Behind the house stood the lye leach — that essential tool in making soap. The Savages pickled some of their meat and cured a portion of it in the smokehouse of a neighbor before they built their own. Each year the sorghum patch provided a crop of cane that the Savages hauled to the mill and evaporator of a neighbor who specialized in preparing sorghum molasses, and who took his pay in a share of the yield or else charged 20¢ per gallon. The wheat flour and cornmeal which Tacy Savage used in cooking had been ground at Oakland Mills from wheat and corn raised on the Savage farm. Tacy Savage did not weave cloth ordinarily, but

[12] "Savage Diary," April 4, 1866.

she did spin a portion of the coarser wool from the annual clip after John had retrieved it from a local carding mill. This yarn Tacy dyed herself with sumac berries and red-oak bark and had some of it woven into cloth in the community. Through many of these years, however, she had a mechanical sewing machine, she did her wash in a mechanical washing machine, and by the late 1870's could listen in the evening to one of her daughters playing a $90 organ.

CONCLUSION

The Threshold of the Golden Age

We have seen the midwestern farmer breaking the prairie, harvesting his crops, tending his livestock, and amassing capital.[1] I have emphasized those farming activities and problems that must usually have held his attention. But the prairie farmer's world had wide boundaries by the 1840's at least. Never a landlocked Crusoe, he owed much thereafter to the expansion of both the domestic and foreign markets for his products and to the developments in transportation, processing techniques, and marketing methods that allowed him to enter those markets on a competitive basis.[2] Local market, frontier post, forty-niner, southern plantation, industrial America, famine-racked Ireland, British mill town, and continental city — the prairie farmer supplied them all in varying degree.

The steamboat age came to the western waters before the farm-maker of the prairies had well begun his task. Supplemented in the down-river trade by the clumsy but efficient flatboat, steamboats plied until the 1850's on Iowa and Illinois rivers, which are now valued only as sources of drinking water or outlets for city sewage. Illinois legislators planned grandiosely during the 1830's to web their state with canals and railroads, but economic depression and mismanagement blasted their hopes.[3] Not until 1848 was the Michigan and Illinois Canal complete. Even more futile were the ambitions of Iowans to develop their water outlets. Hawkeye legislators abandoned the effort to improve the channel of the Des Moines River after contractors had already completed considerable work on the lower reaches of that stream.[4] The pleas of residents in the Burlington region of Iowa for aid in improving a channel

[1] Although I have not had occasion to cite them directly, readers should not ignore the discussions of prairie agriculture and its problems in Fred A. Shannon, *The Farmer's Last Frontier: Agriculture, 1860–1897* (New York, 1945); and Paul W. Gates, *The Farmer's Age: Agriculture, 1815–1860* (New York, 1960).

[2] Rodney C. Loehr presents a thoughtful reconsideration of the concept of self-sufficiency in "Self-Sufficiency on the Farm," *Agricultural History*, XXVI (April, 1952), 37–41.

[3] John H. Krenkel, *Illinois Internal Improvements, 1818–1848* (Cedar Rapids, 1958).

[4] Leonard F. Ralston, "Iowa Railroads and the Des Moines River Improvement Land Grant of 1846," *Iowa Journal of History*, LVI (April, 1958), 97–128.

through the rapids in the Mississippi below that city went unheeded.[5] Between 1850 and the 1880's, however, the railroads gridded the midwestern states so thoroughly that there could have been few prairie farmers living beyond earshot of the locomotive's whistle in 1885. Although the railroad car displaced the steamboat and barge as the pre-eminent carrier of agricultural produce, lake, canal, and river continued to provide valuable alternate transportation routes from early spring to late fall.

As the railroads revolutionized transportation in the Midwest, the marketing structure became increasingly complex. The expeditions of forty to sixty miles, which prairie neighbors had once made to Chicago or other shipping points with wagonloads of wheat, faded into fond reminiscence at old settlers' reunions. Now the farmer hauled only to local warehouse or elevator, knowing that ultimately his grain would probably pass through the more elaborate storage facilities of Chicago or St. Louis.[6] Now, too, although only dimly understood by many prairie men, began the system of futures trading, which facilitated the orderly marketing of the small grains, corn, and pork.[7] And where once farmers and drovers had sold their livestock directly to butchers or packers, they now relied increasingly on commission men operating at the great stockyards of the major livestock markets — above all in Chicago.

Although important changes occurred in the milling industry, notably in the introduction of the steel-roller process in flour-milling, in the rise of the oatmeal industry, and in the increased scale of operations generally, developments in the meat-processing industry were even more striking.[8] From the refuse of the slaughterhouse, ingenious men conjured a vast array of useful by-products, ranging from hairpins to nitroglycerin. An old staple of the meat trade appeared in new guise when lard oil became important as an illuminant during the 1840's. Still a seasonal industry in the 1830's, meat-packing by the 1870's had become a year-round operation as packers learned the techniques of ice-cooling and refrigeration generally. When inventors and packers developed the refrigerated railroad car in the 1870's, they set the

[5] George A. Boeck, "A Decade of Transportation Fever in Burlington, Iowa, 1845–1855," *Iowa Journal of History*, LVI (April, 1958), 131–32.

[6] Guy A. Lee, "The Historical Significance of the Chicago Grain Elevator System," *Agricultural History*, XI (January, 1937), 16–32.

[7] James C. Malin has included a very perceptive essay on such matters in *Confounded Rot About Napoleon: Reflections upon Science and Technology, Nationalism, World Depression of the Eighteen-Nineties, and Afterwards* (Lawrence, 1961), pp. 21–51.

[8] Charles B. Kuhlmann, *The Development of the Flour-Milling Industry in the United States with Special Reference to the Industry in Minneapolis* (Boston, 1929), pp. 113–25; Harrison J. Thornton, *The History of the Quaker Oats Company* (Chicago, 1933); Despite various popular treatments of leading figures in the packing industry, the standard work is still Rudolph A. Clemen, *The American Livestock and Meat Industry* (New York, 1923). Lawrence A. Cheever, *The House of Morrell* (Cedar Rapids, 1948) is a very helpful company history.

stage for a massive invasion of eastern markets by midwestern dressed beef and gave new impetus as well to the sale of fresh pork.

Midwestern grains and meats did not conquer eastern and foreign markets without some difficulties. Carriers must set rates that allowed producers some margin of profit; consumers must agree that midwestern products were tasty and wholesome. When dressed beef began to move eastward in quantity, eastern butchers protested to the last man, and railroad executives initially set rates that the midwestern packers considered to be unfair in comparison to those set for live cattle. Farmers complained of high railroad rates and warehousing charges generally. When they reinforced their protests with political action during the 1870's, they undoubtedly hastened the fall of freight rates and middleman charges. But urban business groups played an important role, perhaps even a more important role than did the farmer, in pressing for changes in rate structures and marketing procedures. Businessmen in the Iowa towns along the Mississippi River believed that railroad rates were unfairly designed to give Chicago firms a competitive advantage in supplying the interior of the state.[9] By the late 1860's Chicago grain-traders wanted warehouse and elevator procedures purified in that city no less than did farmers, and the traders played an important role in drafting the constitutional provisions and legislation that ultimately brought reform.[10] Undoubtedly the pressure and maneuvering of the Chicago meat-packers played a highly important role in winning satisfactory freight rates for dressed beef. In justice to an industry that sometimes did justice to its patrons unwillingly, improvements in efficiency and competitive pressures among the various railroads serving the Midwest also contributed to declining freight rates.[11]

Livestock disease, or rumors of disease, affected the marketing of both American pork and cattle abroad. In 1879 European nations began to exclude pork products from the United States because American hogs and pork were allegedly infected with trichina. Importing some 60 per cent of American pork exports, Great Britain never took action, but Germany and France, countries that together imported 18 per cent of America's foreign shipments, did so, as did such minor importers as Italy, Portugal, Greece, Spain, Austria-Hungary, Turkey, Rumania, and Denmark. The rising spirit of protectionism and irritation at the protectionist policies of the United States may have been just as important in producing exclusion as fear of trichina. When the Congress of the United States passed a meat-inspection act in 1890, the ostensible grounds for exclusion vanished. Of itself, this was not enough to break the boycott. But a tariff concession to Germany and a number of benevolent

[9] George H. Miller, "Origins of the Iowa Granger Law," *Mississippi Valley Historical Review*, XL (March, 1954), 657–80; Mildred Throne, "The Repeal of the Iowa Granger Law, 1878," *Iowa Journal of History*, LI (April, 1953), 125–29.

[10] Harold D. Woodman, "Chicago Businessmen and the 'Granger' Laws," *Agricultural History*, XXXVI (January, 1962), 16–24.

[11] Edward C. Kirkland, *Industry Comes of Age: Business, Labor, and Public Policy, 1860–1897* (New York, 1961), pp. 93–96.

gestures toward France brought action from these countries; other countries followed suit. The episode, however, cost Americans over $260,000,000, if the estimate of the American Secretary of Agriculture is to be taken at face value.[12]

Although Europe's fear of contaminated meats injured the American pork trade, American cattlemen benefited from Great Britain's action in restricting cattle imports from Germany, Belgium, and Russia when pleuropneumonia broke out among the continental herds in 1877. Americans had tried to breach the British market as early as 1868, but only a few hundred American cattle reached British ports in 1875 and 1876; in 1877 the numbers greatly increased. Unfortunately for American shippers, cattle aboard the "Ontario" were reportedly suffering from pleuropneumonia when that ship reached England from the United States in January, 1879. Despite a ruling of the Privy Council that American cattle were to be slaughtered at the port of entry within ten days after docking, more than 154,000 animals reached Great Britain from the United States during 1880, if British tabulations are used. Although American officials tried to have the annoying restriction removed, they failed to convince British authorities that American herds were free of pleuropneumonia, and in retrospect British suspicions were probably well founded. As a result the British trade in American cattle never attained the size or returned the profits that might have been possible if shippers could have sent their cattle to inland markets or given them a short finishing period on British pastures or even supplied British cattlemen with feeders. As it was, more than 800,000 cattle reached Great Britain from the United States in the years before 1886, representing some 6 per cent of the total value of American beef products at the time. But during the 1880's the dressed-beef trade with Great Britain was growing, and ultimately this commerce displaced the shipments of livestock.[13]

There is a time-hallowed tradition that the years between 1866 and 1896 were years of almost unalloyed agricultural depression in the United States. There is certainly evidence to support such a position. The prices of agricultural commodities fell during this period, as did prices in general, and it is generally agreed that primary producers are particularly hard hit in periods of declining prices. Both in the 1870's and the 1890's there were bursts of protest from the farmers of mid-America. On the other hand one need only read a few of the biographical sections in the many histories of prairie counties that were published during the last quarter of the nineteenth century to realize that a great many farmers in Illinois and Iowa prospered exceedingly in the years after the Civil War. On the pages of these county "mug

[12] Bingham Duncan, "Protectionism and Pork: Whitelaw Reid as Diplomat: 1889–1891," *Agricultural History*, XXXIII (October, 1959), 190–95; John L. Gignilliat, "Pigs, Politics, and Protection: The European Boycott of American Pork, 1879–1891," *ibid.*, XXXV (January, 1961), 3–12.

[13] Wm. D. Zimmerman, "Live Cattle Export Trade Between United States and Great Britain, 1868–1885," *Agricultural History*, XXXVI (January, 1962), 46–52.

books" are spread the success stories of almost countless farmers who started
with little and who in the 1880's or 1890's were able to report broad holdings
of valuable land.

Certainly it is true that there began a period of almost unrivaled prosperity
for midwestern farmers in the late 1890's and that this continued until the
end of the first world war. In only one year between 1900 and 1920 were
there as many as five mortgage foreclosures in Story County, Iowa. During
the twenty years, 1880–99, the number of foreclosures reached thirteen in
one year but was above ten in only three; these figures were far below the level
of foreclosures during the previous thirty years in the county. In the years
1865, 1876, and 1877 there were twenty-five farm mortgages foreclosed in
Story County. During 1871 the number was twenty-six, and in 1879, the
nineteenth-century high, thirty-eight. In three widely scattered Iowa townships the percentage of real estate mortgages that went to foreclosure proceedings between 1852 and 1896 was 3.2. But of the mortgages filed between
1870 and 1874 inclusive and between 1875 and 1879 inclusive, the average
number going to court was 5.2 per cent in both cases. By contrast the failure
rate on mortgages filed in the years 1885–89 and 1890–96 was 1.7 and
1.8 per cent. Somewhat less precise evidence reveals a similar picture in
Illinois. Clearly the 1870's were the years of greatest tribulation for prairie
farmers. Midwestern farm protest in the late 1880's and early 1890's
emanated from the plains states rather than from the prairies. Here farmers
were already entering the golden age of midwestern agriculture. Even in the
1870's, there was no disaster on the prairies comparable to the crisis that
occurred in portions of the plains states in the Populist era.*

Undoubtedly declining prices did press hard upon prairie farmers during
the thirty years after the Civil War. But at the same time horsepower technology was allowing them to increase their productivity greatly. Farmers
who exploited machinery effectively could and did prosper. It is clear, too,
that the man who studied his markets and was alert to relative changes in
the prices of farm products could outstrip his neighbor. The index of Iowa
wheat prices, for instance, declined relatively far more between 1866 and
1896 than did the indexes of oats, corn, hogs, or beef. On the other hand the
index of beef prices showed considerable stability throughout most of
the post Civil War period despite the bitter complaints of many Illinois
feeders after 1885. Almost invariably, too, during these years the relationship between corn and hog prices made it almost always profitable to feed

* Some six months after I submitted my manuscript, including the two paragraphs
above, to the University of Chicago Press, Professor John Bowman of the University
of Illinois showed me his unpublished paper "Trends in Midwestern Farm Profits
during the Period of Agrarian Discontent, 1870–1900," which he wrote several years
ago and in which he used the increase in midwestern land values and opportunity cost
theory to attack convincingly the idea that farming was uniformly unprofitable in the
Middle West between 1870 and 1900.

hogs. One hundred pounds of pork was worth less than 10 bushels of corn in only three years between 1861 and 1900 in Iowa.

Evidently also, there were subregional differences in farm income in the prairie states. In a recent study, Frank T. Bachmura discovered that the gross returns for each member of the agricultural labor force in nine sub-

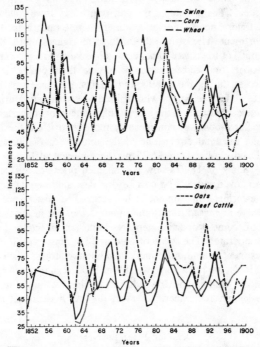

Fig. 11. — Iowa price indexes, 1851–1900 (currency prices adjusted to gold values, 1862–78)

divisions of Iowa differed substantially in state and federal census years from 1869 to 1930. His findings also suggest that returns per agricultural worker were usually low in frontier regions. In 1869 and 1875 gross returns per agricultural worker in the twelve counties of northwestern Iowa were the lowest in the state. By 1910 this district led all others.[14]

The more progressive farmers of the prairie triangle evidently entered the 1880's aware that their best future lay in increasing the size of their farm units to take advantage of the new technology. They had learned, too, that profit lay in judicious combinations of corn, hogs, and cattle while not discarding

[14] Frank T. Bachmura, "Geographical Differentials in Returns to Corn Belt Farmers: 1869–1950" (unpublished Ph.D. dissertation, University of Chicago, 1953), pp. 70–71.

the small grains, particularly oats, nor ignoring tame grasses and clovers — a necessity as the prairie grass commons disappeared. Corn rootworm and smut convinced farmers who case their lost unreservedly with the corn crop that some rotation paid. They found now, too, that tiling rewarded the investment. The farmers of the Illinois black-earth counties took up this task seriously in the 1880's, although there had, of course, been much ditch drainage earlier. The farmers of the wet prairies in Iowa followed suit in a few years time. Cheap labor and falling interest rates helped speed the tasks of adjustment. The usual rate on farm mortgages in 1878 in central Illinois and much of Iowa was 10 per cent; it had fallen to 6 per cent by 1896.

If owner-operators were apparently solving their problems with considerable success during the 1880's and 1890's, the same was hardly true of the tenants or farm laborers who aspired to ownership. During the last half of the nineteenth century, the increased productivity of agricultural labor benefited the farm-operator considerably more than it did the laborer. At the same time the land equivalent of the monthly agricultural wage fell drastically. Land obtained for $1.25 per acre in central Illinois or eastern Iowa in the 1830's or 1840's now commanded prices of $40 to $60 and, in many cases, even more. The cost of drainage alone could add from $5 to $20 to the farmer's investment in his acres. The cost of necessary machinery had also increased during the same period, but in the face of rising land values it became proportionately less important in the total investment of the owner-operator. The value of land and buildings was 76 per cent of the total investment in land, machinery, and livestock for the "average farm" of 1850 in Illinois; the percentage was 89 in 1900. Tenancy rates, therefore, edged upward in Illinois and Iowa during the last years of the nineteenth century. We should remember, however, that no agricultural area in the

TABLE 29

AVERAGE FARM BUSINESS*

	Acres	Total Investment	Value Land & Bldgs.	Per Cent of Total	Value Mach. & Implements	Per Cent of Total	Value Livestock	Per Cent of Total
IOWA								
1850	185	$1453.54	$1125.13	77	$79.22	6	$249.19	17
1860	165	2477.07	2010.75	81	89.33	4	376.93	15
1870	134	4266.48	3376.52	79	176.36	4	713.60	17
1880	134	3892.69	3061.38	79	158.46	4	672.85	17
1890	151	5451.53	4247.49	78	181.59	3	1022.45	19
1900	151	9496.62	8023.48	84	253.52	3	1219.61	13
ILLINOIS								
1850	158	$1666.64	$1261.00	76	$87.97	5	$317.67	19
1860	146	3503.47	2873.04	82	121.08	3	509.35	15
1870	128	5447.83	4538.91	83	170.49	3	738.43	14
1880	124	4597.50	3947.72	86	131.93	3	517.85	11
1890	127	6139.90	5247.07	86	143.16	3	749.67	12
1900	124	8491.54	7587.76	89	170.27	2	733.51	9

* Based on federal census materials, 1850–1900.

national history of this country has been able to absorb all of its would-be farmers.

On the prairies of Illinois and Iowa — as in adjacent states — a mobile energetic population made the Corn Belt. Spurred by technological achievements and expanding markets, commercial farmers built one of the most prosperous agricultural economies the world had ever seen in this land, where each year the rains, the summer heat, and productive soils produced the broad-leafed fields of dark green. Here work often brought success; work plus good luck often brought great success. In the biographical sketches of the county histories there are implicit the values that the Corn Belt farmers cherished in the fading years of the nineteenth century. It was good to have pioneered here, to have been an "old settler," and made virgin prairie "productive" by stocking it with fine animals and raising bountiful crops. He had lived a good life who started with little and added to his acres so that in middle or old age he could start his sons on farms or rent to others. These, of course, were the values of the successful and only part of the reality of farm life in the prairie peninsula. More farm-makers got a head start in the race for success than admitted it in their biographies. There were two sides to tenancy; many farm boys could not win the prize of unencumbered ownership. Some owners failed miserably. Land was often a lucrative speculation no less than a factor of production. But in sum the achievements had been striking. By the 1890's the work of the pioneers was done; their successors were moving forward into the golden age of middle-western agriculture.

Bibliography

MANUSCRIPTS

Berry, Don L., Letter to George M. Sheets, Iowa City, Iowa, March 1, 1958 (in possession of author).

DANIELS, GEORGE, H. "Notes on Population and the Decline of the Democratic Party in Iowa." Unpublished paper.

CHICAGO, ROCK ISLAND AND PACIFIC RAILROAD COMPANY. "Land Grant Tract Books."

DUBUQUE LAND OFFICE. "Pre-emption Entry Documents." National Archives, Washington, D.C.

"John and Ira Davenport Papers," Cornell University Collection of Regional History, Ithaca, New York.

"Henry Eno Papers," Special Collections Department, Library, State University of Iowa, Iowa City, Iowa.

"Federal Agricultural Census, Illinois, 1850, 1860, 1870, and 1880," Illinois State Archives, Springfield, Illinois.

"Federal Agricultural Census, Iowa, 1850, 1860, 1870, and 1880," Iowa State Historical Society, Iowa City, Iowa.

"Federal Land Office Tract Books, Illinois," Illinois State Archives, Springfield, Illinois.

"Federal Land Office Tract Books, Iowa," Office of Secretary of State, Des Moines, Iowa.

"Federal Population Census, Bureau County, Illinois, 1850, 1860," General Services Administration Microfilm.

"Federal Population Census, Iowa, 1850, 1860, 1870, 1880, Iowa," State Historical Society, Iowa City, Iowa.

"Nathaniel Gordon Papers," Manuscript Division, Baker Library, Cambridge, Massachusetts.

"George F. Green Diary," in the possession of Mrs. Curtis Frymoyer, Wilton Junction, Iowa.

LeDuc, THOMAS. "Report of Investigation of the Value of the Land, But not including the Value of Lead Mineral Thereon, Ceded by Treaty of 29 July 1829." Presented before the Indian Claims Commission, Docket No. 217, *Citizen Band of Potawatomi Indians of Oklahoma and Potawatomi Nation v. The United States of America* (1958).

"Joseph Morton Papers," in the possession of Mrs. Charles M. Ellsworth, Iowa City, Iowa.

"Croft Pilgrim Diary," Iowa Department of History and Archives, Des Moines, Iowa.

"Cyrus H. McCormick Papers," Wisconsin State Historical Society, Madison, Wisconsin.

"Cyrus Sanders Papers," Iowa State Historical Society, Iowa City, Iowa.

"John Savage Diary," Iowa State Department of History and Archives, Des Moines, Iowa.

"Edwin Terril Papers," Iowa Department of History and Archives, Des Moines Iowa.

COUNTY RECORDS

BREMER COUNTY, IOWA. "Book of Original Entries," "Index of Deeds," "Deed Registers," "Mortgage Registers," "Minute Books of the Board of Supervisors," Waverly, Iowa.

BUREAU COUNTY, ILLINOIS. "Deed Registers," Princeton, Illinois.

DAVIS COUNTY, IOWA. "Book of Original Entries," "Index of Deeds," "Deed Registers," "Mortgage Registers," "Minute Books of the Board of Supervisors," Bloomfield, Iowa.

EMMET COUNTY, IOWA. "Quit Claim Deed Book, 1," Estherville, Iowa.

HAMILTON COUNTY, IOWA. "Book of Original Entries," "Index of Deeds," "Deed Registers," "Transfer Books," "Minute Books of the Board of Supervisors," "Tax Deed Book," and "Treasurer's Tax Receipt Books," Webster City, Iowa.

HENRY COUNTY, IOWA. "Deed Registers," "Mortgage Registers," "Will Record," Mount Pleasant, Iowa.

HUMBOLDT COUNTY, IOWA. "Book of Original Entries," "Index of Deeds," "Deed Registers," Dakota City, Iowa.

JOHNSON COUNTY, IOWA. "Book of Original Entries," "Index of Deeds," "Deed Registers," Iowa City, Iowa.

LUCAS COUNTY, IOWA. Chattel Mortgage Registers,1856–1900," Chariton, Iowa.

MUSCATINE COUNTY, IOWA. "Treasurer's Tax Receipt Books, 1852–1896," Muscatine, Iowa.

POWESHIEK COUNTY, IOWA. "Book of Original Entries," "Index of Deeds," "Deed Registers," Montezuma, Iowa.

STARK COUNTY, ILLINOIS. "Deed Registers," Toulon, Illinois.

WEBSTER COUNTY, IOWA. "Book of Original Entries," "Index of Deeds," "Deed Registers," Fort Dodge, Iowa.

FEDERAL AND STATE DOCUMENTS

BAILEY, LIBERTY H. *Farmers' Institutes: History and Status in the United States and Canada* ("U.S. Department of Agriculture, Office of Experiment Stations, Bulletin, 79.) Washington, 1900.

Census of Iowa for 1880 . . . with Other Historical and Statistical Data . . . Des Moines, 1883.

Iowa State Agricultural Society, Reports, 1854–1895.

Iowa State Auditor, Reports, 1860–1890.

Iowa, Laws, 1852–53, 1856–57, 1868, 1870, 1872, 1874.

HALL, JAMES, and WHITNEY, J. D. *Report on the Geological Survey of the State of Iowa: Embracing the Results of Investigations Made During Portions of the Years 1855, 56, and 57*. Des Moines, 1858.

HAMILTON, JOHN. *History of Farmers' Institutes in the United States* ("U.S. Department of Agriculture, Office of Experiment Stations, Bulletin," 174.) Washington, 1906.

KAPPLER, CHARLES J. *Indian Affairs, Laws and Treaties* (57th Cong., 1st sess.; Sen. Doc. 452.) Washington, 1903.

KENDALL, EDWARD C. "John Deere's Steel Plow," *Contributions from the Museum of History and Technology*, Papers 1–11 ("United States National Museum, Bulletin," 218). Smithsonian Institution, Washington, 1959.

LOOMIS, RALPH A., and BARTON, GLEN F. *Productivity of Agriculture: United States, 1870–1958*. ("U.S. Department of Agriculture, Technical Bulletin, 1238.") Washington, 1961.

MILLER, MERRITT F. *The Evolution of Reaping Machines*. ("U.S. Department of Agriculture, Office of Experiment Stations, Bulletin", No. 103.) Washington, 1902.

OWEN, DAVID D. *Report of a Geological Exploration of Part of Iowa, Wisconsin, and Illinois, made under instructions from the Secretary of the Treasury of the United States in the Autumn of the Year 1839: with Charts and Illustrations*. (28th Cong., 1st sess.; Sen. Doc. 407.) Washington, 1844.

Public Lands Commission, Report (58th Cong., 3d sess.; Sen. Doc. 189.) Washington, 1905.

"Report on Trials of Plows," in the *New York State Agricultural Society, Transactions, 1867*. Albany, 1869, pp. 385–656.

ROYCE, CHARLES C. *Indian Land Cessions in the United States*. ("Bureau of American Ethnology, 18th Annual Report, 1896–1897." [56th Cong., 1st sess., H.R. Doc. 736.]) Washington, 1899.

RUSSELL, E. Z. *et al.* "Hog Production and Marketing," ("U.S. Department of Agriculture, Yearbook, 1922,") Washington, 1923, 181–280.

THOMPSON, JAMES W. *A History of Livestock Raising in the United States, 1607–1860*. ("U.S. Department of Agriculture, Agricultural History Series," No. 5.) Washington, 1942.

U.S. BUREAU OF THE CENSUS, *Historical Statistics of the United States, Colonial Times to 1957*. Washington, 1960.

U.S. CENSUS OFFICE, *Statistical View of the United States . . . Being a Compendium of the Seventh Census . . . .* Washington, 1854.

――――. *Agriculture of the United States in 1860 . . . .* Washington, 1864.

――――. *The Statistics of the Wealth and Industry of the United States . . . .* Washington, 1872.

――――. *Report on the Productions of Agriculture as Returned at the Tenth Census*. Washington, 1883.

――――. *Report on Real Estate Mortgages in the United States at the Eleventh Census: 1890*. Washington, 1895.

――――. *Report on the Statistics of Agriculture in the United States at the Eleventh Census: 1890*. Washington, 1895.

U.S. COMMISSIONER OF AGRICULTURE. *Reports*, 1862–88.

U.S. COMMISSIONER OF PATENTS. *Agricultural Reports*, 1845–61.

U.S. DEPARTMENT OF AGRICULTURE. *Wages of Farm Labor in the United States* ("Division of Statistics, Misc. Ser.," 4.) Washington, 1892.

U.S. INDUSTRIAL COMMISSION. *Report*, XI (57th Cong., 1st sess., H.R. Doc. 181.) Washington, 1901.

U.S. SECRETARY OF AGRICULTURE. *Reports*, 1889–95.

U.S. SECRETARY OF THE INTERIOR. *Report*, 1871, 1921.

AGRICULTURAL COLLEGE PUBLICATIONS

CASE, H. C. M., and MYERS, K. H. *Types of Farming in Illinois, an Analysis of Differences by Areas.* ("University of Illinois, Agricultural Experiment Station, Bulletin," No. 403.) Urbana, 1934.

HARTER, WILLIAM L. and STEWART, R. E. *The Population of Iowa: Its Composition and Changes. A Brief Sociological Study of Iowa's Human Assets.* ("Iowa State College of Agriculture and Mechanic Arts, Bulletin," No. 275.) Ames, 1930.

DAVENPORT, EUGENE, and FRASER, W. J. *Corn Experiments, 1895.* ("University of Illinois, Agricultural Experiment Station, Bulletin," No. 42.) Urbana, 1896.

HOLMES, C. L. *Types of Farming in Iowa.* ("Iowa State College of Agriculture and Mechanic Arts, Bulletin," No. 256.) Ames, 1929.

HOPKINS, CYRIL G. *et al. Thirty Years of Crop Rotation on the Common Prairie Soils of Illinois.* ("University of Illinois, Agricultural Experiment Station, Bulletin," No. 125.) Urbana, 1908.

MORROW, G. E. *Field Experiments with Corn, 1889.* ("University of Illinois, Agricultural Experiment Station, Bulletin," No. 8.) Champaign, 1890.

——. *Field Experiments with Corn, 1888.* ("University of Illinois, Agricultural Experiment Station, Bulletin," No. 4.) Champaign, 1889.

——. and Hunt, T. F., *Field Experiments with Corn, 1890.* ("University of Illinois, Agricultural Experiment Station, Bulletin," No. 13.) Champaign, 1891.

MURRAY, WILLIAM G. *An Economic Analysis of Farm Mortgages in Story County, Iowa, 1854–1931.* ("Iowa State College of Agriculture and Mechanic Arts, Agricultural Experiment Station, Research Bulletin," No. 156.) Ames, 1933.

NORTON, L. J. and WILSON, B. B. *Prices of Illinois Farm Products from 1866 to 1929.* ("University of Illinois, Agricultural Experiment Station, Bulletin," No. 351.) Urbana, 1930.

ODELL, R. T. *et al. Soils of the North Central Region of the United States: Their Characteristics, Classification, Distribution, and Related Management Problems.* ("University of Wisconsin Agricultural Experiment Station, Bulletin 544.") Madison, 1960.

STRAND, NORMAN V. *Prices of Farm Products in Iowa, 1851–1940.* ("Iowa State College of Agriculture and Mechanic Arts, Research Bulletin," No. 303.) Ames, 1942.

NEWSPAPERS AND AGRICULTURAL PERIODICALS

BURLINGTON *Hawkeye and Iowa Patriot*, October 24, 1839.

Iowa Homestead and Western Farm Journal. 1858–83. (Begins as *Northwestern Farmer and Horticultural Journal*.)

Northwestern Farmer and Horticultural Journal. 1856–58.

National Live Stock Journal. 1870–77.

Prairie Farmer. (Published originally as *Union Agriculturist and Western Prairie Farmer*, Chicago). 1841–90.

Webster City *Hamilton Freeman*. 1858–90.

COUNTY HISTORIES

HANCOCK, ELLERY M. *Past and Present of Allamakee County, Iowa: A Record of Settlement, Organization, Progress and Achievement*. 2 vols. Chicago, 1913.

WESTERN HISTORICAL COMPANY. *History of Appanoose County, Iowa*. . . . Chicago, 1878.

UNION HISTORICAL COMPANY. *The History of Boone County, Iowa*. . . . Des Moines, 1880.

GRAWE, J. F. *History of Bremer County, Iowa*. . . . 2 vols. Chicago, 1914.

UNION PUBLISHING COMPANY. *History of Butler and Bremer Counties, Iowa*. . . . Springfield, 1883.

AURNER, C. RAY. *A Topical History of Cedar County, Iowa*. . . . 2 vols. Chicago, 1910.

WESTERN HISTORICAL COMPANY. *The History of Cedar County, Iowa*. Chicago, 1878.

WOLFE, PATRICK B. *Wolfe's History of Clinton County, Iowa*. . . . 2 vols. Indianapolis, 1911.

WESTERN HISTORICAL COMPANY. *History of Clinton County, Iowa*. . . . Chicago, 1879.

UNION HISTORICAL COMPANY. *The History of Dallas County, Iowa*. . . . Des Moines, 1879.

STATE HISTORICAL COMPANY. *The History of Davis County, Iowa*. . . . Des Moines, 1882.

WESTERN HISTORICAL COMPANY. *The History of Des Moines County, Iowa*. . . . Chicago, 1879.

OLDT, FRANKLIN T., and QUIGLEY, PATRICK J. *History of Dubuque County, Iowa*. . . . Chicago, 1911.

PIONEER PUBLISHING COMPANY. *History of Emmet County and Dickinson County, Iowa*. . . . 2 vols. Chicago, 1917.

LEWIS PUBLISHING COMPANY. *A Biographical History of Fremont and Mills Counties, Iowa*. Chicago, 1901.

S. J. CLARKE PUBLISHING COMPANY. *A Biographical Record of Hamilton County, Iowa*. Chicago, 1902.

LEE, J. W. *History of Hamilton County, Iowa*. 2 vols. Chicago, 1912.

LEWIS BIOGRAPHICAL PUBLISHING COMPANY. *Biographical Record and Portrait Album of Hamilton and Wright Counties, Iowa*. . . . Chicago, 1889.

Union Publishing Company. *History of Hardin County, Iowa.* . . . Springfield, 1883.

Smith, Joseph H. *History of Harrison County, Iowa.* . . . Des Moines, 1888.

Union Historical Company. *History of Iowa County, Iowa.* . . . Des Moines, 1881.

Western Historical Company. *The History of Lee County, Iowa.* . . . Chicago, 1879.

——. *The History of Jasper County, Iowa.* . . . Chicago, 1888.

History of Johnson County, Iowa. . . . Iowa City, 1883.

Union Historical Company. *The History of Keokuk County, Iowa.* . . . Des Moines, 1880.

——. *History of Kossuth, Hancock, and Winnebago Counties, Iowa.* . . . Springfield, 1884.

Western Historical Company, *The History of Lee County, Iowa.* . . . Chicago, 1879.

Union Historical Company. *The History of Mahaska County, Iowa.* . . . Des Moines, 1878.

Donnel, William M. *Pioneers of Marion County, Consisting of a General History of the County.* Des Moines, 1872.

Wright, John W., and Young, William A. (eds.). *History of Marion County, Iowa, and Its People.* 2 vols. Chicago, 1915.

Mueller, Herman A. *History of Madison County, Iowa.* . . . 2 vols. Chicago, 1915.

National Publishing Company. *History of Monona County, Iowa.* . . . Chicago, 1890.

Western Historical Company. *The History of Monroe County, Iowa.* . . . Chicago, 1878.

Western Historical Company. *History of Muscatine County, Iowa.* . . . Des Moines, 1879.

Peck, John L. E., Montzheimer, Otto H., and Miller, William J. *Past and Present of O'Brien and Osceola Counties, Iowa.* . . . 2 vols. Indianapolis, 1914.

Brigham, Johnson. *Des Moines, The Pioneer of Municipal Progress and Reform of the Middle West, Together with the History of Polk County, Iowa.* . . . 2 vols. Chicago, 1911.

Parker, Leonard F. *History of Poweshiek County, Iowa.* . . . 2 vols. Chicago, 1911.

Union Historical Company. *The History of Warren County, Iowa.* . . . Des Moines, 1879.

Pratt, Harlow M. *History of Fort Dodge and Webster County, Iowa.* . . . 2 vols. Chicago, 1913.

Alexander, W. E. *History of Winneshiek and Allamakee Counties, Iowa.* Sioux City, 1882.

A. Warner & Co. *History of the Counties of Woodbury and Plymouth, Iowa.* . . . Chicago, 1890.

GENERAL WORKS

ALLEN, LEWIS F. *The American Herd-Book Containing Pedigrees of Short-Horn Cattle, with Introductory Notes.* Buffalo, 1855.

————. *American Cattle: Their History, Breeding and Management.* New York, 1868.

ARDREY, R. L. *American Agricultural Implements: A Review of Invention and Development in the Agricultural Implement Industry of the United States.* Chicago, 1894.

BAILEY, LIBERTY H. (ed.). *Cyclopedia of American Agriculture: A Popular Survey of Agricultural Conditions, Practices and Ideals in the United States and Canada.* 4 vols. New York, 1907–09.

BARDOLPH, RICHARD. *Agricultural Literature and the Early Illinois Farmer.* ("University of Illinois Studies in the Social Sciences," Vol. XXIX.) Urbana, 1948.

BIDWELL, PERCY W., and FALCONER, JOHN I. *History of Agriculture in the Northern United States 1620–1860.* Washington, 1925.

BILLINGTON, RAY A. *Westward Expansion: A History of the American Frontier.* 2d ed. New York, 1960.

BIRKBECK, MORRIS. *Notes on a Journey in America from the Coast of Virginia to the Territory of Illinois.* London, 1818.

BLEGEN, THEODORE C. *Norwegian Migration to America: 1825–1860.* Northfield, 1931.

————. *The American Transition.* Northfield, 1940.

BOGUE, ALLAN G. *Money at Interest: The Farm Mortgage on the Middle Border.* Ithaca, 1955.

BOGUE, MARGARET B. *Patterns from the Sod: Land Use and Tenure in the Grand Prairie, 1850–1900.* Springfield, 1959.

BOGGESS, ARTHUR C.*The Settlement of Illinois, 1778–1830.* ("Chicago Historical Society's Collection," Vol. V.) Chicago, 1908.

BRINDLEY, JOHN E. *History of Taxation in Iowa.* Iowa City, 1911.

BRYANT, WILLIAM CULLEN. *Letters of a Traveller; or, Notes of Things Seen in Europe and America.* New York, 1850.

BUCK, SOLON J. *The Granger Movement: A Study of Agricultural Organization and its Political, Economic and Social Manifestations, 1870–1880.* Cambridge, 1913, 1933.

————. *Illinois in 1818. (Centennial History of Illinois.)* Springfield, 1917.

BUFFUM, H. S. *Federal and State Aid to Education in Iowa.* Iowa City, 1907.

CASEY, CHARLES. *Two Years on the Farm of Uncle Sam: With Sketches of His Location, Nephews, and Prospects.* London, 1852.

CAVANAGH, HELEN M. *Funk of Funk's Grove: Farmer, Legislator and Cattle King of the Old Northwest, 1797–1865.* Bloomington, 1952.

CARLSON, THEODORE L. *The Illinois Military Tract: A Study of Land Occupation, Utilization and Tenure.* ("Illinois Studies in the Social Sciences," Volume XXXII, No. 2.) Urbana, 1951.

CHEEVER, LAWRENCE A., *The House of Morrell.* Cedar Rapids, 1948.

CHICAGO, ROCK ISLAND AND PACIFIC RAILROAD COMPANY. *Description of Six Hundred Thousand Acres of Choice Iowa Farming Lands, for Sale by the Chicago, Rock Island and Pacific Railroad Company.* Davenport, 1871.

CHRISTENSEN, THOMAS P. *A History of the Danes in Iowa*. Solvang, 1952.

CLARK, NEIL M. *John Deere; He gave to the World the Steel Plow.* . . . Moline, 1937.

CLEMEN, RUDOLPH A. *The American Livestock and Meat Industry*. New York, 1923.

CLOSE, WILLIAM B. *Farming in North-Western Iowa, United States of America, A Pamphlet for Emigrants and a Guide to North-Western Iowa*. Manchester, 1880.

COLE, ARTHUR C. *The Era of the Civil War, 1848–1870*. (*Centennial History of Illinois*.) Springfield, 1919.

CONNOR, L. G. *A Brief History of the Sheep Industry in the United States*. ("American Historical Association, Report, *1918*" Vol. I).

CURTI, MERLE. *The Making of an American Community: A Case Study of Democracy in a Frontier County*. Stanford, 1959.

DONALDSON, THOMAS. *The Public Domain*. Washington, 1884.

ENFIELD, EDWARD. *Indian Corn: Its Value, Culture and Uses*. New York, 1866.

FARSETH, PAULINE, and BLEGEN, THEODORE C. (trans. and ed.). *Frontier Mother: The Letters of Gro Svendsen*. Northfield, 1850.

FAUST, ALBERT B. *The German Element in the United States: with Special Reference to its Political, Moral, Social, and Educational Influence*. 2 vols. Boston, 1909.

FEHRENBACHER, DON E. *Chicago Giant: A Biography of "Long John" Wentworth*. Madison, 1957.

FERGUSON, WILLIAM. *America by River and Rail, or Notes by the Way on the New World and its People*. London, 1856.

FLAGG, EDMUND. *The Far West: or, A Tour Beyond the Mountains. Embracing Outlines of Western Life and Scenery: Sketches of the Prairies, Rivers, Ancient Mounds, Early Settlements of the French, Etc., Etc.* 2 vols., New York, 1838. (Reprinted in REUBEN GOLD THWAITES, [ed.]. *Early Western Travels, 1748–1846*. Vols. XXVI and XXVII.) Cleveland, 1906.

FLINT, RICHARD F. *Glacial and Pleistocene Geology*. New York, 1957.

FLOWER, GEORGE. *History of the English Settlement in Edwards County, Illinois, Founded in 1817 and 1818 by Morris Birkbeck and George Flower*. Chicago, 1882.

FORDHAM, ELIAS P. *Personal Narrative of Travels in Virginia, Maryland, Pennsylvania, Ohio, Indiana, Kentucky; and of a Residence in the Illinois Territory: 1817–1818*, (ed.) FREDERICK A. OGG. Cleveland, 1906.

FOREMAN, GRANT. *The Last Trek of the Indians*. Chicago, 1946.

GARLAND, HAMLIN. *A Son of the Middle Border*. New York, 1928.

GATES, PAUL W. *The Illinois Central Railroad and Its Colonization Work*. ("Harvard Economic Studies," Vol. XLII.) Cambridge, 1934.

———. *Frontier Landlords and Pioneer Tenants*. Ithaca, 1945.

———. *The Farmer's Age: Agriculture, 1815–1860*. New York, 1960.

GERHARD, FRED. *Illinois As It Is*. . . . Chicago, 1857.

GOODELL, JOHN. (ed.). *Diary of William Sewall, 1797–1846, Formerly of Augusta, Maine, Maryland, Virginia and Pioneer in Illinois*. Beardstown, 1930.

GRINNELL, JOSIAH B. *Men and Events of Forty Years: Autobiographical Reminiscences of an Active Career from 1850 to 1890*. Boston, 1891.

HAGAN, WILLIAM T. *The Sac and Fox Indians*. Norman, 1958.

HAIG, ROBERT M. *A History of the General Property Tax in Illinois*. ("University of Illinois Studies in the Social Sciences, Vol. III," Nos. 1 and 2.) Urbana, 1914.

HANSEN, MARCUS L. *The Atlantic Migration*. Cambridge, 1940.

———. *The Immigrant in American History*. Cambridge, 1942.

HAWGOOD, JOHN A. *The Tragedy of German-America: The Germans in the United States of America during the Nineteenth Century and After*. New York, 1940.

HENLEIN, PAUL C. *Cattle Kingdom in the Ohio Valley, 1783–1860*. Lexington, 1959.

HIBBARD, BENJAMIN H. *A History of the Public Land Policies*. New York, 1924.

HOPKINS, JOHN A. JR. *Economic History of the Production of Beef Cattle in Iowa*. Iowa City, 1928.

HULME, THOMAS. *Journal of a Tour in the Western Countries of America, September 30, 1818–August 8, 1819*. London, 1828. (Reprinted as Vol. X of REUBEN GOLD THWAITES [ed.], *Early Western Travels, 1748–1846*.) Cleveland, 1904.

HUTCHINSON, WILLIAM T. *Cyrus Hall McCormick*. 2 vols. New York, 1930 and 1935.

IOWA RAILROAD LAND COMPANY. *Choice Iowa Farming Lands: 1,000,000 Acres for Sale at Low Prices, on Credit or for Cash by the Iowa Railroad Land Company, in Tracts to Suit Purchasers*. Cedar Rapids, 1870.

KIRKLAND, EDWARD C. *Industry Comes of Age: Business, Labor, and Public Policy, 1860–1897*. New York, 1961.

KIRKLAND, JOSEPH. *Zury: The Meanest Man in Spring County: A Novel of Western Life*. Boston, 1887.

KRAUSE, HERBERT. *The Thresher*. Indianapolis, 1946.

KRENKEL, JOHN H. *Illinois Internal Improvements, 1818–1848*. Cedar Rapids, 1958.

KUHLMANN, CHARLES B. *The Development of the Flour-Milling Industry in the United States with Special Reference to the Industry in Minneapolis*. Boston, 1929.

LATROBE, CHARLES J. *The Rambler in North America, MDCCCXXXII–MDCCCXXXIII*. New York, 1835.

LEA, ALBERT M. *Notes on the Wisconsin Territory; Particularly with Reference to the Iowa District or Black Hawk Purchase*. Philadelphia, 1836. (Reprinted by the STATE HISTORICAL SOCIETY OF IOWA as *The Book that Gave to Iowa its Name*. Iowa City, n.d.).

LEAMING, J. S. *Corn and its Culture, by a Pioneer Corn Raiser, with 60 Years' Experience in the Cornfield*. Wilmington, O. 1883.

LOKKEN, ROSCOE L. *Iowa Public Land Disposal*. Iowa City, 1942.

McCoY, JOSEPH G. *Historic Sketches of the Cattle Trade of the West and Southwest*. Kansas City, 1874. (Reprinted Washington, 1932).

MACY, JESSE. *Institutional Beginnings in a Western State*. ("Johns Hopkins University Studies in Historical and Political Science," Series 2, No. 7.) Baltimore, 1884.

MALIN, DONALD F. *The Evolution of Breeds: An Analytical Study of Breed Building as Illustrated in Shorthorn, Hereford and Aberdeen Angus Cattle, Poland China and Duroc Jersey Swine.* Des Moines, 1923.

MALIN, JAMES C. *The Grassland of North America: Prolegomena to its History with Addenda.* Lawrence, 1956.

——. *Confounded Rot About Napoleon: Reflections upon Science and Technology, Nationalism, World Depression of the Eighteen-Nineties, and Afterward.* Lawrence, 1961.

MARSH, CHARLES W. *Recollections: 1837–1910.* Chicago, 1910.

MERRILL, JAMES W. *Yellow Spring[s] and Huron. A Local History Containing Sketches of All the People, Institutions, and Events, from the Earliest Settlement to Date of Publication.* Mediapolis, Iowa, 1897.

NEELY, WAYNE C. *The Agricultural Fair.* New York, 1935.

NEWHALL, JOHN B. *Sketches of Iowa, or the Emigrant's Guide.* New York, 1841.

OLIVER, WILLIAM. *Eight Months in Illinois; with Information to Emigrants.* Newcastle upon Tyne, 1843. (Reprinted Chicago, 1924).

ORNDUFF, DONALD R. *The Hereford in America.* Kansas City, 1957.

OVERTON, RICHARD C. *Burlington West: A Colonization History of the Burlington Railroad.* Cambridge, 1941.

PEASE, THEODORE C. *The Frontier State, 1818–1848. (Centennial History of Illinois.)* Springfield, 1918.

PECK, JOHN M. *A Guide for Emigrants; Containing Sketches of Illinois, Missouri, and the Adjacent Parts.* Boston, 1831.

——. *A New Guide for Emigrants to the West.* Boston, 1836.

PLUMB, CHARLES S. *Types and Breeds of Farm Animals.* Boston, 1906.

POOLEY, WILLIAM V. *The Settlement of Illinois From 1830 to 1850. (University of Wisconsin Bulletin,* "History Series," Vol. 1.) Madison, 1908.

POWER, RICHARD L. *Planting Corn Belt Culture: The Impress of the Upland Southerner and Yankee in the Old Northwest.* Indianapolis, 1953.

QUICK, HERBERT. *Vandemark's Folly.* New York, 1921.

——. *The Hawkeye.* Indianapolis, 1923.

——. *One Man's Life.* Indianapolis, 1925.

QUALEY, CARLTON C. *Norwegian Settlement in the United States.* Northfield, 1938.

ROBBINS, ROY M. *Our Landed Heritage: The Public Domain, 1776–1936.* Princeton, 1942.

ROGIN, LEO. *The Introduction of Farm Machinery in its Relation to the Productivity of Labor in the Agriculture of the United States during the Nineteenth Century.* Berkeley, 1931.

ROSS, EARLE D. *Iowa Agriculture: An Historical Survey.* Iowa City, 1951.

ROSS, HARVEY L. *The Early Pioneers and Pioneer Events of the State of Illinois Including Personal Recollections of the Writer of Abraham Lincoln, Andrew Jackson, and Peter Cartwright, Together with a Brief Autobiography of the Writer.* Chicago, 1899.

SANDERS, ALVIN H. *At the Sign of the Stockyard Inn.* Chicago, 1915.

——. *Shorthorn Cattle: A Series of Historical Sketches, Memoirs and Records Of the Breed and its Development in the United States and Canada.* Chicago, 1916.

————. *History of the Percheron Horse.* Chicago, 1917.

SCHAFER, JOSEPH. *Wisconsin Domesday Book, II: Four Wisconsin Counties.* Madison, 1927.

SHAMBAUGH, BENJAMIN F. (ed.). *Constitution and Records of the Claim Association of Johnson County, Iowa.* Iowa City, 1894.

SHANNON, FRED A. *The Farmer's Last Frontier: Agriculture, 1860–1897.* New York, 1945.

SHIRREFF, PATRICK. *A Tour through North America; Together with a Comprehensive View of the Canadas and United States, as Adapted for Agricultural Emigration.* Edinburgh, 1835.

SINCLAIR, HAROLD. *American Years.* New York, 1938.

STEPHENSON, GEORGE M. *The Political History of the Public Lands from 1840 to 1862: From Pre-emption to Homestead.* Boston, 1917.

STEWARD, JOHN F. *The Reaper.* New York, 1931.

STEWART, CHARLES L. *Land Tenure in the United States with Special Reference to Illinois.* ("University of Illinois Studies in the Social Sciences, Vol. V." Urbana, 1916.

SWEDISH HISTORICAL SOCIETY OF AMERICA. *Year-Book, VII. 1921–22.* Chicago, 1922.

TEAKLE, THOMAS. *The Spirit Lake Massacre.* Iowa City, 1918.

THOMAS, JOHN J. *Farm Implements and Farm Machinery, and the Principles of their Construction and Use: with Simple and Practical Explanations of the Laws of Motion and Force as Applied to the Farm.* New York, 1869.

THORNTON, HARRISON J. *The History of the Quaker Oats Company.* Chicago, 1933.

TOWNE, CHARLES W., and WENTWORTH, EDWARD N. *Pigs: From Cave to Corn Belt.* Norman, Oklahoma, 1950.

VAN DER ZEE, JACOB. *The Hollanders of Iowa.* Iowa City, 1912.

WEAVER, JOHN C. *American Barley Production.* Minneapolis, 1950.

WEAVER, JOHN E. *North American Prairie.* Lincoln, 1954.

WENTWORTH, EDWARD N. *America's Sheep Trails: History, Personalities.* Ames, 1948.

WITTKE, CARL. *The Irish in America.* Baton Rouge, 1956.

————. *We Who Built America: The Saga of the Immigrant.* New York, 1939.

WOODS, JOHN. *Two Years' Residence in the Settlement on the English Prairie, in the Illinois Country, United States. . . .* London, 1822.

WYMAN, WALKER D., and KROEBER, CLIFTON B. *The Frontier in Perspective.* Madison, 1957.

ARTICLES

"Across the Plains in 1850," *Annals of Iowa, Third Series,* IX (July-October, 1910), 447–83.

ADE, GEORGE. "Prairie Cattle Kings of Yesterday," *Saturday Evening Post,* July 4, 1931, pp. 14, 75–8.

ANDERSON, EDGAR, and BROWN, WILLIAM L. "The History of the Common Maize Varieties of the United States Corn Belt," *Agricultural History,* XXVI (January, 1952), 2–8.

ATWATER, CALEB. "On the Prairies and Barrens of the West," *The American Journal of Science. . . ,* I, No. 2 (1818), 116–25.

BERGMANN, LEOLA N. "Scandinavian Settlement in Iowa," *The Palimpsest,* XXXVII (March, 1956), 129–60.

———. "The Norwegians in Iowa," *The Palimpsest,* XL (August, 1959), 289–368.

BOECK, GEORGE A. "A Decade of Transportation Fever in Burlington, Iowa, 1845–1855," *Iowa Journal of History,* LVI (April, 1958), 129–52.

BOGUE, ALLAN G. "The Iowa Claim Clubs: Symbol and Substance," *Mississippi Valley Historical Review* (September, 1958), 231–53.

———. "Pioneer Farmers and Innovation," *Iowa Journal of History,* LVI (January, 1958), 1–36.

———. "Social Theory and the Pioneer," *Agricultural History,* XXXIV (January, 1960), 21–34.

———. and BOGUE, MARGARET B. " 'Profits' and the Frontier Land Speculator," *Journal of Economic History,* XVII (March, 1957), 1–24.

BOGUE, MARGARET B. "The Swamp Land Act and Wet Land Utilization in Illinois, 1850–1890," *Agricultural History,* XXV (October, 1951), 169–80.

BUCK, SOLON J. (ed.). "Pioneer Letters of Gershom Flagg," *Illinois State Historical Society, Transactions, 1910,* 139–83.

CLARK, DAN E. "The Westward Movement in the Upper Mississippi Valley During the Fifties," *Mississippi Valley Historical Association, Proceedings, 1913–1914,* VII, 212–19.

———. "Frontier Defense in Iowa, 1850–1865," *Iowa Journal of History and Politics,* XVI (July, 1918), 315–86.

COFFIN, L. S. "Breaking Prairie," *Annals of Iowa, Third Series,* V (July, 1902), 447–52.

COX, LAWANDA F. "The American Agricultural Wage Earner, 1865–1900: The Emergence of a Modern Labor Problem," *Agricultural History,* XXII (April, 1949), 94–114.

DANHOF, CLARENCE H. "Farm-Making Costs and the 'Safety Valve': 1850–1860," *Journal of Political Economy,* XLIX (June, 1941), 317–59.

———. "The Fencing Problem in the Eighteen Fifties," *Agricultural History,* XVIII (October, 1944), 168–86.

———. "Gathering the Grass," *Agricultural History,* XXX (October, 1956), 169–73.

DUFFIELD, GEORGE C. "Youthtime in Frontier Iowa," *Annals of Iowa, Third Series,* VII (April, 1906), 347–60.

DUNCAN, BINGHAM. "Protectionism and Pork: Whitelaw Reid as Diplomat: 1889–1891," *Agricultural History,* XXXIII (October, 1959), 190–95.

EDWARDS, EVERETT E. "Reid, James L.," *Dictionary of American Biography,* XV, 477–478.

GATES, PAUL W. "Disposal of the Public Domain in Illinois, 1848–1856," *Journal of Economic and Business History,* III (February, 1931), 216–40.

———. "Southern Investments in Northern Lands Before the Civil War," *Journal of Southern History,* V (May, 1939), 155–85.

————. "Land Policy and Tenancy in the Prairie States," *Journal of Economic History*, I (May, 1941), 60–82.

————. "The Role of the Land Speculator in Western Development," *Pennsylvania Magazine of History and Biography*, LXVI (July, 1942), 314–33.

————. "Hoosier Cattle Kings," *Indiana Magazine of History*, XLIV (March, 1948), 1–24.

————. "Cattle Kings in the Prairies," *Mississippi Valley Historical Review*, XXXV (December, 1948), 379–412.

GIGNILLIAT, JOHN L. "Pigs, Politics, and Protection: The European Boycott of American Pork, 1879–1891," *Agricultural History*, XXXV (January, 1961), 3–12.

GOODWIN, CARDINAL. "The American Occupation of Iowa, 1833 to 1860," *Iowa Journal of History and Politics*, XVII (January, 1919), 83–102.

HAYTER, EARL W. "Barbed Wire Fencing — A Prairie Invention: Its Rise and Influence in the Western States," *Agricultural History*, XIII (October, 1939), 189–207.

————. "The Western Farmers and the Drivewell Patent Controversy," *Agricultural History*, XVI (January, 1942), 16–28.

HEBARD, ALFRED. "Recollections of Early Territorial Days," *Annals of Iowa, Third Series*, II (July–October, 1895), 212–20.

HEWES, LESLIE. "Some Features of Early Woodland and Prairie Settlement in a Central Iowa County," *Annals of the Association of American Geographers*, XL (March, 1950), 40–57.

————. "The Northern Wet Prairie of the United States: Nature, Sources of Information, and Extent," *Annals of the Association of American Geographers*, XLI (December, 1951), 307–23.

————. and FRANDSON, PHILIP E. "Occupying the Wet Prairie: The Role of Artificial Drainage in Story County, Iowa," *Annals of the Association of American Geographers*, XLII (March, 1952), 24–50.

HILL, HOWARD C. "The Development of Chicago as a Center of the Meat Packing Industry," *Mississippi Valley Historical Review*, X (December, 1923), 253–73.

KELLAR, HERBERT A. "The Reaper as a Factor in the Development of the Agriculture of Illinois, 1834–1865," *Illinois State Historical Society, Transactions, 1927*, pp. 105–14.

LEAVITT, CHARLES T. "Some Economic Aspects of the Western Meat Packing Industry, 1830–1860," *The Journal of Business of the University of Chicago*, IV (January, 1931), 68–90.

LEDUC, THOMAS. "State Disposal of the Agricultural College Scrip," *Agricultural History*, XXVIII (July, 1954), 99–107.

LEE, GUY A. "The Historical Significance of the Chicago Grain Elevator System," *Agricultural History*, XI (January, 1937), 16–32.

LOEHR, RODNEY C. "Self Sufficiency on the Farm," *Agricultural History*, XXVI (April, 1952), 37–41.

MILLER, GEORGE H. "Origins of the Iowa Granger Law," *Mississippi Valley Historical Review*, XL (March, 1954), 657–80.

MITMAN, CARL W. "Deere, John," *Dictionary of American Biography*, V, 193–94.

PETERSEN, WILLIAM J. "The Pioneer Cabin," *Iowa Journal of History and Politics*, XXXVI (October, 1938), 387–409.

RALSTON, LEONARD F. "Iowa Railroads and the Des Moines River Improvement Land Grant of 1846," *Iowa Journal of History*, LVI (April, 1958), 97–128.

RASMUSSEN, WAYNE D. "The Impact of Technological Change on American Agriculture, 1862–1962," *Journal of Economic History*, XXII (December, 1962), 578–91.

ROSS, EARLE D. "The Evolution of the Agricultural Fair in the Northwest," *Iowa Journal of History and Politics*, XXIV (July, 1926), 445–80.

ROZMAN, DAVID. "Land Credit in Walnut Grove Township, Knox County, Illinois," *Journal of Land and Public Utility Economics*, IV (August, 1928), 305–12.

SHAMBAUGH, BENJAMIN F. "Frontier Land Clubs or Claim Associations," *American Historical Association, Annual Report, 1900*, 2 vols. Washington, 1901, I, 67–85.

SHIMEK, BOHUMIL. "The Prairies," *Bulletin of the Laboratory of Natural History*, VI (State University of Iowa, 1911), 169–240.

TAYLOR, HAWKINS. "Squatters and Speculators at the First Land Sales," *Annals of Iowa, First Series*, VIII (July, 1870), 269–74.

THRONE, MILDRED. "The Grange in Iowa, 1868–1875," *Iowa Journal of History*, XLVII (October, 1949), 289–324.

———. "'Book Farming' in Iowa, 1840–1870," *Iowa Journal of History*, XLIX (April, 1951), 117–42.

———. "The Repeal of the Iowa Granger Law, 1878," *Iowa Journal of History*, LI (April, 1953), 97–130.

———. "A Population Study of an Iowa County in 1850," *Iowa Journal of History*, LVII (October, 1959), 305–30.

THRONE, MILDRED (ed.). "Iowa Farm Letters, 1856–1865," *Iowa Journal of History*, LVIII (January, 1960), 37–88.

WARNTZ, WILLIAM. "An Historical Consideration of the Terms 'Corn' and 'Corn Belt' in the United States," *Agricultural History*, XXXI (January, 1957), 40–5.

WEAVER, JOHN C. "Changing Patterns of Cropland Use in the Middle West," *Economic Geography*, XXX (January, 1954), 1–47.

WHITE, CHARLES A. "The Early Homes and Home-Makers of Iowa," *Annals of Iowa, Third Series*, IV (October, 1899), 179–95.

WIK, REYNOLD M. "Steam Power on the American Farm, 1830–1880," *Agricultural History*, XXV (October, 1951), 181–86.

WOODMAN, HAROLD D. "Chicago Businessmen and the 'Granger' Laws," *Agricultural History*, XXXVI (January, 1962), 16–24.

WOODMANSEE, MRS. ELMER. "Reminiscences," Webster City *Daily News*, May 3, 1923.

ZIMMERMAN, WM. D. "Live Cattle Export Trade Between United States and Great Britain, 1868–1885," *Agricultural History*, XXXVI (January, 1962), 46–52.

THESES AND DISSERTATIONS

ANDERSON, RUSSEL H. "Agriculture in Illinois during the Civil War Period, 1850–1870." Unpublished Ph.D. dissertation, University of Illinois, 1929.

BACHMURA, FRANK T. "Geographical Differentials in Returns to Corn Belt

Farmers: 1869–1950." Unpublished Ph.D. dissertation, University of Chicago, 1953.

BEATTIE, MARGARET R. "Matthew Scott, Pioneer Landlord, Gentleman Farmer, 1855–1891." Unpublished M.A. thesis, Cornell University, 1947.

BEARD, EARL S. "Railroads in Iowa, 1865–1875, A Study in Attitudes." Unpublished M.A. thesis, State University of Iowa, 1950.

CHAPMAN, CHARLES E. "History of Deere and Company, 1837–1911." Unpublished M.A. thesis, State University of Iowa, 1949.

CLYNCH, DANIEL F. "An Introduction to Swamp Land Disposal in Iowa: 1850–1880." Unpublished M.A. thesis, State University of Iowa, 1957.

COOPER, CLARE C. "The Role of Railroads in the Settlement of Iowa: A Study in Historical Geography." Unpublished M.A. thesis, University of Nebraska, 1958.

GREENE, DONALD P. "Prairie Agricultural Technology, 1860–1900." Unpublished Ph.D. dissertation, Indiana University, 1957.

HAWK, DUANE C. "Iowa Farming Types: 1850–1880." Unpublished M.A. thesis, State University of Iowa, 1957.

JACKLIN, KATHLEEN B. "Local Aid to Railroads in Illinois, 1848–1870." Unpublished M.A. thesis, Cornell University, 1958.

KEFFER, KARL K. "Original Land Entry in Eastern Iowa." Unpublished M.A. thesis, State University of Iowa, 1954.

LEAVITT, CHARLES T. "The Meat and Dairy Livestock Industry, 1819–60." Unpublished Ph.D. dissertation, University of Chicago, 1931.

LINDSEY, ADRIAN H. "The Nature and Cause of the Growth of Iowa Land Values." Unpublished Ph.D. dissertation, Iowa State College of Agriculture and Mechanic Arts, 1929.

MEIKLE, DOUGLAS L. "James Oliver and the Oliver Chilled-Plow Works." Unpublished Ph.D. dissertation, Indiana University, 1958.

NELSON, PETER. "A History of Agriculture in Illinois with Special Reference to Types of Farming." Unpublished Ph.D. dissertation, University of Illinois, 1930.

RALSTON, LEONARD F. "Railroads and the Government of Iowa, 1850–1872." Unpublished Ph.D. dissertation, State University of Iowa, 1960.

RICE, MARY L. "The Role of the Osage Orange Hedge in the Occupation of the Great Plains." Unpublished M.A. thesis, University of Illinois, 1937.

SCHILZ, G. B. "Rural Population Trends of Iowa as Affected by Soils." Unpublished Ph.D. dissertation, Clark University, 1948.

SCHMIDT, HERBERT G. "An Economic and Social History of Bond County, Illinois, before 1850: A Type Study of the Development of a Prairie-Forest Region in the Middle West." Unpublished M.A. thesis, University of Chicago, 1936.

THRONE, MILDRED. "A History of Agriculture in Southern Iowa, 1833–1890." Unpublished Ph.D. dissertation, State University of Iowa, 1946.

Index

Adams, Uncle Jimmy, 52–53, 199
Agricultural fairs, 204–6
Agricultural ladder, 56
Agricultural periodicals, 202–4
Aldrich, Charles, 196–97, 201
Alexander, John T., 93–94
Allen, Lewis F., 87
American Emigrant Company, 41
Animal diseases, 199, 271, 282–83
Apples, 269
Ardrey, R. L., 149
Arthur, A. D., 99
Atkins reaper, 155
Atwater, Caleb, 7

Bachmura, Frank T., 166, 285
Ballou, V. A., 196, 198
Bank of Illinois, Jacksonville, 250
Bardolph, Richard, 203
Barley, 138, 223–24
Barney, Charles, 49
Barrett, Richard, 172
Bartlett, C. K., 75
Birkbeck, Morris, 7, 74–76
Black, Johnny, 158
Black Hawk Purchase, 10
Blair, John R., 96
Book farmers, 146, 203
Breaking prairie, 70–73
British, 15, 17, 62
British North America, 17
Broadcast seeder, 153, 165
Broomcorn, 143
Brown, Garret, 163
Brown, George W., 160
Brown, James N., 88, 91
Brown brothers, 101
Bryant, Henry, 98
Bryant, William Cullen, 68
Buckwheat, 140, 245, 270
Burt, D. R., 208–9

Business men: and freight rates, 282; and marketing reform, 282; in agricultural societies, 204
Butter, 252, 256, 261, 275

Canals, 17, 188, 280
Campbell, Samuel, 90
Capital shortage, 145
Capron, Horace, 90
Case, J. I., 157
Cattle: Aberdeen Angus, 90; Devon, 90; feeding, 197, 213, 252–53; feeding methods, 100–102; French Canadian, 87; Hereford, 90; Jersey, 201; markets, 100, 249, 273, 283; milk cow production, 229–30; numbers, 86; other cattle production, 230–31; oxen, 86, 119–20, 254–55, 270; prices, 94–95, 98, 285; raising, 86–102, 247, 256, 261; Shorthorn, 87–92, 201; Texan, 89, 93, 96; wintering contracts, 100, 130
Centennial Exhibition, 265
Chattel mortgages, 181
Cheese, 252
Chicago, Rock Island, and Pacific Railroad Company, 180–81
Civil War: and farm machinery, 156, 165; inflation, 190
Claim clubs, 13, 31–39, 171
Clarkson, Coker F., 91
Clearing timber, 70
Clovers, 138, 140–43, 197, 245, 278
Coal, 50
Cole, Cyrenus, 113
Commission men, 249, 281–82
Cook, Ira, 49
Corn: binder, 162; cultivators, 160–61; culture, 1, 7, 129–37, 197, 245–46, 252, 254, 261, 270; harvest, 133–35, 161–62, 270; markets, 130–31; planters, 159–60, 272; planting, 131, 159; prices, 130–31,

Watermelons, 254
Weare, John, 173, 177
Wearin, Josiah and Otha, 95
Wells, 69–70
Wentworth, Edward N., 237
Wentworth, John, 88, 90
Western farming: criticized, 144–47; described, 202
Wheat: culture, 123–29, 196–97, 245, 252, 254–55, 260–61, 270; importations, 128–29; markets, 249, 257; pests, 125–27; prices, 257–58, 285; production, 128, 217–20; soils, 124–25; varieties, 127–28; winter killing, 125

Williams, Thomas, 250
Willingham, William W., 49
Wilson, William Duane, 138
Windmills, 70
Wittke, Carl, 21
Wood, Jethro, 149
Woods, John, 105, 108, 133, 137
Wool: markets, 118, 273; prices, 114
Wool Grower, 118, 203

Yancy family, 103
Yankees, 15–16, 20, 24–25, 47–48, 133, 144, 152, 195, 211, 236
Yorkers, 14–15, 25, 152, 195

American History

Frederick Lewis Allen.
The Lords of Creation. (QP35)
Lewis Atherton.
Main Street on the Middle Border. (QP36)
Thomas A. Bailey.
Woodrow Wilson and the Lost Peace. (QP1)
Thomas A. Bailey. *Woodrow Wilson and
the Great Betrayal.* (QP2)
Charles A. Beard.
The Idea of National Interest. (QP27)
Carl L. Becker.
Everyman His Own Historian. (QP33)
Ray A. Billington.
The Protestant Crusade. (QP12)
Allan G. Bogue.
From Prairie to Corn Belt. (QP50)
Kenneth E. Boulding.
The Organizational Revolution. (QP43)
David M. Chalmers.
Hooded Americanism. (QP51)
John Chamberlain.
Farewell to Reform. (QP19)
Alice Hamilton Cromie.
A Tour Guide to the Civil War.
Robert D. Cross. *The Emergence of
Liberal Catholicism in America.* (QP44)
Chester McArthur Destler.
American Radicalism, 1865-1901. (QP30)
Robert A. Divine.
The Illusion of Neutrality. (QP45)
Elisha P. Douglass.
Rebels and Democrats. (QP26)
Herman Finer. *Road to Reaction.* (QP5)
Felix Frankfurter.
The Commerce Clause. (QP16)
Lloyd C. Gardner.
A Different Frontier. (QP32)
Edwin Scott Gaustad. *The Great
Awakening in New England.* (QP46)
Ray Ginger. *Altgeld's America.* (QP21)
Louis Hartz. *Economic Policy and
Democratic Thought.* (QP52)
William B. Hesseltine.
Lincoln's Plan of Reconstruction. (QP41)
Dwight W. Hoover.
Understanding Negro History. (QP49)
Stanley P. Hirshson.
Farewell to the Bloody Shirt. (QP53)
Frederic C. Howe.
The Confessions of a Reformer. (QP39)
Louis Joughin and Edmund M. Morgan.
The Legacy of Sacco and Vanzetti. (QP7)
William Loren Katz. *Teachers' Guide to
American Negro History.* (QP210)
Edward Chase Kirkland. *Dream and Thought
in the Business Community,
1860-1900.* (QP11)
Edward Chase Kirkland.
Industry Comes of Age. (QP42)
Adrienne Koch.
The Philosophy of Thomas Jefferson. (QP17)
Gabriel Kolko.
The Triumph of Conservatism. (QP40)
Walter LaFeber. *John Quincy Adams and
American Continental Empire.* (QP23)
David E. Lilienthal.
TVA: Democracy on the March. (QP28)
Arthur S. Link.
Wilson the Diplomatist. (QP18)
Huey P. Long. *Every Man a King.* (QP8)
Gene M. Lyons.
America: Purpose and Power. (QP24)
Jackson Turner Main.
The Antifederalists. (QP14)
Ernest R. May. *The ...
American Isolation...*
Henry F. May.
The End of America...

George E. Mowry.
The California Progressives. (QP6)
Frank L. Owsley.
Plain Folk of the Old South. (QP22)
David Graham Phillips.
The Treason of the Senate. (QP20)
Julius W. Pratt.
Expansionists of 1898. (QP15)
Moses Rischin.
The American Gospel of Success. (QP54)
John P. Roche.
The Quest for the Dream. (QP47)
David A. Shannon.
The Socialist Party of America. (QP38)
John Spargo.
The Bitter Cry of the Children. (QP55)
Richard W. Van Alstyne.
The Rising American Empire. (QP25)
Willard M. Wallace.
Appeal to Arms. (QP10)
Norman Ware.
The Industrial Worker, 1840-1860. (QP13)
Albert K. Weinberg. *Manifest Destiny.* (QP3)
Bernard A. Weisberger.
They Gathered at the River. (QP37)
Robert H. Wiebe.
Businessmen and Reform. (QP56)
Bell I. Wiley. *The Plain People
of the Confederacy.* (QP4)
William Appleman Williams.
The Contours of American History. (QP34)
William Appleman Williams.
The Great Evasion. (QP48)
Esmond Wright. *Causes and Consequences
of the American Revolution.* (QP31)

European History

William Sheridan Allen.
The Nazi Seizure of Power. (QP302)
W. O. Henderson. *The Industrial
Revolution in Europe.* (QP303)
Raul Hilberg. *The Destruction of the
European Jews.* (QP301)

Philosophy

F. H. Bradley. *The Presuppositions
of Critical History.* (QP108)
William Earle. *Objectivity.* (QP109)
James M. Edie.
An Invitation to Phenomenology. (QP103)
James M. Edie.
Phenomenology in America. (QP105)
Manfred S. Frings.
Heidegger and the Quest for Truth. (QP107)
Moltke S. Gram.
Kant: Disputed Questions. (QP104)
George L. Kline.
European Philosophy Today. (QP102)
Lionel Rubinoff.
Faith and Reason. (QP106)
Pierre Thévenaz.
What Is Phenomenology? (QP101)

Political Science

Charles O. Lerche, Jr.
Last Chance in Europe. (QP207)
David Mitrany.
A Working Peace System. (QP205)

Social Science

George and Eunice Grier.
Equality and Beyond. (QP204)
Martin Oppenheimer and George Lakey.
A Manual for Direct Action. (QP202)
... *To Change a Child.* (QP209)
... *Get Children.* (QP208)
... *The Puerto Ricans.* (QP201)